AIRCRASH DETECTIVE

**Also by the same author,
and available in Coronet Books**

Sex Slavery

Aircrash Detective

The search for air safety

Stephen Barlay

CORONET BOOKS
Hodder and Stoughton

Copyright © 1969, 1975 by Stephen Barlay

First published in Great Britain by
Hamish Hamilton Limited 1969

Coronet edition 1975

_____

Printed and bound in Great Britain for
Coronet Books, Hodder and Stoughton, Limited,
St. Paul's House, Warwick Lane,
London, EC4P 4AH
By Cox & Wyman Ltd.,
London, Reading and Fakenham

ISBN 0 340 19890 7

CONTENTS

FOR MY MOTHER

ACKNOWLEDGMENTS

People to whom this author is greatly indebted for generous help, guidance and advice are too numerous to list in full. Many individuals in a dozen countries have wished to remain anonymous, anyway, for various reasons. (Among these, I am particularly grateful to several German and French scientists and aviation specialists and two U.S. airlines.)

Some organisations, however, rendered outstanding assistance by permitting time-consuming interviews with their staff and by giving access to files which had been treated as highly confidential until then, and so setting a precedent which led to my gaining further co-operation in the highly sensitive field of accidents.

This is to express my gratitude towards:

Accident Investigation Branch, Department of Trade and Industry
Air Ceylon
Air Registration Board
Air Transport Association of America
Air Safety Group
Alitalia
American Airlines
(The) Boeing Company
British Aircraft Corporation
British Airways, the former British European Airways and British Overseas Airways Corporation
Cornell-Guggenheim Aviation Safety Center

International Federation of Airline Pilots
Institute of Aviation Medicine
Institute of Pathology and Tropical Medicine
Lloyd's Aviation Underwriters' Association
National Transportation Safety Board (formerly CAB)
Qantas Airways
Royal Aeronautical Society (for use of their library)
Royal Aircraft Establishment, Accident Investigation
  Division
Royal Air Force Directorate of Flight Safety
RAF Transport (now Air Support) Command
Scandinavian Airlines System
(The) Society of Air Safety Investigators
Swissair
U.S. Air Force Transport Service

AUTHOR'S NOTE

The aim of this book is to show how investigators of aircraft accidents work, and how they contribute to aviation safety. Therefore the cases which are mentioned briefly or dealt with in detail have been selected merely to serve the above purpose as representative examples of various aspects of investigation. It is meant to imply no criticism of performance that mishaps of some airlines, aircraft types or countries have more frequently been referred to than those of others. This is in no way to compare their safety for, in fact, some of the more notorious ones may have not even been mentioned while the frank and open co-operation of some of the best helped greatly to produce the most revealing examples.

S.B.

LIST OF MORE FREQUENTLY USED
ABBREVIATIONS

AIB   Accident Investigation Branch, British Department of Trade and Industry

ALPA   (American) Airline Pilots Association

ARB   Air Registration Board, British Board of Trade

ATC   Air Traffic Control

BALPA British Airline Pilots Association

CAB   Civil Aeronautics Board, now NTSB, of the United States

CAT   Clear Air Turbulence

FAA   Federal Aviation Agency of the United States

F/O   First Officer

FSF   Flight Safety Foundation

GCA   Ground Controlled Approach, also PAR – Precision Approach Radar

IATA   International Air Transport Association

ICAO   International Civil Aviation Organisation

ILS   Instrument Landing System

NASA   (U.S.) National Aeronautics and Space Administration

NTSB   National Transportation Safety Board, successor of CAB

QFE	barometric pressure setting of altimeter so that on landing, aircraft altitude will read zero
QNH	barometric pressure setting of altimeter so that on landing, aircraft altitude will read equal to elevation of airport above mean sea level
RAE	Royal Aircraft Establishment, Farnborough
RAF	Royal Air Force
RVR	Runway Visual Range
USAF	U.S. Air Force

CHAPTER ONE

WASTED LIVES

On Tuesday, forty-year-old Captain Philip Guy Watts was off duty. With his wife, he did a spot of gardening, spent the rest of the day pottering about the house and was in bed soon after ten. On Wednesday at seven in the morning he was at London Airport, met Reg Smalley, his twenty-nine-year-old First Officer for the day, and five minutes later they began the mundane activities that precede a dull, routine flight. There were the maps and navigation data to be picked up, meteorological briefing to attend, and all the paper work before a flight plan to Stavanger, in Norway, would be filed at 7.45. Strong winds with rather wild gusts were forecast, but in a good old workhorse like this fifteen-year-old Viking with two Bristol Hercules engines and with pilots who, between them, had had some 4,000 hours' flying time on Vikings alone, there was nothing to fear. Just in case the weather deteriorated, Captain Watts took for the 150-minute journey enough fuel to keep him in the air for 315 minutes and take him safely to an alternative airport if necessary.

At 8.35, the Viking G–AHPM taxied out for take-off, but it returned to the Central Area only ten minutes later. Captain Watts reported that his port engine had not come up to scratch and he would take no chances with his rather special load: thirty-four pupils and two masters of the Lanfranc Secondary Modern School, Croydon. Passengers had to disembark, but while a minor fault was being traced and repaired, they had a good meal at the airport restaurant. At last, at 13.29 they took off.

11

It was an uneventful flight, checking in and out of control zones, making radio contacts with various stations and then with cloud-bound, storm-lashed Stavanger. To prepare an ILS (Instrument Landing System) approach, the Viking had to fly over the airfield at a given heading, height and speed for a certain distance so that the airport tower could pinpoint the aircraft, then had to make a controlled turn of 180 degrees and return along a predetermined track at given speed for an instrument let down.

Papa Mike (the last two registration letters of the Viking) was cleared to descend from 4,000 to 2,000 feet. Homing on direction-finding radio beacons, it passed over the airfield at about 16.18 hours, received instructions to check in when, during final approach, it reached the Outer Marker of the glide path to a landing on runway 18, and requested QFE, the atmospheric pressure at official aerodrome elevation, so that it could set its altimeter correctly. This was given as 999 millibars, but later, forty-four seconds after 16.22, was corrected to 1,000 millibars, and duly acknowledged '1,000 millibars Papa Mike, thank you'. No further communication was now expected from Papa Mike for about three minutes until it checked inbound at the Outer Marker.

But the silence persisted. Thirty-eight seconds after 16.29, the tower called Papa Mike. There was no answer. The call was repeated several times. Twenty-two seconds later, the Search and Rescue Centre was informed that the flight was three or four minutes overdue.

A search began immediately. If there was a crash, the fate of the survivors might depend on the speed at which help came. Three aircraft and seven surface vessels began to comb the mountainous, rugged coastline of the fjords. In the evening, the Norwegian radio announced that the Viking was 'overdue'. But there was little doubt that the truth was much more sinister than that. The Norwegian Investigation Commission prepared to go to the scene of an accident at a moment's notice and the British AIB (Accident Investigation Branch) was notified. Due to darkness and weather conditions, the search had to be abandoned towards midnight. At 3.33 in the morning, it was resumed. Less than two hours later, a light aircraft sighted pieces of wreckage embedded in the face and only ten feet below the top of an almost vertical rock wall, with the rest of the Viking littered over a small plateau at 1,600 feet and, beyond that, in a valley.

Soon after midday, Norwegian investigators were on the spot, and next morning Principal Inspector Norman Head and Godfrey Feltham, Senior Investigating Officer of the AIB, joined them, as accredited British Representatives. (In the AIB, Inspectors were generally ex-pilots who dealt with witnesses and mainly the operational aspects; Investigating Officers examined the wreckage and handled the technical side of accidents. Now all are known as Inspectors of Accidents.) Godfrey Feltham* recalled:

'It was difficult terrain and we had to go in by heavily-loaded helicopters — a controlled operation but not without hazards at that altitude. The site was guarded although it was very unlikely that those who try to take pieces of wreckage as souvenirs would ever get there.

'It was not a pleasant sight. Usually, by the time we get to the wreckage, the bodies have been taken away. This was one of the exceptions. When I began this kind of work, the thought of frequently coming face to face with the physical aspects of human tragedy concerned me somewhat as I believe it would most people. But then, like doctors, one gets used to the idea. I don't think I've ever grown thick-skinned, but the importance and size of the job grew to occupy my mind fully. To some, I imagine, the job could become routine. To me, it has never lost its sense of urgency. The pressure is there from all sides, and one finds it difficult to work always in a relaxed state of mind. However . . . one must find

* Now Assistant Principal Inspector (Engineering).

the way of making the personal adjustments necessary in this work.

'Yet this case was different. They were all so young ... There were school uniforms all over the place ...'

Although investigators struggle constantly to keep a completely open mind, suspect everything and take nothing for granted, in this case an overwhelmingly obvious question arose to gain precedence over hundreds of others from the very first moment: *why was the aircraft at that spot at all?* It was supposed to be in the safety of the beaten track to runway 18, and, judging from the radio contacts with the ground, the pilot must have thought he was.

The time of the accident was one important element. A calculation based on the last known position and speed of the Viking was supported by witnesses and by the fact that the watches of both pilots and the stewardess all stopped just before 16.29. (Crew watches, usually of good quality, set to GMT, are acceptable as supporting evidence if, apparently, the movement of more than one ceased on impact.)

What happened then in those final six minutes between the last radio contact and the crash? Did the pilot know he had deviated from his prescribed flight path? Was he trying to correct his heading? Or was he, after all, struggling with some mechanical malfunction? Perhaps that engine repair in London ... The answers were mostly disappointing.

Although the many clues hidden in wreckages will be dealt with at some length elsewhere in the book, this case has provided some noteworthy examples of site and wreckage examination. The first question was: did the aircraft get to the point of impact intact or was anything missing which could thus account for the crash?

As the aircraft had driven into the rock, there must have been an explosion and devastating fire which hampered the identification of some disintegrated major parts, but finally

14

they all were accounted for. Structural failure in the air was ruled out.

What were the heading and attitude of the aircraft? Perhaps the pilot realised the deviation and tried some desperate manoeuvre to get clear of the rocks in the clouds. The marks on the rock, only some ten feet away from the safety of the plateau, provided half the story. Some of the port wing navigation light glass was embedded in a crevice. Next to it were bits of the port-wing leading-edge de-icer strips. Then the slash marks only a propeller rotating at considerable speed could make. (Later, although the engines and the parts showing their settings were very badly damaged, the fact that propeller blades had left their hubs and come to rest widely scattered supported the evidence that there must have been considerable centrifugal and lateral inertia forces at the time of the break-up and thus showed that the engines were operating.)

The various marks on the rock face were in a near horizontal line indicating that the aircraft was probably in a slightly left-wing low attitude, which could be accounted for by just a gust or a very slight turn — still farther away from Stavanger! More detailed examination of the marks showed that the port wing and the nose must have hit the rock at almost exactly the same time, and that the aircraft was flying nearly horizontally. Its attitude revealed that the pilot was not suspecting any hazard.

The speed of the aircraft in such cases would make little difference to the damage caused by the impact and explosion. But extremely low or high speed could give some indication of in-flight trouble. Therefore the wreckage spray, all places where wreckage had been thrown, had to be mapped and measured. It was now found that the starboard wing tip, almost undamaged because it had broken away on impact and had been hurled over the plateau without hitting the rock face, was the farthest-flung large piece of wreckage. It had landed some 165 yards away from the rock face. To investigators the indication was that 'the speed of the aircraft was not unusual'.

The wreckage distribution gave supporting evidence of the heading of Papa Mike because the aircraft, as it breaks up, projects itself along a certain line creating a wreckage pattern that also indicates the angle of impact.

The site of disaster carefully mapped, each piece of wreckage meticulously labelled, where it was found and in what position, the arduous business of removing remains by helicopter for detailed examination began. And this, as usual, was a desperate moment. One investigator who participated in the case recalled:

'We started a many-pronged attack on the puzzle. But we knew it would be a long, long process. Somewhere in the wreckage, in the history of the aircraft, crew and flight, in the weather factors, radio communications or even in the two pilots' bodies there could be a clue to some mysterious hazard that endangered the lives of thousands flying in and out of the Stavanger area or anywhere in Vikings at the time. And one couldn't help growing more and more desperate as the days went by, results of examination began to trickle in — and everything we found was negative: this couldn't cause the accident, that couldn't cause the accident . . .'

The report of the pathologists was negative: the injuries indicated that the crash was not survivable, all occupants must have been killed instantaneously; the crew's medical history indicated no likely factor of sudden incapacitation, tests excluded the possibility of the crew having been affected by either alcohol or carbon monoxide.

Nor did the technical examination give any clue. The rock impact marks on the wreckage — port-wing leading-edge, etc. — confirmed earlier findings on heading and attitude; no major part was missing; the disintegrated, twisted, badly

16

burnt pieces of the structure, ailerons, flaps, rudder, elevator, power units, fuel and oil systems gave no indication of pre-crash abnormality.

Was the weather, 'unusual for the season', the cause of the accident? The wind speed was found to be considerably greater than the early-morning forecast in the meteorological information given to the pilot. Did then the meterologists slip up? No, there was a revised forecast issued at 11.55 — exactly ninety minutes before Papa Mike's delayed departure. This was available on request, but the Captain never asked for it. So was that perhaps the cause of the accident? The answer was yet another unhelpful 'no'. The revised information was not vitally different from the original. The strong and gusty winds created turbulence near the ground and made landing probably more difficult at Stavanger — but that should not have caused the crash for several reasons: that afternoon and evening, eight other aircraft — another Viking among them — landed at Stavanger's Sola airport without difficulty, and, when flying over the airport for the first time, an experienced crew such as that on board Papa Mike should have had ample opportunity to assess the angle of the drift.

To confirm the validity of this latter point, it became specially important to learn the exact wind conditions in the crash area in the moments of impact. As nobody lived on the top of that particular plateau and there was no way to obtain witness accounts or a reliable measurement of wind conditions at the precise time and place of the crash, the carefully mapped wreckage trail had to give a clue. Documents, bits of paper and torn light cabin-furnishings had been blown out of the disintegrating aircraft by the wind. These pieces were all found and plotted with precision on the map, and showed two direction patterns — both away from the heavier wreckage trail. There could be no doubt that this had been done by the wind. But which of these lines indicated the direction and velocity of the wind at the time of the accident, and which was the result of subsequent wind conditions?

The first men to arrive to guard the wreckage had already given evidence: they did remember which way the wind tried to blow them off the top of the fjord. This was one line in the two patterns indicating the change of wind direction. The other had to account for the conditions at the time of the crash; each piece of paper and shred of textile had been blown to a point where it was captured or hooked by some heavier object, caught in pools of water or rock crevices. Wind direction and speed thus obtained were confirmed by reports from other aircraft at that time in the area and by an appreciation made by meteorologists. But this factor could still not account for the disaster because the pilots, with the aid of their radio equipment, should have known they were on the wrong course.

The radio: was it faulty or was it misused? Most of the equipment was smashed and widely scattered, but was found and identified. A small bagful of these charred tangles of wire and crumpled bits and pieces was collected and sent to Britain for detailed laboratory examination at the Royal Aircraft Establishment (RAE), Farnborough.

The basic question that came with them — was the various radio equipment in good working order before the crash? — was not unusual. It was unanswerable by routine methods of testing the parts. But in this case, the answer was predictably 'yes'. After all, only six minutes before the crash, Papa Mike was still in radio contact with the tower and homing on various beacons. Therefore a second, even more important question had to be asked for the first time in accident investigation: *was the radio actually working at the moment of impact?*

The question had vast implications. If the answer was yes, a finger would be pointed at human performance. If the answer was no, questions like 'was there a sudden loss of power?' or 'could the equipment have accidentally been switched off?' would have to be answered.

'If you're asked such questions, it may have a maddening effect on you,' John Forsyth of the RAE Accident Section said. 'How the hell do you go about it? It's like trying to locate the fifth side of a square! You just sit and think and talk in the office knowing that the boys out there among the fjords wait desperately for an answer that may help to save crews and passengers flying, perhaps right now, into some fatal trap by pure repetition of circumstances.'

These puzzle-solving exercises at Farnborough lack all the elements of heroism and romanticism to be found in other kinds of life-saving detective work. The sobering graveyard of sometimes hundreds of aircraft wreckages under the window will always see to that, and the men who do such work are merely fighting for the preservation of sanity. There is constant and intense activity about the place. There is plenty of gaiety, too. Anything goes that keeps the mind away from tragedy. Fred Jones, head of the Accident Section, is a shooting enthusiast. John Forsyth a keen bird-watcher. In lunch-breaks, the whole accident section may walk along the barbed-wire fences surrounding the establishment and watch with binoculars anything that flies — birds, bees, aircraft. While they worked on the Viking case, a limping pigeon came into the hangar. They tried to nurse it back to health, but failed.

Fred Jones is a lean, tall, zealous man, who thinks fast, talks fast and intensely 'lives his part' as a specialist of considerable international renown. His room is a mixture of an office, a workshop, a laboratory, a lecture hall, a store and a museum, where model aeroplanes dangle from the ceiling, and where he and his colleagues 'think aloud' about possible and apparently impossible ways of solving a particular problem like that posed by the radio of the Viking.

In these odd cases, they find, the greatest difficulty is to choose the right approach. When after several days of 'conversation', Fred Jones suddenly hit on the right question, John Forsyth was ready with the right answer. In a radio, what part does change its state when it is switched on and remain permanently changed? The *valve*.

Briefly, their line of thinking was this: valves contain a heater filament, consisting of a very fine tungsten wire which is heated and cooled always in a vacuum so that it never oxidises. If the glass envelope is broken when the filament is cold, superficial oxidation will be such a slow process that within a few months after the breakage it will be hardly measurable. If, however, the filament is hot when the vacuum is disrupted by a shattered or punctured envelope, the filament will be discoloured, practically burnt.

To support their theory, they smashed dozens of valves with hammers and missiles, and then hurled hot and cold valves with varying degrees of force against hard objects. Finally, laboratory tests proved that the filament cools so rapidly when power is switched off that, unless power is actually on at the moment of breaking the envelope, the filament will always remain clear of oxidation. (Since then, further research has gone into the interpretation of oxidation and permanent damage to other parts of valves, but the evidence is not yet sufficient.)

In this way, it was established that the radio of Papa Mike was actually switched on at the moment of impact. It not only meant that the equipment was functioning but also that the electrical supply was uninterrupted — further evidence supporting the fact that prior to impact nothing was wrong with the structure otherwise the much weaker electrical installations would have been damaged too.

Now the conclusion of some navigational error by the pilots seemed inevitable. But in face of dozens of grief-struck parents and relatives, nobody could shrug his shoulders and notch up lightly yet another 'human error'. Besides there was no material evidence to show that the pilots did err. Perhaps some circumstances made them do so. Perhaps there was still a one in a billion chance of repeating the coinciding factors that may kill others.

After one recent accident which had killed dozens of people, a Middle East official actually laughed at the investigators: 'Oh, you pedantic British! You know now that the pilot was a bloody fool who climbed too steeply, stalled the aircraft, crashed and that's all there is to it. What else do you want to know?' In that case, it turned out that 'the bloody fool' had a perfectly good reason to believe that he was not climbing too steeply, and had he been branded a fool, a mysterious killer might have been allowed to endanger other pilots.

Were the crew of Papa Mike convinced that they were on the *right* course? If the answer was yes, as seemed probable, what was it that had lulled them into a false sense of security?

Those 'pedantic' Norwegian investigators, and the 'pedantic' British specialists who helped them, explored all avenues. The reconstruction of the flight did not disclose any single startling fact. But various tiny errors that might have caused an accumulating work-load in the flight deck were revealed. From the radio communications and the wreckage the investigators sorted out how the pilots had used their various sets. And there were traces of minor confusions. At 16.18 the First Officer, who would normally be concerned with the tuning of the various navigation aids and whose voice was, in fact, identified on the tape recording at the control tower, reported, for instance, 'We estimate the Lima India beacon in approximately two minutes.' That Lima India caught the Tower's attention: LII is the identification signal of a non-directional radio beacon irrelevant to the approach of the aircraft. The Tower replied,

'Understand you estimate Zulu Oscar in about two minutes.' The operator put the emphasis on Zulu Oscar, standing for ZO, the identification signal of the relevant and vitally important landing aid. The aircraft simply replied: 'Roger.'

Investigators now found that the type of route chart used by the First Officer showed Lima India and other beacons — but not Zulu Oscar, for this chart was mainly concerned with route facilities but not landing aids.

Although the mistake had been corrected by the Tower, was the aircraft really navigating towards that Zulu Oscar signal? After its northerly run over the airport, to the *west* from Zulu Oscar, Papa Mike turned back and steered to the east, on its left, to line up with runway 18. But it crashed into the rock face, well to the *east* of Zulu Oscar and, as the impact marks showed, it was still turning slightly to the left as if the pilots had believed that they were still on the other side. Could they not hear the Zulu Oscar signal properly? Did they tune their set to the wrong frequency?

To answer the question, a long series of tests was carried out. It was found there could have been some interference from a radio beacon in Denmark. Godfrey Feltham, himself a pilot as well as a qualified engineer, knew the Viking thoroughly. He experimented on board another Viking to see how wrong the tuning can be. He found that the mechanical function of the tuning controls might cause some error, the size of which would depend on the direction of turn — from left to right or vice versa. With only a small tuning error it was possible to get interference from the overlapping, much stronger Danish radio beacon. This would account for the misleading radio compass indication — but not entirely for the pilot's belief that he was still on the west side of Zulu Oscar.

And here the final blind alley investigators could venture into was reached. For whatever the radio compass had indicated, there was still the so-called ILS localiser needle, which would move automatically into three possible main positions during the final approach and say to the pilot that he was 'on course' or should 'fly left' or 'fly right' to line up with the runway. Even if the pilot missed the movement of the needle — unlikely in normal circumstances — he could not avoid seeing that the needle was instructing him to 'fly right' during the four or five minutes he continued to fly left. Was he trying to avoid some collision with other aircraft? No. Traffic at the time was well distributed and separated.

The investigating Commission was finally 'unable to explain how the crew in a situation of this nature could continue on the heading indicated for the time stated unless they either did not note or were misinterpreting the ILS Indicator readings . . .' In other words: a probable pilot error that cannot be proved. 'The cause of this accident was a deviation from the prescribed flight path for reasons unknown.'

'These cases are the most frustrating of them all,' a French investigator said in an interview. 'If I had lost a son or a relative in an accident, I would long for at least the slim comfort of knowing what exactly went wrong and that the findings would save others so that their lives were not just utterly wasted. When I work, this is one thing I want to achieve for the sake of the relatives. If I fail, I feel I let them down.'

The American CAB (now NTSB) has solved ninety-four per cent of its air carrier cases since 1938, and initiated corrective action in about half of its reports. British authorities have no exact statistics of success, but the indication is that the cause of the overwhelming majority of accidents has been found. How Papa Mike came to grief remained one of the few mysteries — with thirty-nine young lives wasted. The investigation did not help to understand human behaviour in the cockpit or the problem of how human mistakes are brought about; its only positive result was the evolvement of the radio valve technique, that has since helped to solve other mysteries. (The method was developed and also made applicable to filament bulbs, for instance warning lights in the cockpit. In the American TWA–UAL collision case, New York 1960, the investigation was still in progress when George van Epps of CAB heard about the technique which then helped him to prove that certain instruments had worked correctly and had *not* contributed to the accident.)

This case of 1961 left behind two incessantly disturbing thoughts in the form of two comments.

One came from a fairly important bureaucrat of international aviation: 'Well, it's one of those things. You must look on the brighter side of investigation work.'

The other was made by an investigator closely associated with this case: 'The Viking used to fly with two pilots and a radio officer. There is a seat for this third man in the cockpit. But then it became standard procedure to fly the Vikings without the radio officer. He was regarded as redundant. A change of philosophy, you know. Without substituting new mechanical aids, his absence meant perhaps extra work-load for the pilots. They could cope with it, no doubt, in normal circumstances. Others have been coping with it ever since. But could they do it when getting tired after the long delay in London, at the end of the flight, when the weather was getting worse and worse, and when signs of slight confusion exerted additional pressure? We don't know. And we don't know if the same would have happened had they had a radio officer on board.'

One point is clear: there will be no room for such comments, attitudes and unanswered doubts when a Concorde or a 900-seater Jumbo eventually comes to grief. They are already an intolerable luxury.

CHAPTER TWO

SOMETIMES GRIM BUT NEVER BORING

THE investigation of the first air accident in which a passenger was killed took only about three seconds. The pilot knew the cause of the accident before the actual crash.

The first powered flight was made in 1903 by Orville Wright. Despite general public scepticism, the machine's efficiency was improving spectacularly and by 1908 the American government and Army, well before most other authorities, decided they could ignore it no longer. Wright had to prove the capabilities of the aircraft in a series of demonstration flights. In September 1908, he circled the parade ground at Fort Myer, Virginia, fifty-seven times in so many minutes. But an essential condition of an eventual government contract was that the aircraft must be able to carry a passenger. Lieutenant Lahm, a light-weight, became the first guinea-pig, and on September 17 Wright accepted Lieutenant Thomas E. Selfridge, a 173-pounder, as his next passenger. The aircraft took off with ease despite the extra weight, reached an altitude of 150 feet, descended to 75 feet — and then suddenly side-slipped. Wright peered out of his birdcage seat and a single glance completed his investigation: a wooden propeller blade had splintered and cut the wires controlling the rudder. The aircraft nose-dived into the ground. Wright's leg was broken. His passenger, pinned under the engine, was killed.

It was the first time the world was to read the dreaded headlines: PASSENGER KILLED. Editors and readers were horrified. This was not a crash in which one of those eccentric air adventurers was killed, but an innocent man, a passenger, who had no control over the weird contraption!

The case not only aroused public interest in the whole question of safety for passenger-carrying aircraft, but also created a tradition of irresistible demand for immediate information: What happened? What went wrong? Wright's answer was promptly available. But even recently after a major jet incident, a newspaper of international renown expressed righteous indignation over the fact that 'the investigator in charge *still* couldn't name the cause of the crash' — thirty-six hours after it happened.

Public alarm, voiced by both well-meaning and vote-catching politicians, is only to be expected on these occasions. Unlike individual mishaps in the house, in the workshop or on the road, aviation accidents come in the form of disasters killing many people in one go. While hardly anybody bothers to raise a murmur about the appalling number of people falling down the stairs, or cares to notice that in Britain alone, each summer, about a thousand people are drowned, thus equalling the toll taken by all the world's commercial aviation in a bad year, a roaring outcry is inevitable in the wake of every aircrash. This and the thirst for reassuring facts are understandable. but to demand hasty explanation means the complete disregard of all the complexities of modern aviation, all the progress made since the first passenger fatality, the great speed and height at which jets fly, and the tremendous weight of new types. Just consider that the VC10 has more than 200,000 individual items in its official description, that an engine is just one of these items, that counting all the nuts and bolts a sophisticated jet has several million parts each of which may fail, that scores of specialists are needed to examine each of the various highly complex systems, and that, in the majority of modern accidents, ground impact and subsequent fire bring about such utter destruction that the mere recovery and examination of bits and pieces may take a couple of years. And that is still not all. No discovered failure or malfunction in the machine is necessarily the *primary* cause of the accident. A mistake or series of mistakes might have originated in design, manufacture, maintenance, ground handling, ground control or flight. This new, baffling army of potential killers has created the counter-force of professional investigators who work for the governments, airlines, manufacturers, insurers and lawyers.

Although some pilots and cynics often suspect (and sometimes claim) that any aviator could do the job and that investigators 'tend to surround themselves with a stylish aura of importance', the truth is that such critics know very little more than the public about what this job entails. The investigators' day-to-day work hardly ever hits the headlines. It is specialised detective work of the highest order, carried out under tremendous pressure from governments, the public and the entire aviation industry, in the gruesome atmosphere of tragedy, under the constant threat of another similar disaster occurring before the real cause of the original catastrophe has been found.

But perhaps their greatest problem, one that creates devastating inner pressure, is what they call the 'state of the art' — the limitation of knowledge at the time of an accident. Perhaps that is why one of them has described the job as 'often frustrating but never boring'. For the men who sit waiting for disaster have learned the hard way that it might cost countless lives not to resist the human weakness of jumping to conclusions, not to learn *all* the lessons from each accident, and not to find the main and all the contributory causes, even if they have to suspect the hitherto unsuspected and probe into totally unknown territories. At the time when the Comet, the world's first jet transport, came to grief, a completely revolutionary fatigue test had to

27

be invented. When swept-wing aircraft came into service, nothing was known about what turbulence could do to them and how pilots could defend their passengers against it. It is in this way, by solving these mysteries, that investigators turn the debris of tragedy into the life-saving equipment of aviation.

In the early days, the findings were crude — and often self-destructive. At about the beginning of World War I, at the time when any pilot who survived a crash was sent up in the air without delay to restore his nerves, a military Court of Inquiry accepted that the cause of a particular accident *'is perfectly clear. What goes up must come down.'*

In 1911 a Board of Officers in Texas examined a bad landing case and found the pilot had made an error of judgment when selecting an unsuitable landing place. Safeguarding the pilot's judgment by limiting the choice of landing places did not occur to anyone.

The regular early findings, blaming 'Pilot error', reflected the ignorant state of the art — investigators accused the pilot so that they themselves should not be accused of failing to find the cause of the accident. Unfortunately, the stigma still sticks: it is often claimed that investigators 'blame the pilot if they do not know the answer'. Although the majority of accidents are attributable to human error rather than technical malfunction, the truth is that, usually, investigators are most reluctant to blame people. This is partly because they are very much aware of the implications of such findings, and partly because not blame but the exploration of accident-causing weak spots is the prime object of their exercise.

With the real or imaginary causes revealed, investigators have always found it their duty to make recommendations on a remedy — sometimes, in the early state of the art, by quite absurd suggestions. In the early 1920's, for instance, a British Inspector investigated an accident and found that the canopy of an aircraft could easily get covered with oil and seriously restrict the pilot's view. His recommendation: never cover the cockpit!

Investigators have learned to doubt even the most obvious. That is why when a case is apparently completed, it is never closed fully. British accident reports used to state 'the cause of the accident' and merely imply that the conclusion had been based on the hitherto available facts. Now they tend to apply the American formula which is copied by many countries whose investigators are trained with the aid of the vast U.S. experience, and which always refers to '*the probable cause*'; for even if the investigators know perfectly well what the answer is, they recognise that some day, in the light of fresh evidence, a cause behind the cause may be found.

New facts and the advanced 'state of the art' may lead to fuller understanding and better interpretation of old cases. The flight of Icarus story, as 'the first structural failure of aviation', could, it seemed, demonstrate what modern approach and new knowledge can do with old well-known data. But what started out as a cursory exercise led to some rather startling conclusions.

Two main questions have been an enigma for centuries: firstly how would the legendary flight have failed? and secondly is there any logical explanation of the oddity that an island and a sea, both named after Icarus, are twenty-five miles apart? In the absence of wreckage, our 'facts' had to come from the least reliable source — witnesses. With the aid of Greek and Roman authors and with advice from the Meteorological Office at Bracknell, the Accident Section of RAE Farnborough carried out some spare-time reasoning and calculations for this book.

Apollodorus, the earliest 'witness' to the legend, reported in about 140 B.C. that Daedalus warned his son 'neither to fly high, lest the glue should melt in the sun and the wings drop off, nor to fly near the sea, lest the pinions should be detached by the damp. But the infatuated Icarus, disregarding his father's injunctions, soared even higher, till, the glue melting, he fell into the sea called after him Icarian, and perished.' Strabo made the same error as witnesses who have related only hearsay ever since. But he adds that 'alongside Samos lies the island of Icaria . . .' and 'Icarus fell here having lost control of their course'. Arrian states that, according to the legend, Icarus fell on this island and also attributes the cause of the accident to the sun melting the wax when Icarus flew too high.

Ovid, having collected details from Greek authors and hearsay, describes in *Metamorphoses* how the wings were made. Daedalus 'lays feathers in order, beginning at the smallest, short next to long, so that you would think they had grown upon a slope'. He then fastened the feathers together with twine and wax. Finally, he 'bent them with a gentle curve' to make them birdlike. The wax he used was quite soft and could be moulded by the thumb. When the wings were ready, the two began the flight from Crete to Sicily.

Daedalus 'balanced his body on two wings and hung poised on the beaten air'. He told Icarus to follow him and he kept turning back to watch and instruct his son 'in the fatal art of flying'. As they flew, flapping their wings, fishermen, shepherds and ploughmen believed them to be gods. Ovid then describes their progress in a slight geographical confusion: Samos, he says, was passed 'on the left and Delos and Paros', and 'Lebinthu was on the right and Calymne' when Icarus flew higher up. The wax was melted by 'the scorching rays of the nearer sun' and he fell into the sea. (Elsewhere he says Daedalus 'buried the body in a tomb and the land was called from the name of the buried boy'. Therefore Icarus either fell on the island or was washed ashore there.) Daedalus, who at this late stage of the journey turned less and less frequently to watch his son, now searched for him and called until 'he spied the wings floating on the deep, and cursed his skill'.

As night-flying is nowhere mentioned, it must be assumed that all this was in a day's flight. But as Sicily is to the west of Crete, why did they fly north-north-east? One possible explanation examined would be the presence of a low pressure system in the Aegean sea area around which the two flew like birds *with the wind* to conserve energy. This theory would explain why they flew north first, intending to turn west later, but in this case, after Icarus lost his wings, his body would fall while the feathers would travel farther along a curve, the trajectory, coming down some thirty miles to the north. *This would mean that either the Icarian sea or the island of Icarus was always wrongly marked on the maps.*

Since many mythological stories have been proved to be based on facts, one is inclined to seek another explanation.

The Icarian sea is part of the Aegean between the islands of Patmos and Leros, and the coast of Asia Minor. It is about thirty-two miles square. The island of Karus lies about twenty-five miles away to the north-west from Patmos which is at the edge of the Icarian sea. Normally, one would expect the island to be inside or on the edge of its sea namesake. But modern accident investigation can see the way the bits and pieces of evidence fall into a neat pattern which excludes 'a silly mistake by some ignorant old Greek'.

According to meteorologists, it is improbable that the present climatic and wind conditions in the area would be very much different from those in mythological times. The wind blows mostly from the north, gales of thirty-four knots or more are infrequent, but completely unexpected gusts and sea breezes blowing towards the shore can often occur. If Daedalus decided to fly into headwinds and chose an *island-hopping route* — across the present air routes of the area — so that they could rest on land at almost any time but at least every night, the flight first towards the north would be understandable and, considering the likely speed of the summer wind, their progress, some 180 miles in daylight, would be feasible.

To calculate the *altitude of the flight*, two points had to be considered: firstly Ovid says that fishermen below thought them to be gods — not birds — so they could not have been flying higher than about 3,000 feet; secondly Daedalus, from the air, recognised the feathers of his son's wings floating on the water — the 3,000 feet maximum limit makes sense once again.

So now we have the two flying north at not higher than 3,000 feet, Daedalus possibly at a lower altitude. The sun must already be going down slowly. Evening sea breezes may now persuade Daedalus to make for the shore by having an easy ride on the back of the wind, or he may continue to fly into head-winds and reach the next island before nightfall. Either way, the wind direction now sets the fatal pattern.

Icarus grows more and more self-confident and ventures higher up. He may get into turbulent conditions and an attempt to restore control may break off his wings — a condition not unknown to today's swept-wing aircraft.

But the Greeks suspected it was the wax that gave way. And this, too, is a possible cause of the accident — except that it must have happened in reverse to what they imagined. *The wax, instead of melting from the heat of the sun, grew brittle and cracked* in the cooler air of the evening breeze and also of the new heights Icarus reached. A 2° or 3°C. decrease in temperature can be expected with every 1,000 feet upwards. Even if he climbed from, say 500 feet to only 3,500 feet, this alone would account for some 6° to 9° loss in temperature.

Once the wax gave way — or some other structural failure

occurred — *the body would plummet down almost verti-*
cally but the feathers would begin to float along a certain
trajectory that can be calculated just as in the case of
modern aviation accidents. (When an aircraft lost a part of
minor importance in the air, the pilots noted the height and
speed at that moment, radioed the data to investigators,
whose calculation on the telephone enabled searchers to recover the lost part many miles away even before the damaged aircraft landed.)

At Farnborough, feathers of various sizes were dropped
in the still air of a hangar from the roof. It was found that the
average feather would fall at the speed of six inches per
second. From a supposed 3,000-feet altitude, the feathers
that formed Icarus's wings would ditch in the sea in 6,000
seconds. At the same time, the wind would move them horizontally. The speed of the sea wind could be put at seventeen knots or thirty feet per second. Therefore, during each
of the 6,000 seconds the feather needs to fall, it is carried
thirty feet towards the shore of the mainland, roughly about
thirty-four miles in all, so that Daedalus could, in fact, 'spy'
them 'floating on the deep' right in the middle of what is
now called the Icarian sea. (If the wings fell off in larger
units than a single feather, their trajectory would be steeper
and shorter, but they would still fall inside the area of the
Icarian sea.)

So the mysterious separation of island and sea can be
explained by twentieth-century investigators. Unfortunately, modern aerodynamics cannot yet explain and
reproduce the secret of Daedalus.

All this reasoning and the resulting deductions are, of
course, completely contrary to modern investigating
methods which aim at the total exclusion of assumptions.
Their various basic rules and principles may be stating the
obvious — like 'Take nothing for granted; do not jump to
conclusions; follow every possible clue to the extent of use-

33

fulness . . . Apply the principle that there is no limit to the amount of effort justified to prevent the recurrence of one aircraft accident or the loss of one life' in the investigation manual of the U.S. Air Force; or like 'Facts are stronger than argument, more impressive than reasoning, more dependable than opinion' formulated by Eric Newton of AIB — but we must take into account that such simplified truisms may help to preserve sanity and order in the maze where the investigator finds himself at an accident site. Aviators often refer to aircraft as 'a million spare parts, including crew, flying in close formation'. It is the investigator who must find the one, perhaps a fourpenny bolt, that started the destruction of the other 999,999.

This is detective work that must utilise the entire scale of technical, aeronautical and medical knowledge, coordinate the work of sometimes hundreds of scientists and specialists in various parts of the world, dissect and disseminate information, suggest the right questions and question even the most likely answers. Therefore it was no exaggeration that Sir Vernon Brown, former head of AIB, called on Conan Doyle for a guiding light, quoting Sherlock Holmes: 'My dear Watson, when you have eliminated the impossible, whatever remains, however improbable, must be the truth.' Yet, he added hurriedly, 'It was only Sherlock Holmes who could get away with the assumption that the victim's watch stopped at the moment of murder — accident investigators have to prove it, and they do.'

Luck may help investigators in their task but this is regarded as quite exceptional. When, in 1945, a military aircraft crashed into the 79th floor of the Empire State Building in New York, the question of engine failure was among the first factors, as usual, to be proved valid or ruled out. But, on this occasion, the answer came from an unexpected quarter. Higher up in the building, a businessman had been working with a dictating machine which had recorded the sound — the perfectly normal, unfaltering hum turning into a roar — of the approaching engines which ceased only on the crescendo of impact.

Yet even in such unusual cases of luck, the investigation must not only prove, often with brilliant originality, logic and perspicacity what *did* cause the accident and what other causes *did* contribute to failure, but also that all the other parts of the 'close formation flight' *could not* and, in fact, *did not* bear any of the responsibility for it. Without this process of elimination, it would be impossible to save many lives at the expense of a few — which is the only true ultimate purpose of the investigation. (Unfortunately, as will be shown, the findings have a great deal more to do with legal proceedings and the apportioning of blame than any investigator would want.)

In 1962 Britain's Minister of Aviation presented a paper on Aviation Safety to Parliament. In this he described the pattern of safety progress — or the lines of defence if taken in a negative sense. 'Progress in aviation safety depends partly on foreseeing problems before they arise, and partly on learning the lessons of experiment and experience and spreading this knowledge to all those concerned, by force of law if necessary. Some of the lessons can be learnt from controlled experiment in industry and in the Ministry's Establishments. These experiments may be expensive in labour, time and money. Some lessons are learnt from the routine of operating and engineering experience. Others are only learnt from the costly results of accidents, and of incidents which might have been accidents.' This fair summary clearly delegates the role of the goalkeeper to the investigator: behind him there is no further line of defence, his is the last opportunity when everything else has failed, to make positive use of a negative event especially if a new and completely unforeseeable hazard can be brought into the spectrum of safety and aeronautical knowledge. And C. O.

Miller, of the University of Southern California, admitted that traditionally 'major advances in safety have been triggered by major disasters'. With the future of the essentially new aviation era at stake, the investigator of tragedies will need more money, more assistance and more professional training. And his word will have to be heeded more often than now. For his objective is not blurred by the idealism of the researcher who seeks the advancement of science and technology, by the cold enthusiasm or despair of the statistician, by the loyalty of industrial employees, by the profit motive of the operator or by the political consideration of the lawmaker. In the fight against technical hazards and the weakness of the 'human factor', he is the 'referee' who represents the public. Or at least, ideally, he should do so.

The aftermath of an air disaster strongly resembles a somewhat obscure Indian rite that requires a gigantic statue of Buddha to be carried from one cliff-capping temple to another each year. It is put on a makeshift cart ready to be wheeled to its new residence for the year. Pilgrims flock to the procession in their thousands and fight for every inch of a mile-long rope so that by giving it a pious pull they register their fervour. Disease is spread indiscriminately, some of the devout drop from exhaustion on the steep mountain road and get trampled underfoot while others are felled by the stampede of the newcomers. Progress is slow and custom does not specify the required duration of piety. Before the Buddha has done half the journey, the rope is left lying in the dust along the road. Then come the professionals, a handful of monks from the temples, to complete the job.

The investigations of accidents are ultimately the responsibility of governments even though a number of people in aviation take the view that they are conducted on either of two levels — by bureaucrats or brains. This malicious or, at its best, fallacious attitude is specially widespread in Britain, where the RAE, with its conglomeration of all kinds of scientists, can be called in to investigate and asnwer any specialist question. But Farnborough must be *invited* to participate — like Scotland Yard experts must be *invited* to help solve a local police problem — and its assistance may mean many months' work, much more than government investigators, even if they had the knowledge, could ever spare without creating a huge backlog of 'routine' cases.

As today more and more specialist experience is needed to solve a major accident, government investigators must use an increasing number of experts including the manufacturers' and bigger airlines' own investigators. But in the end, they are on their own. It is left to them to complete the donkey-work, tie up all the loose ends, prove or disprove everything, give evidence if necessary, produce a report — and face the music if they are wrong and are caught out.

The men who do this extraordinary job tend to lead very ordinary lives. In fact, there appears to be a sometimes indefinable yearning to blend into suburban communities, take up very ordinary hobbies and spare-time activities perhaps to counterbalance the numerous occasions when their job intrudes into their leisure. This and an ardent compulsion to solve stubborn mysteries, and to serve the cause of aviation safety, are characteristics that help to shape an international community of investigators.

What is a typical aircrash investigator like? There is, of course, no such bird. But they share numerous attitudes and characteristics. Nearly all of them could, for instance, hold a much more lucrative job in some other field of aviation. They all struggle against frustrations, get their 'kicks' out of a job well done, and while each seems to put it differently, they would all agree with Thomas Saunders of the American NTSB: 'Our job is to light a little candle each time' — a

37

sentence that sounds pompous and phoney without the clarion ring of sincerity in his voice.

How do they live? How do they react to tragedy and to the gruesome aspects of this work? How does a wife put up with living in her husband's suitcases? Many of the scores of interviews with investigators took four days, but it would be unfair to them to pretend a full understanding of each one. Some sketchy profiles, notes and quotes may still answer these questions.

Eric Newton, M.B.E., Principal Inspector of Accidents (Engineering) of the British AIB, ex-engineer, ex-pilot, has more than a third of a century's experience in aircraft accident investigation. Calm, well dressed, always ready to smile and question everything under the sun. Tremendous attention to detail; to watch him clean a burnt, oil-soaked cockpit document is like watching a mother handling her ten-minutes old baby. 'They say we are waiting for disaster. Perhaps. Yes, there's a register to make sure that everybody's immunisations and visas to everywhere are always up to date. Bags packed, everything ready to go — yet there's always a last-minute rush. Unlike murder to the M. Squad or arson to the fire brigade, a crash is a shock, perhaps a surprise, too, to us. If we consciously waited for it, it would depress us. The worst is the trip out to the scene. Once there, too many loose ends want to be tied up to leave time for depression.'

George van Epps, fifty-four and father of three sons, Chief of the NTSB New York field office looking after the whole of north-east United States. Did almost everything in aviation — pilot, airport manager, flight instructor, mechanical rating, etc. Air safety investigator for sixteen years. Left better paid job for CAB 'to contribute to aviation safety, and anyway, part of the pay is satisfaction'. His life is centred round the work: 'Everything here seems to be done in preparation for cases. I have a bag packed at home. But I have another one here,' he feels it with his feet under the desk. 'Never go without it. One must be ready to push paper-work into the drawer or leave the lawn half cut. I have a little workshop at home. I put in a safety switch so that all electricity can be turned off at once if I have to leave in a hurry. And there's, of course, an extension line to every room in the house. If the 'phone rings, it must be picked up at the first bell, not the second.

'Some men, and some wives, never get used to it. They quit the job, that's the only way. I don't blame them. Rules here cannot be enforced. And wives must understand, instinctively, that long-standing holiday arrangements can be upset in one second, that we must let the office know if we go to a restaurant. I'm lucky, I suppose. My wife has never objected to the interruptions.

'I used to like bowling. Played in a team, but had to let them down frequently. I couldn't do that to the team. So I gave it up. At first, neighbours were surprised that I couldn't volunteer to hold a responsible job in the community. In church the men's group wanted me to be more active. I had to explain it all to them — and now they understand that my job comes above everything.'

He emphasises that he is no idealist: 'I just happen to like the job.' The pictures of farm-life on the walls of his office suggest simplicity and peace with plenty of time on hand. His books, model aircraft, desk, conference table — all spotlessly neat. A reaction to the job, the confusion, the rush?

He is definite about everything he says. Whenever he is slightly uncertain, he looks up the answer to the question at once. He hesitates only when asked about his attitude to tragedy. He touches his sparse, dark red hair, then the bow-tie, and then hesitation is over. 'My answer for it is to push on and on. It must never happen again. Some get used to the gore. I can't. Just lay it aside. The worst comes when a friend is killed. Hard to restrain oneself. But there's no time to waste on sympathy. It's not being cold or lacking in compassion, you just have to suppress it, swallow it, adjust to it or quit.'

An American insurance assessor who helps at investigations: 'I take about a hundred trips a year — never by train. Nobody likes to be exposed to death, who wants to go to a morgue? — but with me it's a matter of business.'

Edward E. Slattery, Jr., director of the Office of Public Affairs of NTSB, Washington. Had a bone infection as a child and learned to fly aeroplanes before he could walk on crutches. Very cheerful, active pilot. Unlike the rest of the staff, he must go to all major U.S. accidents and subsequent Public Hearings. Notification of the last thirteen big cases came in between 2 and 5 a.m. His wife drives him to the airport — a good-bye kiss before dawn is a regular feature of his life.

Group Captain P. G. Tweedie, CBE, engineer and pilot, spent thirty years in crash investigation; retired Chief Inspector of Accidents, AIB; amateur magician, Member of the Magic Circle. 'The job left no room for private life. Telephones everywhere, radio in the car, had to call at police stations during driving holidays. Usually Sheila, my wife, picked up the 'phone. If she said "Oh, hello dear" I paid no attention. Only if she said "Yes, yes of course, I'll fetch him ..." did I sit up. Hard life? Yes, but you're a professional. Professionalism disciplines you. It lessens anxiety until the case is solved. The job leaves no room for sentimentality.'

David Cuthbertson, AIB, investigating officer: a small man with great reserves of stamina; lighthearted chain-smoker, aircraft engineer. 'I used to read about the works of Major Cooper, the first British investigator, and about the AIB. It fired my imagination. Always enjoyed puzzles, and it fascinated me how one can find out what could go wrong with aircraft. They seemed safe enough, yet early in my career I had to learn that when aircraft fly, aircraft come to

40

grief. Why? Wish I knew all the answers. In fourteen years, I had several scores of cases. Each of them was different. But in one way they are the same: to me they are a challenge and leave behind them on occasions the question — how close did we get to the real cause?

'That's what drives you all the time. Once I had to deal with a wreckage in the Arabian desert. It was buried by a sandstorm. In tremendous heat, I had to go on and on until I had learned all there was to know about that wreckage. Or when that Britannia struck the top of an Austrian mountain in '64. There was a big show, helicopters, mountaineers. A helicopter landed us on the peak at 9,000 feet where we had to crouch on a narrow ridge while it left us. Then a team of mountaineers guided me, using ropes and tackle, to the site. There we had to wait until the sun dropped behind the rocks and the snow hardened or else we'd have slipped and started avalanches. But I found I couldn't do much even then, for the wreckage was somewhere deep under the snow. I returned four months later — with one guide and an Austrian colleague. I was forty-nine then. Perhaps it's never too late to start mountain-climbing.'*

Lennart Bergstrom, forty-four, father of two, never discusses work at home; ex-air force and airline pilot; set up Swedish Accident Investigation Section, the first such independent specialised government bureau in 1965. 'I had a good basic training for four weeks at Oklahoma City, where American investigators are trained, but would like to take an advanced course somewhere. We are very much at the beginning. I have only a technician and a clerk, but can call in specialists. Sometimes fourteen or fifteen people are working for the section. Still, perhaps we are a little ahead of

* This attitude he retained throughout his career. He drove himself on and on, anxious to clear up every detail of his cases, and died prematurely — but not before completing an important investigation in 1972.

Norway and Denmark, where now, I think, a former pilot is specialising in this business, within the framework of the aircraft inspection division.' He has now produced the first Swedish annual accident survey.

Joseph Fluet, Chief of NTSB Central Investigations Division, sixty, looks much younger, face would fit a priest or marriage counsellor. Twenty-five years in crash detection — from the time when major crashes were single-handed jobs. Today he partly supervises the elaborate team system which he helped to create. He knows how much more specialist knowledge is needed (in a GO team, under the investigator in charge, there are about a dozen NTSB specialists who in turn form their own groups with outside assistance for the investigation); perhaps a little nostalgic about the one-man-show.

Teams are, of course, the most efficient answer to the bigger, more sophisticated crashes. The view is endorsed in Britain, the other leader in crash detection, where assistance is brought in, but where the team system is sometimes casual and often limited partly by shortage of manpower and partly by some resistance in principle against the more rigid predetermined pattern of team-work. The individual objections are based on many grounds: conflicting interests, distorted view of specialists, difficulty of communications, and so on. One brilliant investigator feels the job needs 'an almost monastic seclusion. I want to see, read, do everything myself and make sure that nothing is lost, overlooked or damaged. I don't want the compromises of team-work. I want to go step by step, have plenty of time, gather all my evidence in a hole or corner, feel that it's all mine, no one else has access to it, and then, only then, formulate the right questions to be asked from the right specialists. But of course, it's time we lack most. We burn the midnight oil, take our problems home and make our wives suffer for it, yet we need more and more brains — and it's all gone beyond the point where one could get a really good grasp of everything.' His wife stopped flying the day he joined AIB.

Said van Epps: 'We can never stop learning. The first lesson is to be ready to admit our own mistakes and short-comings. When we handled the first 707 accident, some of my men came to me saying that they were not familiar with the terminology. Even if they knew the right questions, they couldn't ask them. So I called a meeting, and asked the specialists to give us a quick, good grounding. Embarrassing? Not at all. We gained their respect — always a main objective — and they knew we had plenty to contribute.'

Raymond Warren, a Principal Inspector, and most of the others at AIB also emphasised the importance of learning all the time, of keeping up with new developments, of being able to discuss any subject with any specialist on a high technical level. But the problems are considerable. The AIB is badly understaffed. The majority of the staff are over fifty. The pay is still not very attractive to new men with high professional qualifications. And some of the old hands say openly: 'Why should I learn more? Retirement is round the corner!'

In the NTSB, perhaps time is the greatest enemy of knowledge. Investigators could have free rides in almost any aircraft, could go to up-to-date courses at factories — if they had the time.

George 'Dick' Baker, GO team captain of NTSB since 1963, aged forty-six, a towering ex-Navy pilot with a crew-cut, has three sons. 'I touched my first Boeing 707 when it was already smashed into pieces and saw a BAC 111 for the first time after it had crashed. Not very helpful, is it? Time is the problem, as my wife knows only too well. When we moved house to New York at nine a.m., there was a 'phone call at eleven hundred and I was gone for three days. She still figures I arranged to get away from moving.

'Neighbours ask me which line or which aircraft is the safest. How can I tell? I only know that my work has made me even more cautious when piloting an aircraft. I sometimes think that more people at least in aviation ought to see the left-over of a major case. But then I know it's not for spectators. You need the work, the endless detail to get lost in and forget the enormity of it all. At the beginning I was not exposed to much blood and carnage and I was concerned how I'd react to it. Then I saw big, burly, rugged highway policemen go pale and sick. If it affects me like this, I'd better quit, I thought. But it was surprising how well I took it. It's so terrifying that it looks unreal.'

Gilbert Jameson, sixty-one, of AIB, a qualified and experienced aeronautical engineer. Witnessed Lindbergh landing at Croydon, and, before this, the place where a friend's father, a pilot, and all his passengers were killed shortly after taking off. Intrigued by an advertisement, he applied for a job with AIB in 1951 and had a forty-five-minute interview. 'It was Eric Newton who asked me all sorts of questions, such as the cause of fatigue in metals and how to identify it. Also, in which direction will the wings of an aircraft bend during pull-out from a dive? — upwards of course, because of the increased lift.

'When he gave me two different views of a light aircraft that had crashed — nose embedded in the ground, tail in the air, broken wings, etc., and asked me whether it had been spinning at the moment of impact it was rather satisfying to be able to spot the deliberate mistake! The photographs were of two different aircraft of the same type, both of which had crashed at different times in a similar attitude!

'When I was subsequently offered a probation appointment I expected that I would have to run errands and carry the bags of some great sleuth for a long, long time. Within three days of starting the new job I had to accompany a senior colleague who was off to investigate an in-

44

flight break-up of a military aircraft. Upon arrival at the scene we found pieces of aircraft scattered over a large area of the countryside. I just didn't know what to make of it. I thought, I've bitten off more than I can chew on this job. How can anyone *start*, let alone finish such an investigation? I was really out of my depth.

'After this I assisted at three more accidents, each of a different type, but I never felt that I knew enough to tackle a technical investigation on my own. Then without warning I was suddenly thrown in at the deep end . . . a telephone call to say that a jet fighter had just crashed killing the pilot. "Do you think you could cope with this one, Jamie?" What could I say? Without being slung right into it I'd never know. But I had a fair amount of stage-fright.

'Anyway, I went to the scene and to my dismay found pieces of aircraft scattered over a wide area — was this another structural failure in the air? Based on what I had recently learnt I began by asking myself three questions: did the distribution of the wreckage indicate an in-flight break up? If so, what part of the structure failed first, and what was the cause of the failure? To the first question the answer was almost certainly "Yes". At the point where the remains of the aircraft had struck the ground there was a shallow crater and after a preliminary look at the wreckage scattered in and around this area it was evident that there were no pieces of the right outer wing in the vicinity. I then walked back a mile or so in the opposite direction to which the aircraft had been travelling when it struck the ground and found myself in a thick wood with almost impenetrable undergrowth.

'After making slow progress in the failing light I noticed a lighter patch in the canopy of trees. As I made my way towards this area I saw what had crashed vertically through the trees. There was the complete outer wing, the top skin of which had diagonal wrinkles, and the main spar was bent in a wing tip upwards direction. I remembered my interview and previous experience. Excessive tip up bending can occur during recovery from a high speed dive . . . well, there it was. I now felt that I knew more about what had happened, but *why*?

'Starting at the beginning of the trail of wreckage I numbered each large piece of wreckage and plotted its position on the map. This gave me an overall picture of the distribution of the wreckage and also enabled me to see if any other large piece of the structure was missing. I then arranged for all the wreckage to be transported to a hangar where I spent about a week matching up the pieces and gradually rebuilding the structure.

'Gradually the picture became manifest — the wrinkled wing and its bent spars. If metal fatigue had caused progressive cracking of either member of the main spar the wing would have been seriously weakened and would have broken long before the excessive lift could have bent it to such an extent.

'One by one my suspicions were eliminated. Why did he go into a dive? What of the controls — had they jammed or malfunctioned? Perhaps there had been some obstruction . . . the pilot would push the stick with more force . . . if then it suddenly cleared, it would cause the aircraft to start to bunt. . . . But if that resulted in break-up at high altitude, then I'd have found a much longer trail of wreckage. Nice theory! But the evidence was much against this.

'It was then that I noticed the oxygen master valve, pretty badly damaged with just the valve spindle protruding out of a piece of mangled cockpit. I was about to put it aside when I sensed there was something odd about the short amount of spindle showing. It was screwed fully in. Wasn't the pilot supposed to have gone to a fair height during the flight? A quick check with another pilot who had flown on a similar exercise confirmed that this aircraft could have been at a fair height and still climbing at about the time the accident occurred. Surely if the pilot was going high he would open the oxygen master valve, or would he? What if he forgot to open it? Supposing lack of oxygen caused him to be less aware of the impending danger and that he had slipped into unconsciousness, what then? Without pilot control the aircraft would eventually go into a power dive. As height rapidly decreased, the increase in atmospheric oxygen would bring the pilot round and seeing the ground rushing up at him he would haul back on the control column in a desperate attempt to recover from the fast dive without breaking the aircraft.

'A reasonable diagnosis but not proved. However, subsequent experiments showed that the oxygen valve required about six turns to open or close it fully and as it was fairly stiff to operate it was not likely that it could have been accidentally shut upon impact with the ground. Although not entirely conclusive, there was a strong possibility that the valve had never been opened during the fatal flight.

'Of course, it was possible that some other unidentified mechanical failure had caused the accident; on the other hand the pilot was relatively inexperienced and could have encountered other difficulties. However, as no other significant evidence was found during the detailed examination of all the pieces, the closed valve seemed the most likely cause of the accident.

'That investigation was quite a confidence booster, for if the valve had disintegrated, or had not been found, or if I had failed to appreciate its significance, I think I would have started to look for another job!'

The kit investigators carry may have to include almost anything. In some countries its contents are left to the discretion of the individual. In others there are long, detailed lists of basic necessities and available extras. In the checklist for SAS investigators, for instance, it is specified that pencils should be of HB hardness, that a certain number of crayons of various colours are the basic minimum, and that rifles and revolvers can be issued according to need. (They were originally used on their over the Sahara and Far East routes, and rifles are still used on their Polar routes in case there's an emergency landing.)

'That kit of mine is at times a real nuisance,' said Jamie, making a slight gesture of resignation. 'I try to restrict it to a minimum but it keeps accumulating as my experience grows. I keep some of the gear in the boot of the car but most of the equipment and clothing I store in a bedroom cupboard so it is readily to hand when it comes to selecting items in a hurry for a local trip or a flight to the tropics or the eternal snows. Come to think of it, the Arctic is one of the few places I haven't been to — yet! The Government gives us most of the stuff, a black briefcase, also a navigator's bag for overalls, small tools, cameras, books, etc. Mind you, I have my own white boiler suit, the official issue is too shoddy to be seen in.

'I have in constant readiness oversocks, an old hat, old shoes, gumboots, climbing boots, passport, shaving and toilet gear, anti-malaria pills, ointment for foot trouble — sometimes there is little in the way of washing facilities — aspirin, glucose tablets to help overcome exhaustion, oilskins, an old mac, anti-diarrhoea tablets — always need them in the hot countries — camera with colour film and exposure meter, compass, maps, first aid kit, leather gloves, fifty-foot flexible steel rule to measure marks on the ground, my own torch — the official issue is not strong enough — wax crayons and tie-on labels to mark pieces of wreckage, magnets, small spanners and other tools like feeler gauges, sets of conversion tables, dental mirrors to look underneath or inside things without moving them, magnifying glass, pocket microscope, maps and manuals for the aircraft — picked up at the last minute from the library — woollies for the cold, or tropical suit. We have £20 allowance for such a suit every five years but one grows out of them round the middle much too soon, and it's not then really good enough to be seen in, especially when one has to meet people like air attachés and local government officials. You have to wear it and hope that it doesn't look too inferior. Of course one could just buy a suit and then not go to the tropics for five years, that's most unlikely, but it's one reason why the allowance is so low.

'Oddly enough, the thought of seeing blood and bodies never occurred to me until I was on my way to my first fatal accident. Some say that one must disregard all personal feelings when faced with an unpleasant job. I don't find that this is so. One often finds that one is working alongside other people who have never experienced such conditions yet they keep going — it's the only way to cope with the situation. It is also said that one can get used to anything. I can't truthfully say "that applies to me," especially the occasions when the rescue operations have not been completed. I don't exactly like working in such conditions but there's much to be done and I suppose the only way to look at it is that I don't take fright or become ill on entering a butcher's shop; but what is the situation going to be in the near future with the five-hundred-seater Jumbo jets?

'In this work, it is essential to have a robust constitution, and considerable physical and mental stamina! Fortunately, you feel the urgency of the situation and the need to work patiently through everything. Nothing must be taken for granted, and if having examined all the available evidence, the cause of the accident cannot conclusively be established, then this must be stated.

'I must admit, though, that there are occasions when I *feel* like taking short-cuts — especially after a long and difficult journey to the scene of the accident. If the wreckage cannot be transported from the site, one is sometimes faced with

49

having to make a daily walk or climb to the scene and then work all day in the heat, rain or cold. It's then that I wonder what on earth I'm doing at such a remote and desolate spot, at my age, and why I still continue in the job at all. Well, I suppose this is a question which every one of us asks from time to time, but it is really the least important of all the questions. It's better just to do the job. Quickly.'

'To remain impersonal and unemotional,' to use the words of Bernard Doyle, NTSB Chief of the Human Factors Group, 'you must learn to remember the real objective of the exercise. This becomes most difficult when a friend is among the victims.'

'It's bad enough with a colleague,' argued Hugh Gordon-Burge, former airline pilot and senior AIB inspector, Air Safety Adviser of BEA* 'Or to interview relatives — it's worse than the inquest. Luckily, I'm not very imaginative. I don't go off my food, but in the first few days of an investigation I don't sleep much. It wouldn't be true to say that it's because of the human aspects of the tragedy, which naturally affect me, but because from the moment the 'phone rings, especially at night, when my wife starts packing my bag before I'm off the 'phone, I cannot stop thinking until some definite line of inquiry begins to take shape. I can't talk about it, I don't want to bring it home, but my wife can sense the tension all right. Well, it's part of the job, I suppose.' A tall, bony, quietly-spoken man who, even without the veneer of a uniform, carries some of the glamour usually attached to pilots. A no-nonsense forty-nine-year-old who has the 'requisites of this job' as defined, off the cuff, by Richard Westlake, fifty-seven, former pilot, AIB Principal inspector:

'What you need here are common sense, background knowledge, an inquiring and understanding mind, plus a

* His sudden death in 1974 was a great loss to the cause of air safety.

good measure of humanity so that you won't think the worst of anyone for whatever has been done. And remember: you might have done the same in the circumstances.' Westlake is hard, outspoken, critical and ready to philosophise without sentimentality. The way he lights his pipe is a statement: no sign of the loving care devoted by many pipe-smokers, it's a pipe, to be filled and lit and smoked, there's no more to it. 'Ruthlessness is out when dealing with people. We're not policemen. I wouldn't do it if it were a police job. Occasionally, guilt may arise at the end of the investigation, never until then. And I'm not interested in guilt and witch-hunts . . . in any case, responsibility is a much better description than guilt. You need a non-compromising attitude and a critical approach in the light of knowledge.'

A softer method of approach, but one of similar single-minded determination, transpires when Ira McInnis of American Airlines, Director of Safety Administration, speaks. A white-haired, fatherly figure, obviously relieved to belong to the small band of U.S. aviators who can keep well away from the rat-race and cut-throat competition among the carriers. He agrees that U.S. airlines are perhaps the most cagey in the world when it comes to talking to outsiders about mishaps: 'But among ourselves, there are no barriers. Where safety begins, everything else, even competition, stops. If there's anything to be learned from the tiniest incident, it must be learned at once by all of us.'

Must be learned — but how? According to the law, any written material — no matter how it fell into unauthorised hands — can be used in litigation against the company. A safety warning might be considered an admission of guilt. Investigators use the telephone to warn others — but legal advisers would prefer them to keep their mouths shut.

Lars Tullberg, Director of Quality Control, SAS, a tense, somewhat ascetic, energetic enthusiast: 'We must learn from others to be ready to investigate in a professional way.

Thank God, it's hard to get experience here — thirty cases with substantial damage to aircraft, six planes destroyed, with fatalities in only three cases in twenty years. But that's no excuse. We must be ready.'

John Goulding, retired AIB investigating officer. Handled almost three hundred big and small cases in twenty-five years all over the world. 'It was quite a sight when in India caravans of coolies had to carry big pieces of wreckage to load the bullock carts because mechanical equipment couldn't get near enough due to seasonal flooding.' He never knocks his pipe out in the street until he finds a bin for litter; polished his desk while talking in the office without being conscious of it; brought roses from home to the office to give it a 'touch of humanity'.

Dr. Jr. Harald Widmer, ex-Chief of the Swiss Büro für Flungunfall-Untersuchungen, sixty-nine, a lawyer; gliding used to be his hobby. Government aviation official since 1939, drifted into investigation and set up this independent accident branch in 1960 with one engineer and six occasional collaborators. 'My first case was a friend burnt to death. In the early days, you knew them all. Now it's more impersonal as the whole thing is getting much, much too big. I've handled some two hundred cases, but mostly small ones where you could put yourself in the pilot's place, think as he would to understand what he did; smaller cases where you could have your personal opinion related to, say, the pilot's character, even if you couldn't put that in the report because you couldn't prove it.

'Today, we still cannot do our job in the highly sophisticated style achieved by the Americans or the British, but we're lucky that we can draw freely on the experience and resources of manufacturers and Swissair. No, I'm not worried about relying on them — it's in their interest to find the cause, and cure any trouble. And at least we can call in men who are professional aviators.'

(After his retirement, Dr. Kurt Lier, another lawyer took over as chief investigator.)

Captain Hugo Muser, a Jumbo pilot, and Jürg Michel, an engineer, are reorganising the Swissair Flight Safety Section: 'Especially to the older generations, the maintenance of and caring for aircraft are a religion. That's the attitude we need in every part of the operation. The best investigation begins before the accidents happen. Accidents and incidents are not the failures of men and machine – not in the first place. It's mainly a failure of prevention.'

William Tench, fifty-three, Chief Inspector, twenty years with AIB; flew with the Fleet Air Arm in the war and in the South American jungle before he became an airline pilot. The effort of going back to study for civil licences after the war was a strain which involved hours of tedious testing by his wife who became quite knowledgeable in aviation matters. 'In the accident investigation business', he said, 'nobody can know everything. We are like general practitioners who know what specialists to call in.' (Dick Baker likened an NTSB man's job to that of a quarterback, the brain, soul and motor of an American football team.) 'There is a strong feeling of comradeship amongst the international community of accident investigators. Friendships tend to last if struck up on the top of mountains or in mangrove swamps with the threat of crocodiles or venomous snakes constantly in the background.'

On reflection, this series of extracts from the investigators' remarks suggests an almost Hollywood-style idea of boffins. Many who have met them at work may believe that for the interviews these men have struck poses for which they have used some time-worn scriptwriters' clichés. But the enduring impression left is that they have clearly meant what they expressed in sometimes rather flamboyant sentences. And it appears that weather beaten remarks ('The idiot! Couldn't he crash into a nightclub instead of a jungle?'), the cynical comments (a pathologist: 'Yes, I suppose the patients I see are somewhat reduced in size and tend to be incomplete') and the general rugged, matter-of-fact attitudes they adopt at work are the façade presented to colleagues merely to 'keep things going' and to cover up for the shock and emotional involvement.

'Sometimes grim, sometimes frustrating, but a fully absorbing job,' summed up Norman Head, an ex-pilot, retired principal inspector of AIB. 'But it's fantastically elating when the pieces of this dreadful jigsaw puzzle begin to fall into place ...'

CHAPTER THREE

THE JIGSAW WALLAHS

IT was an American military accident. Nobody saw it happen. It demolished part of a house — fortunately unoccupied at the time. The aircraft broke up, exploded and burned so fiercely that the first people who tried to pull out the bodies of the crew were driven away by the flames. The destruction seemed to be complete: parts of the jet's structure that had survived the tremendous impact — one mammoth engine had been crumpled and compressed into an outsize cannon-ball — were now consumed by the fire.

The beefy and impassive colonel just stared at it with no more apparent comprehension than the rest of the rescuers displayed. He walked round without a word, seemingly in a daze: to the tail, lying upside down some ten feet to the right of what once had been the cockpit, to two old beech trees side by side — part of a wing was hanging on a branch — to the road beyond, past a willow and up a hill a quarter of a mile away.

'What a waste,' he mumbled finally. Then thinking aloud, he demonstrated his 'track-reading technique' when he began to retrace his steps to the wreckage. 'It was probably coming in along this line. Had he been controlling the aircraft at all, he would have avoided the trees. Plenty of open fields here, so why go for a lonely farmhouse?

'He was losing height rapidly, but wasn't in a dive. Or he wouldn't have touched the willow. Mind you, no major branch is broken,' he picked up a handful of twigs from the ground, none of them longer than three inches, all with fresh, still moist, fractures. 'Just brushed the crown.'

At the two beeches he stopped, looked back towards the willow, then to the demolished corner of the farmhouse: 'Yes, that's the line of approach. Between the beeches. The tree on the left is almost undamaged, the other lost a lot of branches and caught the tip of a wing. To get through like this, the plane must have been banking . . . to the right. That would break the starboard wing. But it's the port wing.' He picked up some red glass of the port navigation light. 'So it came in upside down . . . banking, say, 45° to the right . . . now the inverted port that is . . .'

He left the trees and studied four significant marks on the ground. Facing the way that jet did in its final moments, there was a long groove on the right — made by the inverted port wing. Then a hole where the engine struck the ground and, to the left, a similar mark made by the inverted starboard engine. Driven into the lawn in the middle lay the top of the cockpit structure without the canopy. 'Of course,' he nodded and walked back to the beeches where he soon spotted specks of perspex on the ground. 'Those branches in the centre must have caught the canopy, probably incapacitating the pilot.'

A quick measurement of the groove in the ground showed it was deeper to the right and confirmed that, apparently, the angle of banking was still about 45° at impact.

The tail: broken free and upside down, it still had the controls in position. 'So, probably, there was nothing wrong with the fuselage, where the controls came through, before the crash.'

There was severe fire on the ground, but was there any in the air? Possibly. Certainly not a serious one. For if a lot of fuel is burning in flight, the slipstream carries it to the rear and there would be plenty of melted metal spatter on the tail. There was no sign of that. The blots in the paint of the tail indicated the vicious heat that had emanated from the burning main wreckage and had affected the tail although it lay some thirty feet away.

The colonel then lay on his back, crawled under the remains of the cockpit and began recording the settings of instruments, throttles, controls, radio. He followed that up with further notes on rudder trimming tab, ailerons, the extension of actuating jacks, etc., to see if the settings corresponded with the actual reaction of the controls. To draw any conclusion was much too premature. Any discrepancy might have been caused by the impact. That would have to be ruled out or confirmed before any meaning would be attached to it.

A specialist arrived from the engine manufacturers and, with the colonel, he began a quick check on the engines: was there any sign of malfunction? Did the engine suck itself full of earth, a sign of running normally on impact?

With this quick preliminary inspection completed, the investigation could now begin.

Today, there is some controversy among investigators about the profound significance of the wreckage. Many would agree with Martyn Clarke of NTSB that 'the utter destruction caused by modern accidents leaves behind less and less readily available evidence in the wreckage. A superficial but typical sign of this is that airlines need not obliterate their names on the wreckage — there's rarely a big enough surface left in one piece'. It was for the same reason that some NTSB investigators were among the first to fight for flight recorders, against strong opposition from airlines and pilots, for without recorders many of the highly complex recent accidents and their intertwined causes would have remained mysteries.

On the other hand, it cannot be disputed that the wreckage is the most factual, tangible evidence for the investigator, whose philosophy and analysing approach has not changed much with the type of aircraft and extent of destruction. In this respect, experience is far more important than any amount of training and academic knowledge, and that is why the British AIB is in a unique position in the world. Half of its staff are engineers who — together with the RAE accident section — must bear the work-load of military accidents, too. This gives them a wealth of information about the design and capabilities of future civilian type aircraft. When the jets entered airline service, they were, to some extent, a novelty to CAB but 'routine' to AIB engineers. The same may be true about supersonic aircraft for which investigators into military accidents have already provided tragic experience.

A classic pioneering application of basic accident investigation technique occurred during the war.

The Germans began the development of the V2 and fired an experimental ballistic rocket. It broke up in the air and parts of it fell on Swedish territory. While the Germans began desperate negotiations about the return of the handful of wreckage, the Swedes sent it all to Britain. At Farnborough, the usual basic question of wreckage analysis was raised: what was it like before break-up?

As in cases of major accidents, the pieces of wreckage were laid out in the hangar to see which part came from the nose and other sections of the rocket. Then a reconstruction was attempted on a skeleton of chicken-wire and the result was a fifty-foot structure — the estimated size and shape of the rocket. (Later, commando raids obtained information that confirmed that the reconstruction was only about an inch off the mark!)

In order to estimate the danger of the rocket, further tests were devised. Chemists analysed the outside paint that had been affected by the flight. As speed develops high temperatures on the surface, the paint becomes discoloured. Now experiments were carried out to determine what kind of paint had been used and how much heat would bring about discolouration to this extent. The last step was to calculate the speed that would develop the necessary heat.

With the size, shape and speed of the rocket known, aerodynamicists could predict the probable flight path and destructive power of a rocket the Germans were only about to build. (The same speed-and-heat relationship has been a serious problem for the builders of the Concorde and a special test-rig was set up at Farnborough to study this possible hazard, predict its effects and determine what precaution might be necessary.)

Sometimes the wreckage has the cause of the accident 'written all over it' — only waiting for a detective who can see as well as look and who will question everything, even the apparently obvious.

On August 17, 1966, a Dakota aircraft of Gulf Aviation Service flew from Bahrain to Doha, Abu Dhabi, Dubai and Azaiba, from where it took off for the return flight at night. Soon after it had left runway 06, it suddenly lost height, struck some palm trees, then hit the ground and came to rest on a dried-up river-bed 565 yards from the end of the runway. Both engines were torn away, one of them caught fire, and there was other serious damage to the aircraft. Miraculously, the two pilots and seven of the eighteen passengers sustained only minor injuries. Less serious crashes have sometimes killed all on board.

Captain R. H. Herrington recalled that, when the nose began dropping, he 'pulled back on the stick but there was no immediate response. It seemed as if the aircraft had no energy, the power just leaked away. I know this is a funny way of putting it but they were my impressions at the time. We were not turning at all while descending. I next heard a crack or thump from the port wing; I assumed it was a tree, we swung to port, I gave full right aileron and at the same time reached out to switch off the ignition switch. I never reached it as we then made contact with the ground and was trying to hold myself in my seat . . .'

Everything was left in the cockpit as it had been at the moment of impact. The airline called in Ben Folliard, then Chief Inspector of Accidents at BOAC, probably the only airline that called a spade a spade by having an 'Accident Section' instead of a department under the usual code-like euphemisms.

He took photographs and detailed notes of the condition of the wrecked aircraft and then looked at the cockpit. Throttles, mixture control levers, pitch control levers, all in appropriate positions. Carburettor air intake heat control levers fully forward as they should be to give cold air to the engines, in this tropical climate. To make any further checks on these levers was like making sure manually that your mouth is open before putting the toothbrush to use. An absurd precaution, but this attitude did pay off on this occasion: Folliard noticed that the 'fully forward' position was marked 'HOT'. But in this climate, the engines needed cold air!

Gulf Aviation had had four Dakotas for some time. On all, the forward positions of these levers were marked RAM AIR and the aft position was HOT AIR (to be used only in freezing weather). On this particular Dakota, the latest acquisition of the company, it was the other way round. Had the pilots taken off by supplying the engines inadvertently with hot air, the events that followed would have been perfectly understandable: in the ambient temperature of 30°C. the carburettor air temperatures would have risen fast to well beyond the 'detonation threshold' and result in sudden loss of power.

Having eliminated all other explanations, the question investigators had to answer was: how could this happen? Both pilots knew that this Dakota was different from the others. They flew the aircraft all day, took off several times without a hitch. Yet neither of them remembered positioning these levers forward for the final take-off. Ben Folliard found that this must have been 'an instinctive movement' by one of the pilots — like a man looking at his watch without a thought about 'on which hand am I wearing it today?' — 'resulting from many flights' on other Dakotas. (Before Folliard, several pilots and experts had looked into the cockpit without one of them noticing what seemed the obvious and checking whether 'forward' on this occasion really meant what it always had.) During the day's previous operations, Captain Walton flew the aircraft from the left-hand seat. For the return flight, the pilots changed seats and, during this, one of them probably 'tidied up' the cockpit automatically. Unlike procedure when taking over an aircraft for the day, the pilots were not required to do a full check including a power check because the unnecessary burst of power might get the engine too hot for a successful take-off. (Had there been a power check, the instruments would have gone haywire and the lack of power would have been apparent at once.)

But why was the lever position reversed? Folliard telephoned to warn London and a quick check there revealed that about a third of the British-registered Dakotas had their air intake controls in this reversed position. The difference was due to a minor technical innovation some *fifteen years earlier* when the various operators had decided for themselves which way to modify these levers. In April 1966, four months before the accident, Gulf gave sufficient warning to its pilots that this latest addition to their fleet of Dakotas was in this respect different from all the others.

Modification of the levers, instead of the warning, would have been a two-hour job.

Rescuers and firefighters cause a great deal of unfortunately inevitable damage to the evidence in wreckages. Therefore it is vitally important that nothing else is destroyed, disturbed, or even handled by unauthorised people. (Had someone moved those levers, the Dakota crash might have remained a mystery.) In this respect, souvenir-hunters are a very real menace to an investigation. Usually, guards are quickly marshalled to surround the wreckage.

In some countries, the guards for an accident site must be armed. Martyn Clarke, for instance, recalled that when investigating a structural failure case in Brazil 'in the heart of the Matto Grosso — true headhunting country with all the pleasures of the jungle — even armed guards meant little protection for both wreckage and investigator'; when the work was over and, as is usual, he mentioned that the wreckage could now be buried, he was laughed at: the natives could clear the site faster than any workman could and, he was assured, would find use for every bit of the tragic litter. 'When the wreckage is somewhere deep down in the water, it can be rather awkward,' he said. 'But I'd much rather calculate how currents move the pieces and learn skin-diving as some of us had to than worry about souvenir hunters.'

Even armed guards are not always a solution. A German investigator who wished to remain anonymous in case he were ever again involved with a Middle East country told me that there 'the presence of armed guards was no guarantee against pilfering, but they were ready to use their rifles to stop us, foreigners, *interfering*. It meant the loss of an entire week-end during which we couldn't find an official to help us, and also meant the total loss of some evidence.'

The investigators' concern is understandable. Until the very end of their detective work, the tiniest scrap of metal and any shred of fabric are just as vitally important as some key instrument from the flightdeck. Take, for instance, the helicopter night-training flight in the Far East in 1963. The pilot radioed the control tower that he was turning. A few seconds' silence — then a very distorted, shaky voice came through: 'May Day, May Day, May Day.' This international distress signal was the pilot's last words. He was killed in the crash.

The investigation revealed no sign of any malfunction in the engine. But something must have been wrong with it for two reasons: the pilot sent a distress signal and the recorded message implied that the 'chopper' was shaking violently.

The few yards of relevant tape were then thoroughly examined. Was it a certain 'g' condition – acceleration or deceleration — that caused the distortion? Volunteers were shaken in a vibrating seat at various 'g' levels and their endless May Day calls were recorded, but the shaky voice could not be reproduced. Suspicion then fell on the pilot's panic that might have caused the distorted pitch of the voice. This again was ruled out after experiments. Finally, radio operators came up with another theory: was it possible that when the helicopter was turning, as reported by the pilot, the rotor blades repeatedly interrupted the line between the transmitting and receiving aerial and caused the distortion? This was confirmed by further experiments that reproduced the original effect on the recording. So now the interruption rate per second and per rotor blade was measured and this gave an indication of the number of revolutions of the rotor in the final seconds before the crash. The jigsaw men were proved right: the machine had given no cause for alarm — the pilot must have been deceived by his own senses, lost direction and crashed.

Such cases only reaffirm that minute pieces of wreckage

must be recovered almost at any cost. One of the latest moves into this field was to train dogs at Farnborough to search for survivors and wreckage in inaccessible areas. The dogs are equipped with transistor radios for two-way communication so that commands could be given to them from a strategic position. They are trained to distinguish between old metal and wreckage, and to bark into microphones when they make a find.

In 1959 the very promising future of the 'Victor 2' bombers seemed to be jeopardised by a mysterious crash into the Irish Sea. Everybody recalled the fate of the Tudor, an excellent passenger aircraft doomed after the crash of 'Star Ariel' had remained a mystery because the wreckage was buried in the sea. Now the Navy moved in with all their latest equipment, but there was no sign of the Victor.

Dr. P. B. Walker, then head of RAE Structures Department, hired a fleet of trawlers and made one desperate bid after another to find and recover the wreckage. One day a fishing trawler reported that its drag-net had caught something big and heavy but lost it when pulling it in. Hanging on to a straw of hope, some red rubbing on the net was examined but it could not be proved conclusively that it came from paint used on the Victor. The cables were lowered on to the seabed and dragged along. When they were obstructed, the cables were hoisted and the rubbings again were subjected to tests.

Despite expert advice and governmental penny-pinching pessimism, the RAE was ready to filter the whole Irish sea with drag-nets if necessary. But Walker's fleet of sixteen trawlers produced no results. Once oil patches were noticed on the waves. Trawlers then skimmed the sea. The cans of oily water they sent in were examined — but there was no proof that the oil had escaped from the Victor.

At last came a stroke of luck: a fisherman pulled in his net with a piece of tangled metal. He reported the find and soon it was confirmed that this beyond doubt had come from the aircraft. The trawlers now really began to filter the sea in the area. They lined up like taxicabs on a rank and moved in circles. Each trawled a predetermined stretch, put the metal catch in green bags, plotted the spot where the contents were picked up and sent immediate radio messages to shore — 'Green Pasture, 2 bits'. As the wreckage trail in the water became more and more identifiable, better direction could be given to the trawlers and the number of bits in the net increased.

Each night, lorries took the bags to a small airfield from where a Hastings, used solely by the investigation, flew them to Farnborough. And each night the hangar where the wreckage was sorted and shifted smelt like a fishmarket. To give the captains new inspiration, Walker invited them to Farnborough, showed them the gaps in the aircraft under reconstruction on chicken-wire and challenged them to find him such-and-such crumpled piece. In almost a year, more than half a million pieces were recovered and the reconstruction — that ultimately solved the puzzle — was eighty per cent complete. The investigation cost about one and a half million pounds.

The result is a military secret and so it has never been published. Because the wreckage trail seemed to extend over a huge area, it was rumoured that the Victor had fallen apart in the air. The fact was that the Victor, on the basis of a successful investigation, justified the expense for it became a long-serving, very reliable aircraft. The secrecy that surrounded the RAE hangar and the findings is explicable in view of the tales a wreckage can tell about the capabilities of the aircraft itself.

The Russians, for instance, fought a desperate battle in 1966 over a doomed twin-engined aircraft supposedly packed with secret equipment such as an anti-radar device that could protect it from ground-to-air missiles. The two pilots flew over West Berlin where their radio was monitored. Allegedly, they lost control at 12,000 feet, but their Russian controller forbade them to use their ejector seats or attempt an emergency landing at West Berlin's Tegel Airport. The instruction was to reach East Berlin dead or alive. They never made it.

One fact the wreckage clearly confirmed was that the pilots had not even attempted to escape by ejecting themselves before they crashed into the muddy water of Stössensee in the British sector. All available Russian personnel, including a busload of guards from the war memorial, rushed to the site, but military police kept them at bay. The Soviet authorities claimed that the pilots had not ejected because they wanted to avoid crashing into a densely populated area of the city. The Russians offered to look after all the recovery or assist in any way, but the British insisted on their right to do all this themselves as a favour to their colleagues from over the wall. The Russians had to satisfy themselves with illuminating the site every night and filming every move the divers and experts made. The Russians were patently worried about what the British jigsaw wallahs might learn about the aircraft — believed to be the latest, top-secret supersonic YAK fighter, the Firebar, capable of carrying nuclear bombs — than about the possibility that Western expertise might snatch the honour of detecting the accident cause from them.

Apart from these games of secrecy, the Russians had a genuine, purely technical problem a crash detective must face constantly: if he does not supervise the recovery and handling of the wreckage himself, he may never be able to detect whether damage to any component has been caused before, during or after the crash.

Any is the operative word, for it is not merely a figure of speech that even the cheapest, tiniest nut in the colossal complexity is under suspicion as the source of a chain of disastrous events. If there were any doubts about the wisdom of this attitude, the first day of March 1962 was to put an end to them.

The 707 of American Airlines made a normal take-off from New York's Idlewild (now Kennedy) Airport on that day. Its crew of eight were to transport eighty-seven passengers to Los Angeles. Less than twenty seconds later all of them lay dead in Jamaica Bay, a notorious, raindrop-shaped spot of water between Brooklyn and the Atlantic Ocean.

Within a further few seconds, everybody from van Epps's CAB office rushed to the government car pool and the investigation was under way. From available witness evidence, it seemed obvious at once that something must have gone wrong with the controls: eight seconds after the powerful, fast climb had begun, the pilot was making a normal left turn when the jet seemed to lose its balance; its left wing started to dip as if in slow motion, the bank became sharper and sharper until the aircraft turned upside down, and then tumbled headlong out of the sky.

The crash shook the entire international aviation world. After a troublesome start, the 707 was by then already regarded as one of the world's safest jets. In nine countries where at that time nearly four hundred of the type were in use, the question of an immediate grounding was raised: if there were control problems on a serious scale, it might have been suicidal to fly the aircraft.

The investigation was one of the most painful, complicated and controversial cases of aviation detection ever undertaken. While the various specialist groups – structures, systems, power plants, maintenance records, flight recorder, operations, air traffic control, weather, witness and human factors groups with the participation of FAA, American Airlines, Boeing, pilots' association and a dozen other organisations — did their routine chores, a concentrated effort was made to scrutinise everything that could lock the 'steering' (rudder) in an extreme position and so render the aircraft uncontrollable.

In true Sherlock Holmes style, having eliminated the impossible, flight tests were carried out to prove or disprove two remaining theories.

The hydraulic mechanism controlling the rudder was the chief suspect. Tests suggested that if a one-inch twenty-cent bolt fell out of its place, it *could* lock the rudder. The bolt was supposed to be held in place by a nut, but as an extra safety precaution there was a cotter pin that ought to have done the job even if the nut worked loose. Investigators who studied the manufacture and maintenance procedures of the 707 could not ascertain whether the cotter pin had been installed properly or not in this particular aircraft. Simulated rudder malfunction flight tests by FAA proved that recovery action would be ineffective if the bolt failed — and on June 12, three and half months after the accident, FAA sent a warning to all airlines operating 707's. George Prill, Director of the agency's Flight Standards, emphasised that the investigation was not yet closed but claimed that the tests eliminated all but the bolt theory.

Some had doubts about the value of further investigation — others about the validity of the bolt theory. Boeing, whatever its experts thought, was not going to take chances: it sent a small safety wire for each aircraft to all users. The airlines were not going to take chances either: they fitted the wire to the bolt.

Although manufacturers and airlines have often been criticised by politicians, insurers and other interested parties, this case emphasised the important point that, usually, remedial action is taken as soon as the investigation produces any even remote hint of the cause of the accident without waiting for the final analysis or the report which is published sometimes years later. Yet such very sensible precautionary acts involve a conflict between law and safety. If a manufacturer publishes some modification after a crash and advises airlines to comply, lawyers claim it amounts to the admission of responsibility even if the modification was not the result of the main causal investigation but only a 'bonus', what Joseph O'Connell, Jnr., Chairman of the NTSB, called in an interview 'the scientific and technological fall-out of the investigation'.

In this case, the CAB was far from being finished with that 707. Their theory, too, confirmed that the rudder was suddenly shoved into an extreme position that forced the aircraft into an irrevocable yaw, sideslip and roll. But they suspected electrical malfunction in the hydraulic system: a generator, if shorted, could have produced all the elements of this tragedy.

The unit was examined meticulously. Investigators found that some wires inside were scratched and punctured. Could these cause the short-circuit? The answer was 'yes'. Could this damage be caused by the crash itself? The answer was 'no' because first the impact would have had to destroy the surrounding parts, which acted as a protective envelope to the wires. So the damage must have been there *before* the crash!

Maintenance was ruled out as a cause of that damage. What about manufacture? Charles Lamb, now one of the four GO team managers of NTSB in Washington, went to the factory and examined similar wires in generator parts coming off the assembly line: he found damaged points identical with those discovered in the 707. Then he followed through the entire operation and at one point he saw a man handle the wire with tweezers in a way that could, once again, reproduce the same damage that would short the generator, deflect the rudder and lead to a loss of control. A new, safer method of handling the wire was therefore introduced.

The CAB accepted this line as the probable cause of the

accident in its report issued some six months after the FAA warning and ten months after the accident. One of the two theories must have been right: there were no more similar accidents.

It is a basic tenet of aircrash detection that 'each accident is different from all others'. (This is true, as shown by the accidents to the 727's, even if the primary cause is apparently the same.) When the sequence of failures is traced to basically identical components, the investigation may still go in any number of ways.

Just to demonstrate this point, it is worth recalling two cases both of which were traced to a valve in a hydraulic system.

One involved two Canadian accidents — clear repetitions of one another. First structural failure, then the manner of piloting was suspected. Finally, the investigator was led to believe that a valve that controlled the 'up' and 'down' selection of flaps had claimed independence from the pilot. When, during take-off, the pilot wanted the nose up and therefore shut the valve, it remained open and put the nose down. X-ray examination of the valve, observation of new valves working on a test rig, and flight tests proved that a speck of dirt, perhaps some screw scraping, had been sealed into the system during manufacture, and it could have kept a spring-controlled small ball in the valve open in spite of any effort by the pilot.

In the other case, the destruction of a prototype aircraft, after the elimination of all other possible causes, suspicion fell on a valve that was set incorrectly, increased the friction between moving parts and possibly jammed. Closer examination revealed that the minute clearances were not there at all. Impact distortion was ruled out: it was in a very protected position and its surroundings were undamaged. The valve just appeared to be of the wrong size!

The valve couldn't have passed the rigorous production

tests in the condition in which it was found, and even if it had slipped through, the aircraft could not possibly have made its earlier flights 'uneventfully'. While all aircraft using similar valves were urgently grounded for a check — similarly suspect valves were changed — Godfrey Feltham, the investigator, came to the somewhat frightening conclusion that the valve must have changed its dimensions, albeit to a small degree, *during its working life*. It was just a loophole, a legal no-man's-land, and Feltham took it upon himself 'to investigate to the bitter end'. The manufacturers and the airworthiness authorities could not have foreseen such a change. The valve manufacturer had produced the unit within the prescribed limits of tolerance. The steel works did not know what their product would ultimately be used but complied with all the regulations.

It was a long scientific battle that opened up an entirely new field of research. At long last, industry and other parties became interested and, with their backing, far-reaching conclusions were drawn. In lay terms these meant that some types of steel, under certain conditions, *without* extreme changes in temperature, can go through dimensional changes.

Both cases helped to advance 'the state of the art', both added new weapons to the impressive armoury of crash detectives. Unfortunately, new methods of investigation are not made accessible to all specialists — and certainly not quickly enough. Just three examples.

O. E. 'Ed' Patton and his flight recorder laboratory at NTSB have developed the fastest methods of deciphering this vital information and devised a 'reading machine' for metallic foil recorders. Yet the machine has been ordered only by Australia, and is scarcely known outside America even among countries that use metallic foil as their recording media. (The machine will face considerable problems soon when the amount of recorded information increases.)

In Britain, recorders use the allegedly more advanced magnetic plastic tape or wire. But when there is a crash with a metallic foil recorder on board a foreign aircraft, the 'reading' is still by a more laborious method than the one used by NTSB.

Farnborough, like all centres of investigation, encountered difficulties in the examination of supposedly damaged ball races, and devised therefore a technique called 'balloscopy' — a special apparatus which reveals hitherto invisible tell-tale marks. It was described in the *Canadian Aeronautics and Space Journal*, but in the course of this research, none of the investigators interviewed outside Britain had any knowledge of it.

Aircraft manufacturers are in close contact. The exchange of their experience is being carried out at commendable speed, as far as safety, in design for instance, is concerned. But there are not yet any regular channels for experience exchange in investigation techniques and rationalised organisation for the sake of a higher degree of preparedness. Like American manufacturers the British Aircraft Corporation has always assigned appropriate specialists to help the investigations according to the particular requirements of the case. But only since 1964 has BAC operated an independent flight safety and investigation department. Prater Hogue, the Boeing investigation co-ordinator, revealed in a recent Washington lecture how his company had improved the readiness of specialists who might be assigned to investigations (they have a pre-selected band of experts whose health is checked regularly, whose temperament and compatibility are judged to see whether they could really cooperate with members of the team, who have visas and immunisations up to date, and who are familiar with basic ways and problems of investigations), but other manufacturers and their investigators know very little about this system.

The difficulty of exchanging such information is, of course, very considerable. In this unruly, ever-changing world of crash detection, it is almost impossible to lay down hard and fast rules of 'reading the wreckage', but there is a fast-growing treasury of special tools, techniques, theories, time-saving mathematical formulae and a wealth of basic codes investigators can apply with discretion. The problem here is that even the best publications — like the ICAO *Manual of Aircraft Accident Investigation* or the USAF handbook *Aircraft Accident Prevention and Investigation* — are not reviewed frequently enough to include the latest achievements, and so show a distinct preoccupation with propeller settings, for instance, when this is already the age of jet engines.

The clues manuals provide are based on experience, and some examples may help to appreciate how crash detectives work.

A steep dive into ground may be indicated by the wreckage being confined to a small circular area around a deep crater where buried parts and completely crumpled engines would be found.

Propeller blades bent forward: indicates engine under power on impact. Extensive damage to the turbo-jet 'compressor rotor blades with all the blades bent opposite to the direction of rotation' is one indication of high rpm during steep angle of impact.

Periodic light spots in dark line of tyre marks on the runway: a blowout hole in the tyre. Short, wide, heavy and erratic tyre mark: may suggest landing hard enough to cause gear failure.

When instrument pointers are lost or torn away, their position at impact may be established by application of ultra-violet light to the instrument face. This 'black light' may also reveal the contents of certain burned aircraft documents.

If there is fire in the air, the smoke pattern will usually follow the slipstream and in the 'shadow' (aft side) of rivet-heads, for instance, there will be smoke-free spots. If the folds of a crumpled sheet of metal are burnt, fire preceded the distortion; if the folds are clean, the piece of wreckage was affected by fire after impact.

Ed Slattery mentioned in his Rome lecture in 1961 that the CAB had pioneered the use of X-ray in search of metal fatigue, and in working out mathematical formulae, for instance, to determine ground speed when engine rpm is known or rpm when speed is known by utilising the number of propeller blades and distance between slash marks on the ground.

Scores, smears, scratches and burns help to determine sequences. When fractured parts of a surface are reassembled by the investigator, discontinuity of a mark would show that this damage *followed* the fracture, continuity would prove the sequence was the other way round. In a collision, for instance, there was a paint smear from one aircraft on the tailplane of the other. The tailplane broke off, its torn pieces were damaged in many ways, but it was the paint smear alone, found on *all* the pieces, that indicated that, at the time of the collision with the other aircraft, the tailplane was undamaged and complete.

When painted metal is torn, the paint is left in a saw-tooth-like pattern; the lie of the saw-teeth helps to tell the analyst in which direction the metal underneath had been torn; in the metal sheet itself, protruding burrs are left on the last edges of contact.

The clothes and equipment of the crew, together with their bodies, are also a source of 'wreckage clues' for the investigator. The precise immediate recording of these clues is vital. The ICAO *Manual* (p. 51) recalls that, after a military accident, one of the first people at the scene made a mental record that the dead pilot's face was blue. 'This colour, a symptom of anoxia, had gone by the time the victim was examined by a doctor', but the observation helped to establish the cause of the accident.

These kinds of clues and 'de-coding' techniques leading to the message in the wreckage are the easiest part of the studies for the aircrash detective constable. Much more difficult is to learn what could be called the investigator's philosophy. After numerous consultations on this subject, it seems best to present one man's views which incorporate the experience of many others, too. Fred Jones of the RAE explained his basic approach to investigation in a paper delivered to the Canadian Aeronautics and Space Institute in 1962 and in a series of interviews for this book.*

He likens the investigator's work to the interrogation conducted by a father whose son limps home with a plastered knee and whose natural 'human faculty of inquisitiveness' is aroused. He will ask *what* happened (I tripped, Daddy), *where* (at the gate) and *when* (an hour ago), *how* did it happen (I ran and that broken paving caught the tip of my foot) and *why* did it happen (Jimmy was chasing me). The investigation completed, the father may get that broken paving repaired and may even give a warning against running in the street — in fact, impose a 'temporary flight limitation'.

An aircraft is a clever string of components, each affecting the behaviour of the others, that ultimately must be looked at as one complex unit. But at the beginning, it is all unnamed 'wreckage'. Then each item must be handled and identified — pieces of the metal skin may only be identified when the aircraft is reconstructed in two or three dimensions — and parts of the various systems must be sep-

* The paper has been published in the December 1962 issue of the *Canadian Aeronautics and Space Journal*. It is most unfortunate, to say the least, that this paper has been used in slightly reworded forms verbally and even in print many times without permission and without giving due credit to its author.

arated. About each piece, each system and the aircraft as a whole, the five basic questions WWWHW are asked: what happened, where, when, how, why?

There is a constant interchange of deductions and feedback: if this component failed in such-and-such manner, it would cause such-and-such damage to other parts; did it in fact cause such damage to the particular other part — or was it the end of a chain of events? Perhaps the other part was no longer even anywhere near when this damage occurred! In this way, a series of failures emerges — independently from one another. Then the whole 'clever string of components' must be related to one another and each failure must be given its place in the sequence that leads to the ultimate primary cause of the accident.

Many of the identified failures and reconstructed sequences will bear negative results. These are a corrective guidance like 'no through road' signs.

A great team of contributing experts is most valuable in examining individual units and systems but sometimes, when a specialist condemns a piece of wreckage by saying that it is 'too damaged' for examination, a jack of all trades may devise ingenious ways of extracting information. Fred Jones sees it all as a basically lone battle in which the specialists play their part by answering specific questions. He sees the investigator in charge as the man who must carry the knowledge and specialist findings across man-made barriers — for example systems of airframe or powerplant — and avoid ultimate judgment of any one failure out of context. (This is apparently a contradiction of the American team system, but in practice, it is not. The Americans avoid this pitfall by daily conferences for all team members, specialist group managers, and also by using an 'inner circle' of all-rounders in Washington who review the team's work step by step and, if necessary, give guidance so that nothing is evaluated out of context.)

The application of the 'WWWHW' system to a not entirely hypothetical case would go like this:

The wreckage pattern on the ground revealed that the starboard wing of the aircraft broke off in the air (it was farthest away from the main wreckage) in a certain manner. While everything else on the aircraft is being fully examined — leading, as expected, to negative results — the brunt of the investigator's attack must be borne by that starboard wing and its relation to the movement of the aircraft. (Until now, the investigator was just looking, and not looking *for* anything in particular.) The step-by-step conclusions in the various phases of the inquiry could be shown on this 'logic tree'.

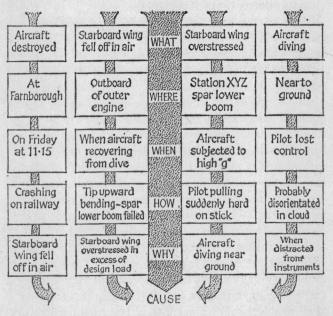

Aircraft destroyed	Starboard wing fell off in air	WHAT	Starboard wing overstressed	Aircraft diving
At Farnborough	Outboard of outer engine	WHERE	Station XYZ spar lower boom	Near to ground
On Friday at 11·15	When aircraft recovering from dive	WHEN	Aircraft subjected to high "g"	Pilot lost control
Crashing on railway	Tip upward bending–spar lower boom failed	HOW	Pilot pulling suddenly hard on stick	Probably disorientated in cloud
Starboard wing fell off in air	Starboard wing overstressed in excess of design load	WHY	Aircraft diving near ground	When distracted from instruments

CAUSE

The manoeuvre indicated in the wreckage would be reconstructed by those who investigate the operational side.

76

The conclusion that the pilot lost control not because of inexperience (training, background had already been looked at separately) but because of disorientation, would again be the result of discussion with experts — like those in the American teams. But why would an experienced pilot be distracted from his instruments when his entire training had aimed at teaching him not to fly 'by the seat of his pants'?

Suddenly, a 'negative' line of the investigation is brought back into the picture: rough running of an engine was indicated but ignored because it did not amount to engine failure. Was the pilot distracted from his instruments by that engine? Was he struggling to diagnose the symptoms and make a decision to cut out that engine or not?

If so, although the immediate cause of the accident is now known, the chain of tragic events could be traced back to some faulty item in the engine, insufficient servicing or supervision, and even perhaps to a design problem that had given trouble before but had never been named, in a report, as the cause of an accident.

CHAPTER FOUR

THEY FELL APART IN THE AIR

THE Bristol Wayfarers carried a sizable work-load in the 1950's. By 1955 the type was about eight years old and had got over its teething troubles a long time ago. All over the world, some two hundred of these aircraft flew, posing only occasional routine problems. Several of them belonged to Iberian Airways and these were now on their way to Britain for some modifications and an overhaul at Bristol. Another Wayfarer, working for West African Airways, was on its run to Lagos. None of the captains knew that the wings of their aircraft were being slowly chewed away. In simple, if melodramatic, terms, it was a race for destruction — which of them would be the first to fall out of the sky without warning?

The aircraft over Nigerian bush country carried thirteen passengers and crew. The captain was already in radio-telephone conversation with Lagos where he would land. He was flying straight and level, reported his height, speed and estimated time of arrival, then went off the air. When he failed to contact the control tower in due course, Lagos called him, but there was no answer.

The increasing delay made it obvious quite soon that there must be a serious reason. As there was no other aircraft in the area, collision could be ruled out in theory. The Wayfarer was in the least demanding phase of the flight — exposing the aircraft and crew to the least stress — so what could have gone wrong? There could have been many causes. But when the wreckage was spotted in dense bush, the airline and the Nigerian Director of Civil Aviation realised at once that there must have been an engineering problem calling for more engineering experience than their own. They asked for immediate assistance from Britain. This was not only a most fortunate decision but also a highly commendable one, for there had been accidents in other countries where national pride, overruling all other considerations, had stood in the way of an appeal for help, and where inexperienced handling of the wreckage had wasted precious time and destroyed evidence.

Bertram Morris was then forty-one and his nine years' experience had already taught him to expect the phone to ring in the middle of any night. His wife, whom he had married a month after taking the job with AIB, got out of bed calmly and, shivering in the February night, helped him to pack. He caught the next flight to Lagos, landed in the tropical heat and had no time to get acclimatised. In the three weeks to come he was to lose 21 lb. in the quickest slimming course on earth — by bushwhacking.

'Officially, I was to stay in The Residency, the place where Edgar Wallace had got the atmosphere for his Sanders of the River stories, but I had no time for pleasant literary memories,' he said. 'The wreckage was some fifty miles inland from Calabar, far from the road. Fifty men with machetes had to cut down the bush so that I could get to it at all. Not that I wanted to, quite frankly, for it was one of the few cases where the wreckage was still untouched and I dreaded going near it.

'The aircraft had come down, almost vertically on a 45° slope of a hill, and in the bush it was difficult to see if all the aircraft was there. As the men cut down a small area, I laid out what I had found and at first everything appeared to be there. Then it became obvious that a major part of a wing "skin" was missing. Knowing the position, height and speed of the aircraft, and also the wind conditions at the time, I could make a quick trajectory calculation of the spot where the skin would fall if it failed in the air. It was about a thousand yards away, and with the aid of machetes we managed to find it in five portions buried in dense, untracked bush.

'As you can imagine, there were a tremendous number of fractures and each had to be looked at and matched with the part it had separated from. But to me, the most important were the parts which could have anything to do with the in-flight failure. So I had to transport all these to Lagos where, when I laid them out in their correct relation to one another, it occurred to me that the various parts of the structure showed no sign of having been overstressed. The wing skin rivets were all torn apart — and the skin just ran off the wing structure like a glove.'

The beginning of this series of rivet failures pointed a

finger at a spot that had been known to be exposed to heavy aerodynamic stress and had already been specially strengthened by design. Morris knew that if there was still a structural problem, every mile the Wayfarers flew was potentially lethal. This particular aircraft had flown some 5,000 hours. There might be others in the air that had clocked up more than that.

Working under tremendous pressure from the impact of this thought — 'it would have been a nasty experience if another aircraft crashed the same way while I was searching for the cause' — Morris retraced the sequence of failures from wing skin to rivets, from rivets to wing structure, which could be described in simple terms like this: the top and bottom spar booms in the wing are connected by the vertical 'spar web'; the wing skin is riveted to the 'skin angle' which, in turn, is attached to the spar boom and web. Morris scrutinised every part looking for signs of a failure which could not be caused by and had in fact, preceded all the others — the primary cause.

One by one all the parts were exonerated. Suspicion now fell on a 'doubler plate' which was supposed to give the required extra strength and 'back up' the web against structural loads. This was the last part in the sequence of failures: it appeared that the doubler plate had still not given the required strength to the web which failed at the point of stress concentration where it was attached to the plate. It was the primary cause of the crash — but why and how did the web fail? Morris suspected fatigue and examined the fracture, but in such very thin sections it can hardly ever be recognised by the naked eye. Therefore he sent the part to Farnborough for micro-examination and sent a signal to AIB giving them the direction and mode of failures and the apparent primary cause. A copy went to the Bristol manufacturers who, in turn, warned all users of the aircraft.

The warning came just in time. While Farnborough

confirmed that the fracture was due to fatigue, the Way-farers from Iberian Airways were examined without delay. One aircraft was found with a fatigue-failing web. The wing of another was far beyond that: the web had already ceased giving support and the first few rivets had already failed. The impending disaster might have been a matter of minutes or a few hours during the next flight.

Was it a design error? Yes. Could it have been foreseen? No, the state of the art was not yet ready for that. Once the doubler plate had been redesigned, the wing gave no more trouble.

Fatigue failures became perhaps the greatest menace to aviation soon after the war. For more than a decade it rode like a jinx on the wing tip of every new aircraft. Dr. P. B. Walker described it as 'a disease of maturity in aeronautical science. In the early days, aircraft did not as a rule last long enough for fatigue to develop'.* As economy began to re-quire longer working life and fuller utilisation of the new expensive machines, designers scored a magnificent success by meeting these demands. But the extended life of the air-craft and its work-load (Dr. Walker estimated that, in ad-dition to the millions of miles flown, 'the average transport aircraft travels a greater distance on its wheels when taxiing than the total distance covered by many land vehicles') in-troduced the crucial time element which permitted aircraft to pass all known tests with flying colours and operate for years without a hitch while harbouring a lurking potential killer.

Fatigue was not a new problem. For several decades it was a mechanical engineer's headache and was considered to have been mainly a result of vibration. Metallurgists com-bated it by providing high-strength aluminium alloys. Manufacturers fought against it by paying great attention to

* 'Aircraft Fatigue From the General Engineering Standpoint', lecture at the Institution of Mechanical Engineers.

the most minute details and so eliminating points of stress concentration caused by corrosion, the simple malalignment of a bolt, scratches and sharp tool marks, etc. Designers, in the throes of the strength versus lift battle, allowed for it by making fuller use of the old 'fail-safe' principle and so creating methods like double structures (two small members doing the job of one large piece), multiple structures to divide the load, and back-up structures where the load is still carried only by one structure although there is another one built in for stand-by duty. This latter concept is, incidentally, the nearest to Leonardo da Vinci's idea some four centuries ago: 'In constructing the wings one should make one cord to bear the strain and a looser one in the same position so that if one breaks under the strain the other is in position to serve the same function.'*

But the state of the art was such that designers tried to meet precisely defined requirements for *static* strength — to be ready 'for extremely severe loading cases but on the assumption that each was applied once only' (Walker). Now their own achievement of longer and harder working life for the same, basically 'flimsy structure' of aircraft meant that smaller, for a while non-hazardous, loads would be applied more frequently over a much prolonged period. Designers worked with an increasing safety margin but could not 'design out' the unknown hazards fully. And when these hazards revealed themselves, it usually meant disaster.

All this set the stage for one of the most brilliant victories of aircrash detection that paved the way to new, higher standards of safety. This was the story of the Comet, the first civilian jet airliner. It has been told many times, yet recapping it briefly may not only pay tribute to those who took part in it, but also help to highlight some points which are

---

* Quoted by Eric Newton in the *Journal of the Royal Aeronautical Society,* March 1964.

accidentally overlooked or conveniently forgotten in practically all accounts.

At the end of the war the de Havilland Aircraft company took an outstandingly brave decision: instead of building yet another type of conventional piston-engined aircraft, they would utilise their experience with jet fighter planes and design a civilian jet-powered machine. Work began in September 1946 and the first Comet flew in July 1949. BOAC started their proving flights in April 1951 and, in the following year, the Certificate of Airworthiness was granted.

The magnitude of the task was fully realised by all concerned. It was not just a new type of aircraft — it was a journey into the unknown. The turbo-jet engines offered high cruising speed, some 500 miles per hour, which, if it was to be used to its full economic advantage, required that the aircraft should fly upwards of 30,000 feet, twice the altitude of earlier machines, where constant oxygen supply and pressure would have to be maintained for the comfort of passengers. Therefore an 'air bubble', a pressurised cabin, was created.

To the best of everybody's knowledge at the time, the engines, the cabin and, in fact, every inch of the Comet was thoroughly tested in extreme conditions such as no aircraft was ever expected to encounter. The cabin strength, for instance, was tested far beyond the magnitude of pressure required by national and international regulations. According to the state of the art, these were static fatigue tests although, strangely enough, the wings were already suspected of possibly giving way under the repeated application by gusts of not very severe loads. The wings were strengthened, but it eluded everybody that there was a strong resemblance between the effects of gusts and pressure. Nobody can be blamed for it, but even when static *and* repeated loading tests became an official requirement for RAF transport aircraft in 1952, the pressurisation weaknesses were over-looked.

In the meantime, a Comet — registration leters G–ALYP, called Yoke Peter, according to the current international alphabet — accumulated 339 flying hours. On May 2, 1952, Yoke Peter became the first jet civilian airliner starting scheduled passenger service for BOAC. It was a great achievement, duly admired by the whole world.

On exactly the first anniversary of that memorable day, another Comet 'crashed in a tropical storm of exceptional severity near Calcutta'. According to ICAO regulations the Indian government held an inquiry which took less than a month. At this time, an international convention known as 'Annex 13', the most important move in international crash detection, had already been in force for almost two years. 'Annex 13' had recognised the increasing complexity of ac-cident investigation and given the state where the aircraft was registered the right of participation in the inquiry. It had also opened the way to delegating 'the whole or any part of the conducting of such inquiry to the State of Registry'. In this way, Farnborough could ask for some of the wreck-age. But not before the official Indian inquiry into this first Comet crash was over and the wreckage released. Then, in accordance with the Indian investigators' recommendation, some parts were sent to Britain. When Dr. Walker, head of the RAE Structures Department, found that the fragments he had seen were not enough and asked for more pieces, he was told they had already been irrevocably disposed of.

The Indian Court's findings — the structure gave way when overstressed *either* by gusts in a thunder-squall *or* by loss of control — have never been disputed. The storm was such that it might have broken any aircraft. But was there any sign of fatigue in that wreckage? We do not know for certain. Most probably the RAE would have confirmed the Indian findings. But could there have been a 'technological fall-out', a sign of fatigue discovered by leading specialists as a bonus for painstaking examination? Again, we do not know.

In the Comet investigation story this remaining uncertainty was the first denial of all previous crash detective experience. But nothing could be done. An American investigator remarked in 1967: 'We have long claimed that if we have all the wreckage, we must get *all* the answers. How could I give evidence at a public hearing otherwise? Could I just stand there and say "Sorry, sir, I haven't looked at it" when I'm asked if a certain part of the aircraft had anything to do with the crash?' On this basis, some indication of fatigue might have been found, for *all* the wreckage had fallen on land and was retrievable.

It is also possible that even if by luck fatigue had been found, only minor importance would have been attached to it for not all fatigue causes disasters. This might have been regarded as a problem that had nothing to do with the accident. But this is what the investigation is all about.

Less than a month later, the British Air Registration Board followed the RAF lead and called for even more strenuous static *and* repeated loading tests for civilian aircraft. De Havillands now did not fail to take the hint. They conducted loading tests — unfortunately, only of a section of the cabin — to establish the Comet's probable safe working life. By the autumn of 1953 these tests had run far in excess of the proposed ARB requirements and were then ended by *a fatigue failure of the skin at the corner of a window*. These loading tests were regarded as so excessive that nobody believed that any aircraft would live long enough to fail like that.

If all this puts undue emphasis on something that could not have been fully recognised at the time, it is done intentionally. To be wise after the event is not as easy as it looks. In aviation it may take dozens of lives or even more to achieve that delayed wisdom. The aircrash detective — like his criminologist colleagues — gets his chance to be wise only *after* the event. But then it is his duty.

On January 10th, 1954, there were some thin and broken layers of cloud over Rome's Ciampino Airport; some mild clear air turbulence was probably created by a 'jet-stream', the narrow, high velocity wind current, but Yoke Peter pierced through them all with the graceful ease and determination of an arrow. On its way to London, it climbed effortlessly towards it cruising height. Its captain reported his position from time to time by radio telephone and told Ciampino that he was, according to flight plan, over Orbetello Beacon at 0950. He also talked to the captain of an Argonaut aircraft (George How Jig for G–ALHJ).

At about 0951 the Comet's radio transmitted: 'George How Jig from George Yoke Peter did you get my . . .' Then silence.

Coming down from a considerable height (later calculated as about 27,000 feet), a blazing torch fell out of the sky near the island of Elba. Some islanders saw it. But the flames were soon put out by the waters of the Mediterranean which buried the broken body of Yoke Peter, its crew of six and its twenty-nine passengers.

The Italians launched an expedition to the scene at magnificent speed, but the salvage haul was pitifully small: fifteen bodies, some mailbags and personal effects, and a few fragments of wreckage.

AIB representatives joined the urgently convened Italian Commission immediately but, within a few days, the Italians realised that this accident should be handled fully by the state of registry *and* of manufacture where the greatest wealth of experience could be rallied to the cause. This was one of the two commendably quick and prudent decisions following the drama. The other was that although the airworthiness certificate was not withdrawn from the aircraft,

BOAC suspended their Comet passenger services as long as the fleet was to be under scrutiny.

The crash was a tremendous shock to Britain. Until then, an unprecedentedly huge market was wide open both to her operators and manufacturers. No other country was anywhere near building a jet airliner. It would remain impossible to assess the subconscious influence exerted by the hurt national pride and profound commercial considerations on the decisions that followed. (Many people might be forgiven for thinking that sabotage was a distinct possibility considering the way the plane had broken up and burst into flames.) Everybody was understandably anxious to participate in the investigation — and now a strange situation developed.

Following the Italians' decision, the AIB was charged with the responsibility of the investigation. Their representatives directed the search for the wreckage, examined the pieces on the spot and asked RAE to work on the parts returned to Farnborough. In the meantime, within twenty-four hours of the accident, BOAC called a meeting with representatives of AIB, de Havillands and ARB. As a result of this meeting, a committee was formed under the chairmanship of C. Abell, BOAC Deputy Operation Director (Engineering) 'to consider what modifications were necessary' before BOAC could fly the Comets again. 'The Committee proceeded to consider what possible features or combination of features might have caused the accident' (quoted from the Report of the Court of Inquiry, published in 1955).

There are three interesting points about this decision: 1, AIB was represented at the first meeting, attended the following meetings, too, but was not a member of the committee; 2, who was now *really* in charge of the investigation — AIB or this committee?; and 3, this committee was charged with seeking modifications right from the start even though it was not yet known whether modifications would be needed or not.

At the crash area, a frantic salvage operation was mounted with specially fitted vessels of the Navy using under water TV cameras for the first time for such a purpose. The search was in full swing within a fortnight, but despairingly little was found. In the absence of a sufficient quantity of wreckage, the Abell committee agreed — and was supported by all other parties including AIB — that there were a number of *possible* main causes of the accident. As a result of this, some fifty major and minor modifications were recommended and carried out.

Fatigue of the cabin was not suspected. The earlier excessive loading tests were still regarded as sufficient. Dr. Walker had a hunch that must have seemed a boffin's far-fetched eccentric idea to many at the time: he thought about loading tests of an entire cabin instead of only a section. It was an expensive idea, too. It would have cost yet another aircraft. As it happened, it was to cost more than that.

By mid-February, only six weeks after the Elba accident, the Abell committee's very careful report was ready. Various authorities and government bodies gave their opinion but the choir ultimately sang this score: there is very little hope of recovering more substantial parts of the wreckage; the definite cause of the disaster was not found but everything humanly possible was done; after the modifications and tests, there is no reason to keep the Comets grounded. The Minister agreed and jet service was resumed on March 23, 1954.

A report by the AIB had not yet been issued. The practice is that the Chief Inspector of Accidents decides what cases should be investigated and in what form. The cases causing major structural damage or serious injury, practically all accidents to public transport and those that seem to be repetitions or following a trend are formally investigated and a report is produced. Others may lead to 'field investigations' without resulting in a formal report, or to the gathering of some information for experience, statistical and other uses. If there is a Public Inquiry ordered by the government, the AIB investigates and helps the Inquiry in every way, which includes giving evidence if necessary, but the report is produced by the Court and not by AIB.

In the Yoke Peter disaster there was going to be no Public Inquiry and therefore, undoubtedly, an AIB report would have followed. It seemed possible that the report would have to call the cause of the accident a mystery, as there was insufficient wreckage uncovered to prove the real causes and clearly disprove all other causes. As it turned out, it is probable that the RAE, working for the AIB, would have found the cause later because the search for wreckage, although apparently hopeless, was never abandoned, and a week before the resumption of the flights some main items were found. On April 4, a major part of the front fuselage was found. And the search went on.

Once again, criticism that a report was not waited for is being wise after the event. But to professional investigators this is a specious argument. As Eric Newton put it, 'no finding is better than wrong finding'. It is true that there was nothing to indicate the existence of a major problem, a trend or a connection with the Calcutta case, but to some extent both were mysteries which might have been acceptable when flying a new type of conventional aircraft but not when it involved an entirely new concept where unknown factors played a part.

The analogy between the Comet and the problems facing air safety today is obvious enough to be disturbing: should the DC-10 be allowed the continued freedom of the air with a known weakness? Should operators who ignore the warnings from incidents be permitted to carry on flying? And when the first Concorde, again the leader in the field, meets with the first accident, will the suspected gremlin on board be grounded – or only subjected to debates in two languages?

In 1954 all this was difficult to foresee. A fortnight after the operations had begun, on April 8, at 18.32 hours, Yoke Yoke (G–ALYY) took off from Rome's Ciampino Airport for Cairo. Radio-telephone conversation went on without interruption. At 18.57 the Comet was above Naples, climbing to 35,000 feet. At 19.05, it reported its estimated time of arrival to Cairo. After that nobody could contact Yoke Yoke any more. It disappeared with a crew of seven and fourteen passengers. The following day a few bodies and some wreckage were found — the rest of the aircraft was at such a depth in the sea that recovery was an even more hopeless proposition than in the previous case.

BOAC grounded the Comets immediately and voluntarily once again and, four days later, the certificates of airworthiness was withdrawn. With the best brains and all available forces rallied, the RAE was entrusted with the desperate task of investigation. Expense and manpower were no longer obstacles. 'I drove my staff, and incidentally myself, well beyond normal limits,' said Sir Arnold Hall, then Director of RAE. The labour force working for him put in eighty hours a week quite regularly. A very large number of scientists and others worked a hundred or sometimes a hundred and twenty hours a week.

This tremendous effort was acclaimed all over the world as 'one of the most amazing pieces of scientific detective work ever done'. The American *Aviation Week* (February 7, 1955) described its results as 'the product of minute examination, probing analysis and deliberate deduction, held together through tortuous hours by British tenacity and national pride'. To appreciate the work fully one really ought to present the records of twenty-two days' court hearings, of the court's visit to Farnborough, and the photographs of all the exhibits. (The transcript of the hearings together with the written and spoken testimony of sixty-five witnesses and the monumental report of RAE ran to more than 800,000 words.)

The investigation was a multi-pronged attack in the best tradition of aircrash detection backed by massive all-round scientific and technological research. There were many lines of specialist investigations including a long series of test flights, model tests and medical probing. All these and every detail discovered had to help to eliminate suspected causes like wing fatigue and fire or had to confirm the findings of the other lines of inquiry.

One of these 'other lines', certainly not a main effort at the beginning, was the pressure cabin loading test. 'I think it was quite incredible at the state of knowledge then that fatigue of a pressure cabin could occur after such a short time [as Yoke Peter and Yoke Yoke had flown],' said Dr. Walker. Sir Arnold Hall decided nevertheless to give him a chance. Dr. Walker got his Comet, Yoke Uncle, stripped it from the inside, packed the empty shell with instruments, built a tank around it with the wings sticking out on both sides and when the tank was sealed the entire tank and the cabin were filled with water.

Now the 'flights' began. A flight cycle was represented by pressurisation of the cabin by more water being pumped in (climb), depressurisation (descent), and as many 'gust loads' on the wings as would be encountered in a flight (imitated by hydraulic jacks). In this way, a 'flight' of Yoke Uncle lasted only from five to six minutes.

While the engines and every suspected movement of the aircraft were studied, the search for Yoke Peter was intensified. Only a month earlier this had seemed as impossible a task as now the Yoke Yoke salvage was. But in April and May further tons of the wreckage, including major parts, were returned to Farnborough where Eric Ripley, then head of the Accident Section, began the reconstruction

91

of Yoke Peter. This led to several important conclusions about the way the aircraft had failed.

A classic piece of detective work concerned the tailplane which was supposed to have broken off early in the sequence of failures. Late in May the tail unit was recovered and sent to Farnborough. It had blue paint smears on it which, when the tail unit was put together with the aircraft, continued along the outside of the fuselage. Examination showed that the smear had progressed from front to aft and this suggested that something thrown backwards might have knocked off the tail. Chemists analysed the paint and found that most probably it was the type used on the seats. This would mean that the tail was in position when something happened in the front from where the seat was catapulted. The proof of the theory was also contained in the tail: a piece of carpet from the main cabin had been captured there by the bent, twisted metal acting like a mouse-trap. The only possible way this could happen was if the carpet had been thrown there *before* or at the moment of the damage to the tail-plane.

Another piece of vital evidence found in the wreckage pointed an accusing finger at the fuselage. There were scratches running along the port wing. Imbedded in the scratches were specks of paint — the type used on the fuselage. This implied two possible conclusions, the first being that the wing was intact when the fuselage failed, and the second being that a part of the side of the fuselage must have been blown out by some extraordinary force, like the cork of a champagne bottle. On June 21 Ripley received a salvaged piece: its paint and jagged edges matched the scratches.

Three days later, Yoke Uncle was making one of its routine 'climbs' in the tank when the water pumped in suddenly failed to increase the pressure inside the cabin. The gauge, marking the difference between the inside and outside (tank) pressure, dropped to nil. The cabin was examined — and there was the proof that the impossible had happened: structural failure due to fatigue at the corner of a window after so few flights! The character of the investigation was changed at once — fatigue and the cabin became suspect No. 1.

The starting-point of the failure was repaired and the tests were continued. But that piece of test evidence was not sufficient to prove what had actually happened to Yoke Peter and Yoke Yoke. Investigators put every inch of the wreckage under the microscope, but there was no sign of fatigue which, if it existed, must have been buried in the sea.

There were large chunks of the Yoke Peter fuselage still missing. Which would contain the evidence? The piece which scratched the wing must have been 'fired' at high velocity, possible only if the fuselage was still otherwise intact when that happened. It seemed a reasonable idea that the initial failure would be in that neighbourhood. But the top of the fuselage was not found. And now, by the end of June, the sea-bed appeared to have been scraped clean.

Investigators reconsidered the trajectory of Yoke Peter. If there was structural failure, it would be like the explosion of a 500-pound bomb in the cabin. It was probable that a fairly large piece, the first to fall, would be blown clear, away from the rest of the cabin. On July 6 the search in the Mediterranean was reorientated. The sea was deeper there, the only way was to use trawlers. Some wreckage was found but nothing significant for a month.

The tank test on Yoke Uncle was the focus of attention. The aircraft was approaching its final flight at top speed. Once again, the structure failed due to fatigue at the corner of a window and the 'explosion' — which did not really take place because the surrounding water could not be compressed — ripped the side of Yoke Uncle wide open.

On August 8 something happened that Dr. Walker later

described as a miracle: an Italian fisherman 'caught' a large piece of metal which, as it turned out, was a part of the centre fuselage with the frame of a skyward-looking window. In the corner of that window — near the 'cork' that had scratched the wing — fatigue, marking the original point of structural failure, was identified.

All the circumstances, explanation and evidence found for the Yoke Peter accident appeared to be applicable to the Naples case, too, and were accepted as such. But, even in the absence of the Yoke Yoke wreckage, there was some material evidence that exactly the same must have happened in both disasters. The link was proved by pathologists.

Italian and British 'medical detectives' were in full agreement that the injuries sustained by people in the aircraft were identical in the Elba and Naples cases. What must have happened to them was also confirmed by scale plastic model tests — the filmed slaughter of dummies at the moment of the pressure cabin break-up left no doubt about that.

There was — and still is — a great deal of dispute about the interpretation of certain injuries inflicted in both cases. Some Italians still believe that these were caused by explosive decompression. Most of their British colleagues who studied this phenomenon deny this: they attributed these injuries to impact with water — experiments with dummies dropped from aircraft helped them to calculate the critical velocity of free fall and impact injuries when hitting the surface. The findings were supported by the examination of some American accidents, the post mortem reports on an airman who trod on a hatch and fell out of an aircraft accidentally, on a German stuntman who had instructed the film company's pilot to go higher than originally briefed so that he could 'make a really spectacular jump', and on a series of suicide cases who had jumped from the Kiel Canal bridge. But throughout these scientific polemics, pathologists never failed to agree that the signs, whatever had caused them, constituted an unbreakable link between the two cases. (This was, incidentally, perhaps the first major occasion when medical crash-detection really showed its capabilities and importance.)

The conclusions of this investigation made aviation history. The manufacturers did everything in their power to 'design out' the newly-discovered hazards, and de Havillands' experience not only lifted the Comets to the ranks of the safest airliners but also helped to establish that high safety level for all other manufacturers building jets and pressure cabins anywhere in the world. The loading tests became standard procedure for all new types ever since. To suspect and recognise fatigue became a routine duty for every investigator.

This latter aspect is especially significant now that structural failures caused by design errors have become almost extinct. Fatigue must be proved or eliminated early in every inquiry when aircraft fall apart in the air. (As it happens, designers have learned so much from the Comet cases and further research that several investigators now 'complain' about the difficulty of giving younger colleagues first-hand experience in diagnosing fatigue.) Without the complete exclusion of fatigue as a primary causal factor, many accidents with structural failures would have remained much-disputed mysteries never leading to discoveries such as the need of new piloting techniques that help to avoid overstressing faster aircraft or to fly more safely in turbulent conditions.

Therefore it is not surprising that the looming shadow of structural fatigue was in the minds of dozens of people who were suddenly pulled out of bed up and down the United States at dawn on January 6 1960.

Only a few hours earlier, most people had never heard of National Flight 2511. To those who had it meant only a chore, a 'New York – Miami non-stop' and the crew of five reported for duty in the evening as usual. To twenty-nine passengers, embarking soon after 1 p.m., it meant leaving a frozen town behind for all the sunshine of Florida. The aircraft, a DC–6B, took off less than half an hour before midnight, flew along the coast, and approached Cape Fear, about its halfway mark. The captain gave routine position reports until, having left Wilmington, North Carolina, he made no more calls. The FAA route traffic controller called him several times but, when there was no answer, the Washington CAB office was alerted: possible accident to Flight 2511. Washington 'phoned New York and, from there, two investigators took the next flight to Wilmington.

Unfortunately, it was not a wasted trip.

The State Police had already found the wreckage in a swampy field partly covered by scrub pine about a mile and a half from Bolivia, North Carolina. The DC–6B had broken into fairly large sections and these fell into a compact area. It did not look like structural failure but at this stage, wandering about in the rain, the investigators were reluctant to come to conclusions. From the nearby military base they borrowed a helicopter search squadron and, as soon as the rain stopped, they flew in widening circles around the wreckage.

They were some eighteen miles from the crash site when they spotted two large pieces of fuselage skin at Kure Beach, right on the shore of the Atlantic Ocean. On closer inspection they also found a three-seat unit. They were lucky; it might have taken a considerable time to reveal that these pieces were missing and find them if they had fallen into the sea.

The implication was clear: no ground impact could have blown these parts that far — there must have been a failure in the air after which the pilot, in a desperate bid to land the crippled aircraft, deviated from its route, away from the sea, descending fast and losing control. With that information, the well-oiled machinery of American investigation swung into action. As the stand-by GO-team system with the automatic assignment of scores of specialists had not yet been developed at that time, the investigator in charge called Washington and asked for specialists. At the same time, he invited experts from FAA, the airline, manufacturers, engine manufacturers, propeller manufacturers, Air Line Pilots' and also Flight Engineers' Associations, and set up his headquarters at the Cape Fear Hotel where he also installed his short-wave radio station.

As soon as about thirty experts had arrived, four specialist groups were organised: one was concerned with the structures — the jigsaw wallahs; the second concentrated on the power plants and propellers; the third, called the Human Factors Group, had to arrange autopsies, study the break-up and see if cabin design could be made any safer on the basis of this new experience; the fourth group reviewed the whole operation, including the flight, maintenance records and the proficiency of the crew. Each morning there was a meeting for all at HQ.

Three days after the crash, a light plane spotted a single body on the bank of the Cape Fear River, near the location of the three odd pieces of wreckage. It was a man, identified as Julian Andrew Frank, a passenger on National Flight 2511. Apart from being found so far away from everybody else, three peculiarities aroused the investigators' interest: he carried more than a million dollars' insurance, both his legs suffered an unusual 'shredded' type of amputation, and there were strange puncture wounds on his body. His injuries were completely dissimilar from those suffered by other passengers. He was put on the top of the autopsy list.

To determine the origin and sequence of the break-up a wreckage reconstruction was now arranged. While a timber skeleton with chicken-wire skin was built for the mock-up, some two dozen convict volunteers from a nearby prison were temporarily released to help move the wreckage.

In the absence of facts, a wild national guessing game began. The presence of so many engine and propeller experts and the known circumstances supported the most popular theory that a propeller blade had been torn from its hub, thrown backwards slicing through the cabin wall, and the consequent explosive decompression of the cabin spewed out the three seats and the body. This idea was accepted even by expert speculators of aviation, but was among the first to be shot down by the evidence literally unearthed at the scene — when all the blades were found to have buried themselves near the four engines.

According to the official report, to an account by Edward Slattery, and to recollections of crash detectives, the investigation now concentrated on the remaining three most likely possibilities: collision, structural fatigue and sabotage.

Collision was then ruled out: no other aircraft had been in the air and nothing had been launched from a nearby missile firing range at the time.

As the wreckage reconstruction progressed, there was no sign of fatigue and strong argument was building up against explosive decompression because the rupture in the cabin wall was too large to be due to that. (Let us recall that designers had learned their lesson: on this DC–6B they had already used a cross-webbing type of wall structure which, unlike the fuselage of the Comet, would now have prevented such fatally extensive spread of the damage.)

During the following weeks, structural experts became more and more convinced that some highly explosive substance had caused the disaster. But with their conviction grew a desperation, for they had only negative proof by virtue of the elimination of other causes, that sabotage of some kind was the culprit.

As the date of a public hearing approached fast, there was a sudden change in the situation: the autopsy revealed various metal particles imbedded in passenger Frank's flesh; laboratory examination showed that among them there were fragments of steel wire which had not belonged to any part of the aircraft; the body indicated the presence of nitrate — the residue of dynamite; laboratory tests on the mock-up also found nitrate in the fuselage near Frank's seat and then, as if to complete the picture, manganese dioxide, a substance used in dry cell batteries, was discovered next to the nitrate. Now it was clear to everybody that dynamite had been exploded by a dry cell battery at the legs of Julian Frank — but crash detectives knew from experience that a scrupulous public hearing would want more proof than mere logical conclusion that there had been a wilful act of sabotage, suicide or murder.

Not that crash detectives were concerned in any way with the criminal aspects and implications of the case — that was in the hands of the FBI who had already established circumstantial evidence such as that Frank had taken out his insurance policies not long before the flight — but they had to prove the cause of the accident and eliminate possibilities like some kind of negligence.

The search area in the mock-up fuselage was widened. Some pieces of torn carpet were now put back into their original position, and those around the blown-out seats were X-rayed. Again, fragments were found that had not belonged to the aircraft.

If there had been an explosion, it would be contained between the rows of seats while blowing a hole in the side of the cabin —but its effect might be shown opposite the ruptured wall. One by one the pieces of wreckage now hanging on the opposite side of the chicken-wire fuselage were examined. It was about a fortnight before the public hearing that the effort paid off: a chunk of twisted metal which had once

99

been a hat-rack held a piece of human bone that had a night-marish tale to tell.

The fragment had come from a lower leg bone. Only Frank had lost his legs, the bone was his. Embedded in the bone was some metal identified as part of the mechanism of an alarm clock that, when blown off, took some shreds of cloth with it. The cloth belonged to the trousers worn by Julian Frank.

The time of the explosion was estimated at thirty-three minutes past two in the morning. The aircraft crashed five minutes later. Yet another 'perfect crime' was solved.

Motives for sabotage are rather limited. Cranks do it sometimes — like the man who blasted a hole in the wall of a Venezuelan airliner and screamed, according to the few survivors: 'Space explorers like me must get the experience of really great emotions!' Such madmen like to borrow ideas from one another. When once a bomb had been placed and exploded in the wastepaper basket of a Vanguard's wash-room, although the plane limped home safely, there were several cases within twelve months when bombs were hidden in the same place.

Politically-motivated assassins also favour the method of blowing up aircraft. They use slabs of TNT because non-fragmentation bombs are harder to detect. Yet in Aden, for instance, a minister was detained in connection with a desert aircrash that killed twenty-eight people as the result of a bomb explosion. Canadian extremists tried to gain attention in this way, only the bombs misfired — the senseless killings failed to increase their popularity. Arab terrorists fare no better: bombs have not won them a single friend.

The most usual motive is, of course, the dream of an insurance fortune from a mystery aircrash. People who tried to turn this fantasy into hard cash included self-sacrificing family-men, a son who insured his mother, men who insured their wives and sometimes even their children, others who tried to dispose of an unwanted wife and used insurance only as a bonus scheme, and ordinary murderers who bore no grudge against their highly insured victims.

Cold-blooded schemers are not deterred by the fiasco in which most of these attempts end. It does not worry them that bombs fail to go off, that the blast does not achieve complete destruction (in November 1967, an American was arrested after the explosion aimed at killing his wife and seventy-seven other passengers had failed to penetrate the fuselage and the pilot could make an emergency landing) and that, sometimes by tragi-comic coincidences, the luggage containing the bomb may end up in the holds of the wrong plane and wipe out the wrong victim.

Alarm stems from the fact that sabotage lives vividly in people's memories because it fires the imagination. In the last twenty years, however, there have been less than three dozen such cases mostly by self-confessed terrorists.

After insurance plots, the blame is borne usually by the insurance vending machines and agents operating at airports. This argument seems to be supported by the fact that such murders feature more prominently in American aviation than in Europe where these facilities are less readily available. Periodically, American pilots start campaigns against the insurance machines but a ban would solve nothing: these plots take considerable planning and preparation; explosives must be bought, detonating devices must be assembled, the criminal must be sure that the victim would take the flight *and* carry the concealed infernal machine; throughout these stages of the scheme, there would be plenty of opportunities for arranging insurance in the more conventional way.

Therefore the FAA stand-point that crash detection and crime detection are the best deterrent is understandable. Apart from some mysterious political killings, in the entire international aviation world there was only one case when, possibly, a killer did go unpunished: one man was blown out of a Mexican airliner, eight others were injured, the plane landed safely, but investigators could not prove a bomb theory. To unravel a sabotage case is always a popular triumph for crash detectives. The aviation industry — not forgetting the insurers — sigh with relief, and fiction writers pocket the fee for yet another original TV script. Newspapers do their job well, they hammer home the message that this is not the perfect crime formula.

But soon, the detection of this crime — together with the tackling of structural failure problems — will grow infinitely more complicated.

As we have seen, in these cases, the solution is in the hands of the jigsaw wallahs and pathologists. Without the wreckage and bodies, they can do nothing. Saboteurs usually plan for the bomb to go off over the sea, jungles, mountains or other rugged terrain. But somehow, at least some part of the wreckage has always been recovered. In an American case, only cabin floor panels were found — but these had buckled upwards above the luggage compartment and gave the vital clue. The October 1967 Comet explosion over the Mediterranean (it was probably intended to kill General Grivas, former EOKA leader, the controversial Greek Cypriot) caused a massive scare among Comet users by reviving the hull failure memories, but the proof of sabotage was provided by the post mortem of some victims, a handful of wreckage and an explosion-torn seat that remained afloat.

Now that aircraft will fly higher and faster, carrying more passengers, the forces of destruction are almost inestimably multiplied. Falling from some 60,000 feet, the trajectory of parts of a supersonic aircraft may stretch halfway across the Atlantic so that the recovery of wreckage may become a superhuman task. Flight recorders and voice recorders, if virtually indestructible, will help the investigators. Tremendously circumspect new tests and military experience with the latest types of aircraft make it less likely that crash detectives will be called upon again as the ultimate line of defence against structural failure. Against sabotage, the work of fanatics and professional killers, the investigators' ingenuity and effectiveness are no deterrent any more. Bombing disasters have nothing to do with air safety.

CHAPTER FIVE

IT WAS ON THE CARDS

A COLLECTIVE farm bought the first electric milking machine in Hungary — but it was delivered in parts without an instructions manual. An exceptionally talented shepherd who had no technical training volunteered to assemble it. During the inaugural run of the machine, the cow howled and struggled to get away. The shepherd had made only one mistake: he connected some part the wrong way round — and that turned the sucking action into blowing.

Considering the tragedies caused to aircraft by similar mistakes, this example may not be the most appropriate, but it certainly demonstrates what 'Murphy's Law' means to everybody in aviation.

If it is mechanically possible to fit any part of an aircraft in the wrong way as well as the right way round then someone, somewhere, some day will assemble it incorrectly.

On both sides of the Atlantic, everybody refers to such cases as 'Murphy's Law' — it is the same in German, French, Arabic, Swedish and Japanese as well as in English — but nobody seems to know its origin. Americans believe it is an Irishism. In Britain it is thought to be an Americanism. And nobody can find a trace of the unfortunate Murphy who gave the law his name.

Wherever this expression crops up, a killer valve is mentioned immediately as the classic example, but its full case-history has never been told before, and even now, it has required special permission from the RAF to retrace the progress of the investigation.

The four-engined transport aircraft took off for an over-seas assignment with a crew of five and thirteen passengers. Soon after take-off, a pilot passenger noticed fuel streaming from the vicinity of No. 1 engine. He informed the captain by inter-comm. After breaking cloud tops, the leak appeared very serious. No. 1 engine was shut down and the captain decided to return to base. The other three engines worked satisfactorily but there was a sudden drop on a fuel gauge — it showed that one of the four port fuel tanks had lost some 3,000 lb. of fuel in ten minutes.

Then No. 2 engine, also on the port side, packed up. While trying to maintain height on two engines, the pilot lost airspeed considerably. And there was a village between them and the airport.

As they struggled desperately to avoid the village and land on open ground, the aircraft, with only the two star-board engines working, went into an uncontrollable turn to port, hit an electrical supply cable, swung round, struck some trees and crashed into the village, demolishing several buildings. Two of the crew, one passenger and two civilians on the ground were seriously injured; all other crew members and passengers, and two villagers were killed.

A Board of Inquiry was convened and technical assistance was requested from AIB. By the time the investigating officer got to the scene only four hours later, the tail, the only large remaining piece of the aircraft, had been pulled from the roof of a building to avoid further damage. The following morning, the investigators had a quick routine look at the maintenance records and noted that some minor servicing had been carried out on the fuel system. While a survivor gave an account of the events on board, the wreckage trail, spread over a vast area, was 'read'. The survivor's report about the leak observed in flight was a second indication that the fuel system must receive special attention. The AIB investigator, never having had anything to do with this type of aircraft, spent the night studying its fuel system. In simple terms, each wing has four tanks leading to a collector tank which feeds two engines. The system is governed by various cocks. The starboard and port collector tanks are connected so that 'cross-feed' from the fuel tanks could be arranged.

In the morning, a third lead emerged from the records: there had recently been some trouble with that port collector tank and a leak had had to be stopped. Was it possible that during the flight a similar but more serious leak had recurred? Walking round the wreckage, still looking for clues and general impressions, the investigator stumbled on a small tank fitted with non-return valves and bits of broken pipes still attached to it. It looked like a collector tank. So he labelled it, marked the spot of the find on his map and put it in his car without examination, because in that moment an army of men, who were to carry out a minute search of the area, had arrived.

He impressed on them particularly the importance of the port side parts of the fuel system because the leak and loss of power had occurred there. Their instructions were not to touch anything, but to call the investigator. By late in the evening three cocks had been found: one controlled port tanks 3 and 4 and was shut; so too was the cross-feed cock; the third cock was open and ought to have permitted the flow of fuel to engine 2. (This was the engine which, after the exclusion of engine 1, lost power and was the immediate cause of the disaster.) The cock controlling No. 2 tank was not recovered but it was accepted as 'shut' because the pilot shut it when the gauge showed the tank was empty.

On the third night after the crash, the investigator — performing an 'old-fashioned' technical one-man show — had two problems to toy with: firstly what could have stopped the flow of fuel between the open cock and the engine? the collector tank? And secondly where was the fuel streaming from in flight? It was seen coming from near engine No. 1. Did it come from an engine leak or from the tank vents near that engine? Those vents acted as overflows — why would any tank be overfilled?

Suddenly a thought emerged from a subconsciously taken mental note: there is a little arrow on each non-return valve fitted to the collector tank showing the right direction of fuel flow — wasn't one of these arrows pointing the wrong way?

At dawn, he looked at the collector tank and found the valve was indeed reversed. The implications were shocking. It meant that the fuel from No. 2 tank flowed into the collector tank and from there it fed two engines *and* tank No. 1. No wonder it was emptied so fast. No. 1 tank was now overfilled and the vent discharged the surplus — observed by the pilots. As a result, to eliminate the risk of fire, engine 1 was shut down.

When tank 2 was empty, the cock was shut and tank 1 was to feed the remaining port engine. But from tank 1 not a drop could come through: the non-return valve did its duty — the wrong way round.

How could it happen? Many more shocks were in store for the investigator.

The origin of the disaster was a plain design error according to the letter of Murphy's Law: the threaded portions at both ends of the valve were identical. Although the valve was marked by an arrow, and although never before had a mistake been made, it was just possible to fit either end into the collector tank.

The result of the mistake was confirmed by an experiment on another aircraft. Now the records came under further scrutiny. During repair and service the valve had been disconnected and reassembled. The inspector did his supervisory duties but then these did not require a fuel flow test that would have revealed the fault immediately.

Five days before the accident the aircraft was test flown for thirty-five minutes. No malfunction was reported. (Because of a different method of fuel management, tank 1 had no time to suck the others empty.) The day before the fatal flight the aircraft was refuelled — and then the forecast of disaster, written clearly on paper, was overlooked. No. 1 port tank had a capacity of 7,500 lb. fuel. The log said it had contained 3,000 lb. before the test flight and therefore, if during that flight none of it had been used, the tank would need 4,500 lb. to be full. That it could take only 2,810 lb. was duly noted in the log — but the implication was not understood. (It meant there was more fuel in the tank after the test flight than before take-off.)

The AIB investigators made several recommendations for the change of valve design, better inspection methods, obligatory fuel flow tests etc., and while a blame-pinning inquiry was being prepared, the Directorate of Flight Safety swung into action with its top-priority cables and telephone calls to ensure that the mistake could not be repeated anywhere else.

Murphy's Law has shown its unrelenting application in practically all parts of aircraft. When a landing gear hydraulic jack was made which it was possible to assemble the wrong way round, a fitter did so — and caused an accident. The oil filter that could be fitted in reverse, permitting unfiltered oil to pass through, incapacitated a vital flying control mechanism.

In the post-war years, it seemed to be an international disease to reverse the aileron controls and thus, when an aircraft tilted a little left, for instance, during take-off, the pilot moved the stick right to restore the balance but instead caused an even further drop of the left wing. The more he did to correct it the worse it became, usually ending catastrophically, for it gave him no time to work out what was going on. This happened in almost identical circumstances in America and in Britain with new designs, and also in Germany where an old, reliable aircraft's aileron control chain had been fitted in reverse — again because it was made possible by an identical screw-thread at both ends. (During the German wreckage reconstruction even individual wires in thick strands of cables were matched because the mistake seemed completely unbelievable until then.)

It is a measure of the investigators' and designers' success that Murphy's Law has lost a great deal of its prevalence. The possible pitfalls are 'designed out' and — with 'the dimmest, least trained, most negligent, tea-time-minded, creditor-chased, family-harassed mechanic in mind'—even extra parts are added to render Murphy's Law inoperative.

And yet, sometimes, even an anti-Murphy device cannot prevent human folly. When it happens, investigators must prove that they can doubt even their own knowledge, skill and senses. This was the case when G–ANRR, a Viscount, crashed at Camberley, Surrey.

The crew was killed, but not before a radio-telephone conversation had been recorded. It revealed that the pilot had had trouble with a 'peculiarly acting elevator'. Working on this tip-off, the investigation concentrated first on the elevator. Together with other parts of the mechanism, a small tab was recovered. The job of this tab is to assist the pilot by relieving him of most of the force necessary to work the elevator.

Thorough examination of the wreckage revealed that one part of the operating mechanism must have been fitted the wrong way round thus forcing the spring tab to work *against* the pilot and pull the stick out of his hands whenever he tried to use the elevator.

Although the investigator did see it fitted in reverse, he knew it could not be fitted like that because the manufacturers, having learned from others' mistakes, had, in fact, produced the part complete with an 'interference pin'. With the pin on, it was just impossible to submit to Murphy's Law.

That pin was found in the correct position — and yet still permitting the reversal.

Running out of valid reasoning, the investigator had a 'mad' idea — and measured the pin. It was shorter than it should have been. Microscopic examination of the end of the pin showed a fine clear cut which, in its protected position, could not have been caused by the crash.

A visit to the maintenance workshop brought a terrifying story to light:

In the maintenance record it was stated that the elevator *trim* tab had been overhauled. It turned out that the fitter who had worked on the *spring* tab thought it was the trim tab, reported the completion of the job and his word was accepted for the record. Now he was shown a spring tab and he said yes, that was the one, with the long pin. He explained that he had found the pin much too long to permit the assembly of the parts and therefore he had sawn off the unwanted length.

For the inspector perhaps it was easy to overlook the mistake — after all, the part was neatly assembled and he, too, knew only too well that it was impossible to do it the wrong way round. When the part was installed in the aircraft, a routine check found it was in working order — in other words it could be moved. Everybody *knew* it could not operate in reverse and so nobody checked that.

No designer can guard against such lunatic mistakes. But fortunately, airlines and manufacturers react violently if there is any indication of a Murphy's Law case in its widest sense. Swissair, for instance, regarded it as a Murphy's Law case when a mechanic mixed up two types of aircraft.

When in March 1967, a Swissair DC-9, was taxiing out for take-off at Brussels airport, a ground mechanic noticed that sparks were coming from the landing gear. Seconds later, the pilot overheard a remark on his radio: 'La Swissair a un frein bloqué.' This not very reassuring sentence was soon followed by the Tower telling the pilot, 'There is something wrong with your brakes.' The aircraft returned and an inspection discovered that a DC–8 nose wheel bearing had been fitted to the DC–9 wheel. The responsible man in the workshop was disciplined, store room procedures with spare parts were made more rigorous, and then a flood of correspondence followed up the case warning all interested departments of the airline, advising other airlines and reporting to the manufacturers that such a mistake was found to be possible.

In a DC–8 case, when the Swiss had a minor incident long after the type had entered service, it was discovered that some engine compressor parts could be assembled incorrectly. An X-ray examination of all engines was ordered and a special inspection was introduced in all their workshops.

It is, of course, comforting to know all the efforts that are being made to expose mistakes and bring them to the widest possible attention. Because of this practice, it is unlikely, for instance, that Northwest Airlines would fall into a similar trap as their Lockheed Electra did on September 17, 1961.

It had flown from Miami to Milwaukee, Wisconsin, the previous day. The crew had spent the night there and started the return flight but only as far as Chicago, Illinois, where another crew of five took over according to schedule. The aircraft took off with thirty-two passengers, climbed to about two hundred feet, began to turn, then banked more and more critically, lost height, struck power lines and then a railroad embankment, cartwheeled, and crashed into the ground, completely disintegrating and killing all on board in less than three minutes.

A tragic tape recording was handed to the investigators: the crew fought for their lives but had no time to save themselves. It was a garbled transmission lasting only seven seconds, delivered rapidly in a high-pitched voice. A special study found that most probably the recording was 'We're in trouble (break) uh and all units holding this is Northwest alert I still don't have release right turn in no control (intake of breath) (garbled phrase)'. The first two words of the garbled phrase were possibly 'can you?' or 'have you?' The phrase 'was higher in pitch and more rapid than the preceding utterances', said the report.

It was presumed that the pilot's unpunctuated message had referred to aileron control problems but, to prove that theory, the investigation took fifteen months. It found that 'the probable cause of this accident was a mechanical failure in the aileron primary control system due to an improper replacement of the aileron boost assembly, resulting in a loss of lateral control of the aircraft at an altitude too low to effect recovery'.

The investigation also revealed that in principle, following prescribed procedures, there were dozens of opportunities to spot the mistake during maintenance. A mechanic did not follow the manual. Another paid little attention to the job which was not his and he only gave a hand to in his spare time. Having finished disassembly of the unit, they passed on the job to another two men in the next shift. These men had not read the manual for the job, completed the installation of the unit, checked one another, signed the log, but did not call for an inspector. Their crew chief had not read the manual, made some checks, but was not sure if he had asked for an inspector. The foreman 'supervised the

111

unit installation through the crew chief', visited the aircraft three or four times to see if there were any problems, but did not check on the work.

And then the work was passed on to yet another shift — and throughout all this no inspector took even a look at the whole procedure. There was confusion over who was supposed to inspect what.

Apart from the scores of regulations which had not been complied with, testimony at the public hearing 'indicated that formal training of personnel in the maintenance of Lockheed Electra aircraft had been sporadic and that no training had been given in flight control systems.' Although the men who carried out the work were not specially trained for it, and although instructor personnel were available to carry out the usual on-the-job training programme, there was no consultation concerning this unfamiliar task.

And so it went on and on. Finally, the aircraft was released for flight tests and its performance was satisfactory. The aircraft went into service.

The designers of the aircraft had known that in that control system a flexible cable could unscrew itself. Therefore they had installed a safety wire that would hold the cable in place. But on this occasion, that safety wire had not been reconnected.

The aircraft made twenty-nine scheduled flights in the two months that followed. Probably that cable unscrewed itself a little during each flight. One crew was lucky. The other was not. Those who could have read what was on the cards — did not look.

A quite fantastic series of coincidences. But it did happen. And when eventually, in the 1970s, the designers of a DC-10 cargo door — and manufacturers, operators and government agencies — were to disregard Murphy's Law, they would open the gates to the worst aircrash on record.

CHAPTER SIX

FLYING ON A BARREL OF GUNPOWDER

IT is probable that most people who are afraid to fly associate aviation — consciously or subconsciously — with accidents in general and with 'being burnt to death' in particular.

Numerically, their fears are groundless. The chances of ever getting anywhere near an air crash are infinitesimal even for those who, like pilots and stewardesses, spend their working lives in the air and at airports. But unfortunately, in a way they are right too. It is fire that greatly increases the number of fatalities and it is fire that turns many survivable accidents into fatal ones.

It is perfectly understandable that safety experts are very much preoccupied with the idea of preventing crashes altogether. But it is surprising that, for many years, comparatively little attention was paid to the second and third lines of defence.

The first big battle was fought over *fire in the air*. Mercifully, the number of such cases has subsequently decreased very considerably.

At the second line of defence, against *fire after crashes* on the ground, the odds are still very much against us and the rapid developments hold almost inestimable threats. A Jumbo carries enough fuel to burn down a small town.

The third battle with fire is staged at the last line of defence. Its objective is the *escape of all alive on board* after the crash and before or even during the fire.

Strategic planning in all three campaigns should lean heavily on the crash detectives' experience.

What this knowledge is worth was proved soon after the war when *in-flight fires* were a very serious threat. Most of them were due to some mechanical failure of the engine. Once the weak spot had been found, a three-pronged attack could be launched: better prevention, quicker detection and more effective control or extinction of fires. (Unfortunately, for some rare types of fires involving alloys with high magnesium or titanium content, there is still no really effective extinguisher that can be carried aboard.) For example, RAF cases of fire in the air reached a peak in 1949 when a campaign for improved design began. 1950 was the worse peace year the RAF had but, after that, the number of in-flight fires was cut in ten years to about an eighth of the 1950 peak and the record has improved even since.

In-flight fires often lead to structural failures. Aircraft used during and shortly after the war usually lost a wing within a minute of the outbreak of fire, and thus no time was given for an emergency landing. Captain MacMillan knew this only too well when in 1947 he reported by radio that his aircraft, a DC-6, was on fire cruising 19,000 feet over Utah. He tried to come down near Bryce Canyon. After a few minutes he realised that the tail was failing . . . 'We may get down and we may not.' He reported trying to find the best spot for an emergency landing. 'We may make it . . . Approaching a strip.' Then, only a few hundred feet from a runway, the fuselage burnt through and the aircraft began to disintegrate. All fifty-two people on board were killed.

Wreckage examination disclosed one possible starting point of the fire but there seemed to be a secondary source, too. This latter was a magnesium landing flare on the wing. (Its white flame was also seen by witnesses of the catastrophe.) While the investigation continued, these flares were removed from all DC-6's as a temporary precaution.

Only a fortnight later, another DC–6 reported fire in flight. That it managed to land before irrevocable damage was caused, was at least partly due to the removal of that flare which had probably added fuel to the blaze and had speeded up the break-up of the aircraft at Bryce Canyon. Now the damaged but complete aircraft and a live crew were able to aid the investigation. This found that when fuel was transferred from one tank to another, an overflow could occur. The escaping fuel would stream into a cabin heater and start an uncontrollable fire.

This exposed not only a design error but also the entire state of the art. For although there were strict regulations aimed at preventing all such specific cases, the design received its airworthiness certificate because government inspectors probably *assumed* that pilots would never permit such an overflow. With real and allegedly 'pilot error' cases we shall deal elsewhere, but this accident underlined one of the chief teachings of crash detection: pilots are not supermen, give them half a chance and one of them will make a mistake for which to blame the pilot automatically is 'the easy way out'.

In-flight fires kept haunting aviation until the late 1950's. They were often caused by design errors and led to break-ups in the air. The later so popular Constellations suffered from electrical fires for several months after coming into service. After one crash it was revealed that a 'crudely deficient design' permitted electrical arcing near a hydraulic line thus starting a disastrous fire. In 1955 it cost thirty lives to find out that Convairs and other aircraft needed better engine firewall protection than that previously used. Even now when fatal fires in the air are rare, designers dread reports like the one issued on September 22, 1966.

It was only three days after the Australian Department of Civil Aviation had praised the excellent safety record of Australian Airlines which had not had an accident since 1961.

Forty-one-year-old Captain John 'Ken' Cooper and his crew of three were flying a Viscount from Mount Isa to Brisbane via Longreach. They had twenty passengers including two children. About a hundred and fifty miles from Longreach, the pilots noticed fire warnings. They reported it on the radio and shortly afterwards they could actually see one fire. The captain had only seconds in which to decide what to do. Such decisions are entirely up to him. Most probably he considered that an emergency landing on rocky ground with a blazing aircraft and no firefighters around was much too risky. So he chose the lesser of two evils — to divert to Winton, Queensland, and make an emergency landing there.

He began his descent with No. 2 fuel tank in the port wing burning uncontrollably. The main spar of that wing was being gradually weakened. The aircraft was at about 4,000 feet when the port wing began to give way and bend upwards from between the two engines. Between 3,000 and 4,000 feet up, about 5,700 feet from a sheep station, the captain's ordeal was over. The port wing folded upwards, broke off and hit the fuselage which began to peel off. Then the tail broke off with the rear fuselage.

More than 400 major pieces of wreckage were scattered over an area of 2,000 by 700 yards. The crash was non-survivable. The fire continued on the ground.

A team investigation began at once. Led by Frank Yeend, Colin Torkington and other Australian investigators, it was the usual 'slave labour' effort: sixty-five-hour, six-day weeks on end. After site examination in the heat, the wreckage had to be moved quickly to Melbourne so that threatening rain would not wash away some vital evidence. A reconstruction of the aircraft was done in an old wool store.

The knowledge of fire in the air, reported by the pilot, was an advantage. The flight recorder, too, helped by giving the point where the pilot had disconnected the autopilot and

116

begun his emergency descent, and by recording sudden changes in speed, heading and altitude, which could be interpreted as effects from the fire. Recorders in general use today do not diagnose the fire itself but help with factual data which otherwise would have to be arrived at only by assumptions and logic. This recorder gave a reliable readout to thirty seconds from the crash.

By 1966, the Viscounts had flown some eight million hours in twelve years. At the time of this investigation, 378 of them were in use by 59 operators all over the world. And despite all the tremendous service the aircraft had given, there had never been a similar accident. The investigation received top priority and BAC specialists rushed to participate. Bob Bishop of the Flight Safety Department was among them. It was one of his first such assignments. Before he became an investigator, he had spent fifteen years as a Senior Flight Test Engineer. It was natural, therefore, that he should ask himself if some additional testing could have possibly revealed a weakness which could be related to this accident or whether the investigation would indicate that the accident could not have been foreseen in any way. But there was no time for soul-searching theories. A repetition of the tragedy might have happened to any of the 378 aircraft in the meantime.

An immediate problem was to separate in-flight and post-crash fire damage. For this job, investigators must rely on common sense assisted by well-known clues like the metal spray, already mentioned, dispersed in the direction of the slipstream in flight. When smoked, folded pieces are opened with great care, clean shiny metal may indicate that the piece was charred on the ground. Soot patterns may show imprints of twigs, grass or leaves — a sign of fire after impact. When a Lockheed Electra broke up in flight near Buffalo, Texas, in September 1959, 'extremely brittle ash residue' of a compressor was noticed. Investigators tried to touch it and

117

it all 'flaked away readily' indicating that the part must have burnt out at the spot where found.

One of the most important clues is the location of a certain part: if it is thrown far away from the site of ground fire but still shows signs of burning, it must have burned presumably in the air.

A copy-book example of this clue was provided in the Australian Viscount case. In the aircraft three compressors look after the cabin pressurisation. Parts located normally near one of these compressors were thrown clear of the ground fire but were still charred. Now the compressors had to be found. One was completely melted by the main ground fire. Another was badly burnt but appeared to be complete. Fortuitously, the third escaped the ground fire — probably it fell out of the disintegrating aircraft. And from this compressor, the metering unit that supplies lubrication oil was missing. The bearing, too, had come off. It meant that the compressor, spinning at high speed, must have rubbed metal to metal and caused the fire.

Although a warning had been sent to all operators about an associated oil pipe only four weeks after the crash, all suspicion now fell on the oil lubricating unit. How did it come off? It used to be held in position by five studs. One end of each stud was threaded into the casing, the other end was secured by a nut. Each of these '2 BA' studs is less than a quarter of an inch in diameter and costs less than 3p. The nuts were not found, but the studs were there. Only one of them was damaged at the end where the nut used to be. Could the other nuts just fall off?

A simple turn of logic gave the answer: if the studs were pulled in any way, the protected thread still inside the casing would also be damaged. An X-ray examination showed that four of the five were not.

BAC sent out an immediate alert to all users in December, less than three months after the accident. They asked all operators to check these studs and nuts (5,670 on 1,134 compressors) and report their findings. China never answered the request by BAC, but the other fifty-eight users sent in their reports within three weeks. It appeared that of the more than five thousand, only two nuts were missing and twenty-nine were incorrectly tightened.

While a new locking device to prevent the accidental un-screwing of the nuts was sent to all operators, laboratory tests established that it was possible to create a very minor compressor malfunction that, in turn, would cause in certain circumstances a particular rhythm of vibration — just right to unscrew these nuts. (One nut was slower than the others, and this was torn away just before the end of its involuntary journey along the stud when the others went.)

It was a freak accident: most unlikely to happen ever again and now, with the locking device, positively excluded for ever. (To prepare the official Australian inquiry took another five months and to put out the official report took another year. These dates only show that responsible oper-ators, guided by the investigators, do not like to wait with corrective action for the ultimate outcome of the inquiry.)

What this author once described as a 'peculiarly Aus-tralian air safety consciousness' of both government and op-erators,* manifested itself particularly in the meticulous attention paid by Qantas to even the most insignificant fire incident in the air — or on the ground:

'Their Safety Department has a separate fire protection section. Their special training scheme for ground staff who work in engineering and other maintenance shops is far su-perior to that of the average industrial plant. Whenever there is *any* fire in any of their premises,' an extremely de-tailed investigation report must be completed by a senior employee wihin 24 hours, irrespective of the extent of the damage.

* S. Barlay: *Fire*, Hamish Hamilton, 1972.

Captain Aubrey Rees, the Safety Controller said: 'I feel we cannot afford to have different attitudes and standards for flying and ground operations. If we continue to insist on the full investigation of any incident or even irregularity in the operation of our aircraft, we must also apply the same principle to our workshops. After all, we are not a mammoth airline. The loss of use of just one of our aircraft would mean a drop of about four per cent of our earning capacity. Delays in maintenance and so in utilisation of an aircraft would also be a proportionately great blow. Safety at all stages is therefore an economic factor, too.'

The result of these investigations was that while in comparable industrial plants there was a steady increase in the number of outbreaks, Qantas workshops had a twenty-five per cent decrease (all minor cases) in the last two years.

'Each industry has its own most notorious trouble-maker. It may be a certain piece of machinery, a fan or a power unit. Whenever it catches fire or begins to emit smoke, it is repaired and then used as before. In case of a single minor occurrence, airlines may do no more than that. But their system is based on defect reports, maintenance logs, exchange information from other airlines, well kept records which are geared to spot recurrences that can ultimately reveal if "the odd mishap" is, in fact, only the tip of the iceberg. At Qantas, they call the process quality analysis, and their Inspection and Quality Control Department gave several good examples of its effectiveness.

'One of these concerned a fault in a high frequency (HF) radio. In May 1964, A Boeing 707 flight crew reported that the No. 1 HF system had become unserviceable. A circuit breaker was found tripped, reset once and again tripped, on the Darwin-Sydney flight sector. At Sydney, during repair, the power supply unit burnt up, causing fire and smoke but no secondary damage on its rack or wiring. The unit was replaced and a number of minor modifications were introduced as additional safeguards for smooth operation. Although the defect was not a hazard to the safety of the aircraft, these measures were regarded only as temporary, and an analysis of records was carried out.

'The first finding was that the company had had similar previous occurrences. Then it was discovered that other airlines had also encountered this problem, and that a Boeing service bulletin ... had already suggested the use of a different circuit breaker which aimed at correcting the fault. A check of maintenance records then revealed that this modification had indeed been carried out by Qantas on some of their similar aircraft, but that this particular 707 was still waiting for its turn. To cure the *symptom* the new circuit breaker was now fitted, and this ensured that if the system failed again it would not burn and cause fire in the unit. Despite these measures, however, the actual *cause* of the illness had still not been found. The analysis ended with the staccato sentence: "Investigations proceeding."

'In many industries, a report like this may be left on file, gathering dust — at least until the next failure. In aviation, this is a less likely course. Seven months after that flight from Darwin to Sydney, another sheet of paper was added to the file. It contained only three sentences but was duly distributed to twelve departments, and it informed everybody that, according to specialists, a diode overheating could have led to transformer overheating and that locally produced diode replacements were being evaluated. This move aimed at curing the ultimate cause. A few months later, with the introduction of these new diodes for all HF radios, the file was closed.'

Unfortunately, international aviation authorities do not always show such utmost care and concern about *fire on the ground* although postcrash fires are just as big a menace as in-flight outbreaks.

In the last twenty years, the aircrash detectives' findings

of ground fires have usually been followed by some patching up of design here and there, rather than by some entirely new concept to prevent the basic hazard.

Infinitely better firewalls have been developed, many ignition points have been neutralised, safer and more sophisticated emergency landing techniques and firefighting equipment have been evolved, and, among other advances, when the first accidents to second generation jets occurred, better protection and integrity have been accorded to the fragile pipelines that run under the belly of the aircraft — like the 727 Trident, DC–9, One-eleven — carrying fuel from the wing-tanks to the rear-mounted engines.

Yet, the real suspects — the tanks and their fuel — have remained almost untouched. Crash-proof fuel tanks were thought about and discussed whenever there was a fire on the ground. But there has never been a really serious public campaign for their development and, perhaps even worse, despite individual crash detectives' strong conviction, their official organisations have never taken the initiative by raising outspoken criticism about the lack of action.

Privately, scores of investigators underline the need for crash-proof fuel tanks now that the One-eleven has a belly-tank for extra long range; now that new planes carry fuel even in the body and, as the Americans put it, 'an aircraft will become a flying gas tank'; and now that a structural advance, the machined wing, may have become a retrograde step in fire protection.

These machined wings have great advantages. They are built of milled planks and without joints, have increased strength and integrity for a given weight so that more fuel or passengers can be carried, and their sealed, hollow insides serve as integral tanks. Using such wings, aircraft like the One-eleven, VC10, 707, DC–8, and DC–9 have become more economical and structurally stronger, but they have lost the possible advantages of the inflatable rubber bag-

122

tanks that work like cells, in the older, stressed 'skin-wings'. If in an accident one such cell is ruptured, there is slightly less chance of fire to all the fuel at once than if a wing-tank is ruptured.

Several investigators suspect that the spread of the fire may be speeded up because of integral wing-tanks by only a few seconds, but they agree that these seconds may be vital to those on board. To prove this point they will need the experience of a whole series of marginal cases.

The wing-tanks, of course, ended the long fruitless argument about tanks which could be jettisoned in emergencies. Now the 'patching up' will be done by better fire warnings, the use of non-inflammable materials, and firewalls to protect not only fuel against hot parts but also passengers against fuel. Washington investigators have some hope that the massive structure of Jumbos, together with the big quantity of mail, luggage and fuel carried on them, may even act as a cushion' separating and protecting passengers from crash impact.

Others in aviation take the more cynical view that the first two-hundred passengers hit by the impact will become a protecting cushion to the rest of the people on board. On which an insurer commented wryly that it would certainly be 'the most expensive cushion in the world'.

Whichever way one looks at it, the fact is that a Jumbo, for instance, carrying up to 490 passengers, takes almost 47,000 gallons of fuel, more than twice as much as a long-range jet, while basic methods of protection, even with improved suppression of ignition points, remain essentially unchanged. (To passengers this extra quantity of fuel makes little difference, but to fire brigades and all the surroundings of a crash site it is an immensely increased threat.)

There are hundreds of research projects in hand all over the world aiming to minimise the ground fire hazard especially in 'low-impact', survivable crashes. There have been experiments like those with systems to cool hot surfaces automatically at the moment of crash, with new flexible 'tough-wall' cell tanks, with several other methods that would prevent either fuel spillage or its ignition, and even with automatically flooding the fuselage with foam when fire breaks out (the foam protects passengers from flames and fumes), but some of these impose very serious weight penalties and, even so, none is advanced enough to be a practicable proposition in the near future.

Yet there is another way to reduce the number and fierceness of ground fires: by using safer, less inflammable fuel.

In the light of expert arguments but in the absence of clear-cut facts and conclusions by accident investigators, public opinion in the last twenty years had the opportunity to apply more successful pressure on the choice of aviation fuel than on any other public matter.* *Did we take full advantage of this unique opportunity?*

When the civilian jets appeared in the skies in the early 1950's, mainly two types of fuel were available. One was of low volatility, generally known as kerosene — similar to domestic paraffin. The other, best known as JP4, was highly volatile, almost a low grade petrol. The flash point of kerosene is around 100° F. (38° C.) while JP4 may easily ignite at any temperature down to —10°. (—23° C.). This means that in take-off and landing accidents in which the occupants survive the initial impact, kerosene will, in principle, often provide some vital extra seconds or even minutes during which passengers can escape before the inferno swallows them. A top British scientific working party, which published a report on the subject in 1962, recognised that in a

* In the fuel controversy, leading authorities in industry were the first to take a stand but their voices became muted by the possible adverse effects of their views on the sales efforts. Then Lord Brabazon and John Rickard, an aircraft fire protection specialist and former Secretary of the Air Safety Group, made the matter a public issue.

few minor aspects the two fuels have similar characteristics, but in the catastrophic major aspects kerosene was the safer fuel. (Lord Brabazon, then Chairman of the ARB, once even challenged the champions of JP4 to a 'fuel-duel'; he would stand in a pool of kerosene, the opposition in a pool of JP4, and both would light a match to demonstrate faith in the respective fuels. The challenge was never taken up.

The arguments raged over the years. Britain was always one of the major champions of kerosene — all British airlines use that fuel — but the government never actually banned JP4 which can still be bought by operators at British airports. The motive was presumably the risk of diplomatic and commercial frictions. International support for a general ban on JP4 was invited several times, but without success. The international organisations of aviation failed to take a stand on the issue. Australia was the first to take single-handed action and ban JP4 in 1962 — but no other country has since followed the example. Most European airlines hold a similar view to that of SAS, that kerosene should be used for safety and standardisation purposes unless in certain parts of the world only JP4 happens to be available. Swissair uses it only as a last resort, and any mixture in the tanks is specially recorded.

JP4 users have employed the better international availability of this fuel as one of their arguments, but recently it lost all its validity. The technical argument in defence of JP4 has never been very strong or convincing and even the most pro-JP4 reports did not go further than emphasising equality between the two fuels. What then are the prime motives for using JP4? One is the lack of clear facts derived from accidents, which could be used as a definite basis for comparison. The other two are purely economic: that JP4 can be some eight per cent cheaper than kerosene and this, in the case of a big national airline, could easily save a couple of million pounds on a year's fuel bill; and that a gallon of kerosene weighs 8 lb. and a gallon of JP4 is only 7·6 lb., an advantage in short-haul operations.

The price difference is eliminated in Britain and in America by a special tax levied on JP4. But in America this tax is applied only to domestic use, resulting in the odd situation that American domestic lines always used kerosene for their jets while Pan American and TWA, the international lines, used mainly JP4. (When they filled their tanks with kerosene, there was still JP4 residue inside.)

But on December 8, 1963, when lightning struck one of Pan American's Boeing 707's, the fuel and the aircraft exploded, killing all the eighty-one people on board. While the investigation had barely opened, there were disturbing indications published that such accidents could not happen with pure kerosene in the tanks. In about May, the U.S. Presidential fleet quietly banned JP4 for Presidential flights and began to use only JP5. (It is by far the safest of all aviation fuels, especially in hot climates, but unfortunately, also the most expensive and least available.)

Then on November 23, 1964, came yet another shock: a TWA 707 aborted take-off in Rome, lost directional control, its No. 4 engine struck a steamroller, fuel spurted from a tank and a fire began. There were seventy-three people on board. Forty-four of them evacuated in a few seconds. Then a series of explosions occurred killing the twenty-nine still in the cabin together with fifteen already on the ground, and injuring others so seriously that ultimately the number of fatalities grew to fifty-one. Once again, the indication was that *with pure kerosene on board the spread of fire would have been slower and the explosions would not have occurred*, thus giving time to escape.

Significantly, only six weeks later, in January 1965, Pan Am announced it would use only kerosene from then on. A fortnight later, TWA followed suit. This was a tremendous breakthrough — but were these airlines really convinced that kerosene was safer? They said they were not. They announced that they saw no difference in safety between the two fuels, but they gave way to public distrust in JP4 and to public pressure for kerosene. This explanation was doubted by determined campaigners because legal implications and public relations principles might indeed persuade airlines to rely on this patently flimsy reason for the change of policy; but, on the other hand, it must also be recognised that the public, led by specialists and pressure groups like the U.S. Airways Club and British Air Safety Group, did play a very considerable part in forcing this decision on these airlines.

Whether all the kerosene users are really convinced about their increased safety level would be difficult to judge. The attitude of American Airlines, a giant domestic operator, may be significant in this respect. Ira C. McInnis of their Safety office said in an interview in New York that they used only kerosene. Then, in a most helpful letter answering more detailed questions for this book, the company reported that, 'On the relative merits of kerosene and JP4, Mr. McInnis states that American cannot make a definite statement that the use of kerosene has prevented a fire in an aircraft accident where JP4 or gasoline would have resulted in fire. The large number of variables involved make it difficult to make such a statement, since the identical circumstances are not present in any two accidents.' The letter then goes on to quote one of the reports that could do the most damage to the 'ban the JP4' camp — 'the Co-ordinating Research Council's exhaustive study of aircraft fires concludes: "Information available on survivable crashes reveals no significant relationship between fuel type and the likelihood of fire." '

Critics of that U.S. report hasten to point out several considerable flaws in the CRC study, and that 'the CRC have hardly touched upon the crash explosion risk with JP4. Presumably the Rome accident occurred too late for inclusion in their report'. (For the argument is not only about how easily fire breaks out with different fuels, but also about what happens *after* it has broken out!)

Fortunately, the number of accidents in general and of applicable crashes in particular is so low that a single case may mean a considerable difference and the statistical approach, aimed at revealing trends, is not as yet really representative. Some statistics for instance, rely on only *five* accidents in which JP4 was the fuel. While five cases may contain some indications, they can hardly be regarded as serious statistical evidence. (An insurer remarked that 'the some 300,000-hour accident-free début of a new type of aircraft is a good start but not statistical evidence and certainly not grounds for a claim for reduction of premium'.)

That there are few accidents with JP4 on board is understandable. First because only four international lines — KLM, Sabena, Japan Airlines and Air Canada — are among those still believed to be using it. Also because some of these – as well as the chief former users, TWA and Pan Am – are among the safest operators who do not give many opportunities for comparisons. (Air Canada, incidentally, like to remind us that they began to use JP4 for safety reasons when it cost more than kerosene. It is true that, at the time, there was no kerosene with a lower freezing point for cold climates. But, since then, such kerosene has become available.)

Accident investigators are also far from being universally convinced or convincing about the advantages of kerosene over JP4 because, taking the practical view, they fail to see decisive differences between the two. In the absence of clear-cut cases one tends to side with the majority of specialists and researchers, but here are some of the crash detectives' views.*

---

* Some of them expressed opinions which are directly opposed to views held by their employers, and some of them gave interviews despite being told not to co-operate. Therefore their names have been omitted.

A German ex-pilot, now a government investigator, said: 'I used to fly with a smaller operator. Officially, we always filled the tanks with kerosene. But there was a premium for the pilot whenever he refuelled with JP4 abroad. To the best of my knowledge this practice has been stopped. But I gave up my bonus long before that, when I saw a colleague badly burnt in a very minor training accident in Pakistan. There was only a very small amount of fuel spilled but the fire spread so fast that the man never had a chance.'

Several American (NTSB) air safety investigators are perfectly convinced that there must be some advantage in using kerosene. Others, however, are rather sceptical even about the Elkton lightning and Rome take-off accidents. 'In both cases,' one of them said, 'the main part of the fuel used was kerosene although, admittedly, there was some JP4 residue in the tanks. For a while it was suspected that such mixtures are even more dangerous. Then we were told that they were not, that what, in fact, happens is that the presence of even a small quantity of gasoline destroys all the advantages of kerosene. It may well be so. But I have yet to see two near-identical cases that would demonstrate the difference. Take that Rome accident. Wasn't there a fire before the explosion? Couldn't that generate such heat that kerosene, even without JP4, would have become explosive?' After the Rome case CAB recommended the sole use of kerosene but, instead of a ban on JP4, a further CRC study was the result.

Pro-kerosene U.S. investigators agreed with the conclusions from examples mentioned in the very comprehensive 'Review of the Aviation Fuel Controversy' (compiled by the Air Safety Group), but emphasised that their agreement was based more on opinion than on facts. Take, for instance, the Aeronaves de Mexico DC–8 which aborted take-off at New York in 1961, crashed into a field and burnt out but only *after* 102 occupants had escaped. (Four in the cockpit died from asphyxia.)

Or there was the UAL DC–8 landing accident at Denver in 1961. The plane caught fire (see page 140), but 105 escaped and only seventeen died supposedly because of the slower spread of fire and absence of explosion. 'It's fine evidence,' an American commented, 'but we don't know what in those particular circumstances would have happened with JP4 on board.'

In Britain, there seems to be a similar split in views. A BOAC investigator recalled: 'In March, 1964, we had an accident in Singapore, with a Comet 4, chartered from us by Malaysian Airways. Its starboard undercarriage snapped off during the landing. The plane was on fire before coming to rest. It was a hot day, the runway was hot, too, and hot kerosene flowed freely. They had a fine crew who did a good job evacuating the aircraft fast without serious injury. Luckily, the fire spread slowly — I'm pretty sure they wouldn't have had a chance with JP4 on board in such circumstances.'

Another undercarriage collapse was mentioned by an AIB investigator. It happened to a 707 at London Airport. 'It was a freezing December day but the metal sliding on the runway generated melting heat and burning kerosene was dripping all over the place. Yet there was no fire. JP4 tanks would have gone up in flames. I have no evidence for that but I'm sure.'

On the other hand, some AIB investigators think 'the controversy has been blown up out of all proportion'. One of them stated in print that in an insufficiently ventilated enclosed space kerosene would ignite spontaneously at a much lower temperature than JP4. (This has been violently disputed by several specialists.) One of his colleagues admitted that in 'one type of accident kerosene has, perhaps, a slight advantage, but as a pilot, flying with JP4 for many years, I never had the slightest reason to distrust my fuel. Some well-meaning but perhaps misguided people pursue this cause with almost religious fervour, but let's face it: a popular demand is not always the right one! The RAF finds kerosene safer – but cannot produce evidence. They use kerosene because they are puppets of the government which in turn is the puppet of voters. If voters want kerosene, let them have it.'

Yet another AIB crash detective argues both ways:

'Fuel is always dangerous whatever type it is, for it's always carried to burn. It depends on the circumstances which is the worse. The JP4 hazard is usually well demonstrated. But few people remember that, with kerosene, there is a delayed yet longer-lasting risk of explosion. When Mr. Menderes, the Turkish Prime Minister, flew to London in 1959, his Turkish aircraft was diverted to Gatwick and some three miles from the runway it crashed in a wood obscured by fog. The aircraft began to disintegrate as it descended through the trees and there was a fire. Most of the cockpit crew must have been killed by the impact. Among the passengers there were survivors. The steward and two stewardesses escaped but re-entered the cabin to help passengers. And then, a few *minutes* after the crash, kerosene exploded killing one and seriously injuring two of these three.' (Of sixteen passengers, nine were killed and seven injured.)

It is difficult to see the disadvantage of the delayed kerosene explosion risk, for this delay is exactly what gives people a chance to escape. In 1968 there was an accident in Holland: according to crash investigators, a short circuit occurred near the booster pump of a DC–8 during maintenance. It caused a tremendous explosion wrecking four aircraft and the hangar. The damage was approximately eight million pounds. The aircraft belonged to KLM, a JP4 user, and allegedly the fuel in the tanks contained twenty per cent JP4. Within a month, at least two major airlines warned their staff once again to adhere strictly to anti-JP4 regulations, first because with pure kerosene the

131

accident would probably never have happened, and secondly because with the JP4 the explosion was so immediate that it was merely fortuitous that there was no loss of life.

On the whole, it appears that the most sensible summing up was given by J. C. Reynolds, BUA flight safety officer: 'It seems probable that the use of kerosene only has a marginal safety advantage. Marginal means a number of lives. It also means we must take that advantage.'

In the late 1960s it appeared that the pro-kerosene — or rather, anti-JP4 — campaigners had not yet won a complete victory because their evidence had not been accepted fully and universally. It was then rumoured that the American government might abolish the extra tax on JP4 and that would open the floodgates with many airlines taking all the financial advantages of the more dangerous fuel.

'In a way, it was a complete vindication of our case that when the Americans did remove that tax, in July, 1970, no airline reverted to JP4,' said Frank Taylor, the Chairman of Britain's Air Safety Group, lecturer at the Cranfield Institute of Technology. And if any further proof of international attitudes was needed, it came in 1973 and 1974, with the major fuel crisis: initially, a few airlines began to use JP4 in a panic, but soon, refuelling regulations were back to normal.

A victory for individuals and voluntary pressure groups such as ASG, indeed, and a marvellous example of the power of public opinion. Yet the review of this major battle makes one wonder how much rosier the outlook would be today if at least part of the good-will, public enthusiasm and specialist talent of these years had been used to promote better and fuller research into gelled or emulsified fuel and to press governments to make a really concerted effort in this direction for the sake of a long-term solution.

Strangely enough, rather unobtrusively, the American FAA, that has received so much criticism for not taking a stronger stand against JP4, is among those who do most for the development of such fuels which have an inflammability level between ninety-two and ninety-eight per cent below that of fuels used today. The FAA, like scores of researchers working for industry or other governments, has not yet solved all the problems of practical application and cost, but drop and crash tests on tanks have already shown the tremendous advantages. Gelled fuel will not splatter all over wrecked aircraft, will not ignite when in contact with hot metal and is sometimes difficult to ignite at all. In June 1966 the Cornell-Guggenheim Aviation Safety Center, an organisation that had, for almost two decades, fostered aviation safety improvements in many ways, sponsored a two-day symposium at Fort Monroe, Virginia, dealing with the fire hazard. There it appeared that international science had advanced considerably although — perhaps because of the lack of public pressure — this research has never received top priority. Engines have already run on gelled and on emulsified fuel, methods have been found to move the fuel from the tanks to the engines, and the way has been cleared to more advanced research.

The idea of gelled and emulsified fuels is certainly not new.*

The Cornell-Guggenheim Center stated in its survey of research projects in 1966: 'Tragic accidents have shown that outside assistance is usually not available within the critical minutes before fires become lethal.' Crash detectives agree and appear to have no doubt that gelled fuel is the answer.

There is a snag: the conversion of aircraft to using gelled fuel carries a forbidding cost tag. But the cost would not be

* See the Beerbower-Philippoff paper in the Bibliography. Kallinokos's Green Fire used a form of gelled fuel in the 7th century B.C., and a better version was applied by Julius Africanus for sabotage purposes in the third century A.D. The main improvements were brought about during World War II when gelled gasoline (napalm) bombs appeared and flame throwers were fed by it.

a problem if the design of a new type started with such fuel in mind.

Unfortunately, supersonic aircraft could not be built for the not-yet-ready fuel. It will use kerosene-type fuel which, together with the skin of the aircraft, will be heated to high temperature by the speed. Very elaborate precautions will take care of that danger, no doubt, but the fact remains: it will be yet another way of patching up.

While we have to put up with highly inflammable fuels, we ought to know a great deal more about how they behave after the crash — how and how fast they can kill. But until recently, comparatively little attention was paid to this aspect of accidents and even today, with the exception of the United States and Britain, many countries' investigators are prepared to be satisfied with their findings without asking questions like: How did the victims die? Were they injured by impact? Were they injured and incapacitated but conscious when death came, say, by fire? Were they knocked unconscious but not lethally injured? Were those who had been injured seriously overcome by fumes or was their escape hindered for some other reason?

These questions are asked by a young branch of crash detection which is manned by human factor and human engineering specialists together with pathologists and other medical investigators who are concerned with the *third line of defence against fire: escape*. The number of low-impact survivable accidents is relatively small. Therefore it is even more imperative that we should learn everything possible from each of them, including the partially survivable ones.

In June 1962 an Air France 707 aborted take-off at Orly but ran off the runway, slid on the ground, and hitting a building killed the crew in the cockpit. Finally the aircraft caught fire. There were only two survivors of 133 aboard. For some reason or other, the exact number of those killed by impact and those burnt to death was never established.

134

When the Air Safety Group made inquiries about this for statistical purposes, the French authorities said it could be *assumed* that about half the victims died by fire. Therefore we shall never know the precise reasons why some sixty people could not escape. Those deaths did not teach us how to save the lives of others.

Medical crash detectives provide contributory evidence to finding the cause of the accident — as in the cases of sabotage or as the link between the Comet crashes, in the absence of wreckage; they also contribute to the improvement of aircraft design for crash-worthiness by investigating the immediate causes of injuries and thus pinpointing particularly dangerous structures and parts that may reduce the chances of survival.

Fire is, of course, one of their main considerations and even their *negative* evidence may help the investigation of a crash. They always work together with the technical investigators and relate their findings to the wreckage. There was, for instance, the case when a part of an aircraft was known to have been on fire in the air. Technical investigators had to know how serious that fire was: could it burn and kill people or just affect the aircraft causing loss of control? The latter was proved to be more probable when pathologists found that everybody on board was killed by impact and none of the bodies revealed signs of life in fire.

These signs are of extreme importance to the medical detective. If, for instance, somebody is alive when the fire begins to affect him, burns could be found in the air passages as far as the lungs. The examination of blood that contains a very great quantity of carbon-monoxide tells the pathologist that the victim was still breathing during the fire for in no other way could the blood become so badly contaminated. Although these are over-simplifications, such are the clues that lead to the next questions about the reasons why people, still alive after the impact, could not escape. One reason could be that they had been incapacitated by non-lethal injury.

In a recent crash of a British-registered aircraft a large number of people died and only less than twenty per cent aboard survived. Medical investigators requested that the cases should not be identified so that causing distress to relatives of the deceased should be prevented.

Among the survivors, typical examples of injury potentially leading to death by fire were found. One person was knocked unconscious by a relatively insignificant bump on the forehead. The cause: during sudden severe deceleration the head flails and may hit the seat in front — a pointer to design hazard. Within minutes, this passenger would have been burnt to death with others but, luckily, a relative in the next seat was almost uninjured and could pull him out of the wreckage. Behind them, another person lay unconscious under a pile of seats and was saved by a friend. A third casualty, whose flailing legs were broken at the ankle, remained conscious and so managed to drag free before the flames consumed the entire fuselage.

A woman, whose husband was killed in the port side seat next to her, tried to get to her son in a starboard row of seats but wreckage and flames in the aisle beat her back. She escaped through the broken wall of the fuselage, ran round the wrecked aircraft and found her son unconscious from a non-lethal head injury. She rescued him in time.

When a passenger who suffers such minor injuries is killed but not completely incinerated, medical investigators may also find other clues. If, for instance, the autopsy shows only a leg injury, it is possible that the blood carried marrow or fat to the heart or lungs causing embolism, an obstruction in the arteries which can now be detected. This would prove that the passenger was alive when the flames reached him — but the absence of this clue would not prove that the passenger was dead before the fire.

Another reason why apparently uninjured people aboard do not escape could be fumes that cause anoxia while practically blinded passengers try to grope their way to safety. The American Airline Pilots' Association suggested, in March, 1966, equipping passengers with smoke masks.

Others recommended that crew members should be issued with masks enabling them to direct evacuation up to the last possible moment. This idea was supported by a case mentioned in a lecture on the Pathology of Fatal Public Transport Aviation Accidents by Wing-Commander Peter J. Stevens, head of a department at the RAF Institute of Pathology and Tropical Medicine, in July, 1967. The aircraft stalled on take-off, pancaked on to soft mud and snow, skidded and burst into flames. Twenty-seven people were on board — seven survived. Sixteen of the fatalities were asphyxiated. Some of these had been incapacitated, apparently, by minor injuries; in eight cases, there was no 'evidence to explain why they failed to escape. It may have been related to their seating position in the aircraft or to their receiving a minor concussive blow causing temporary partial incapacitation while the products of combustion enveloped them . . .'

Together with the autopsies the survivors' accounts gave some indication that, initially, most people in the aircraft must have been so dazed that it took them time to realise there was a break in the cabin wall which would allow them to 'escape by clambering on to the wings and thence on to the ground'. (On the whole, considering the nature of the injuries and the damage to seat structures, the 'evidence on the significance of seat orientation was . . . equivocal in this case; however, although backward-facing seats *might* not have increased the number of survivors, it was difficult to escape the impression that they would have done so to some degree'.)

How did those who had not been badly injured succumb

to the fumes? Were all the cabin crew incapacitated? One survivor helped to solve this riddle. He escaped through an open door. That door, at the rear, had not been torn open but manually operated in the proper manner from inside. To operate that door a crew seat had to be tipped up first. That seat was occupied by a cabin crew member at the time of the crash — but that crew member was ultimately found to have died from asphyxiation in the cabin, far from his seat.

The reconstruction of his fate thus clarified that he must 'have recovered from the jolt of the accident quickly enough to begin to take the correct action. He had released himself from his seat, tipped it up, opened the door to facilitate escape and then gone forward to help passengers. He . . . must have succumbed while trying to rescue passengers . . .'

With a mask he might have saved not only himself but also others who were too stunned to escape.

And this stunned, dazed condition of uninjured survivors is yet another reason why people fail to do the obvious and get away. Aircrash detectives who study this condition call it *negative panic*. Reading any number of first-hand accounts and newspaper reports about accidents, the words 'there was no panic' and 'wonderful passengers! nobody screamed!' appear with disturbing frequency. But, in fact, there is panic — the negative panic renders the mind dazed and the body paralysed. One aircraft engineer told Wing-Commander David Fryer, a physiologist: 'After the aircraft came to rest with nobody injured, there was a burning rivulet of fuel flowing slowly down the aisle. We all sat and watched it in silence. And it was long before anybody moved.'

Or there was the miraculous accident to a Hawker Siddeley 748 owned by Skyways Coach Air Ltd. at Lympne Airport, near Folkestone. 'Eye-witnesses said the aircraft plunged twenty feet to the ground,' reported the *Daily Telegraph* on July 7, 1965, 'and ploughed off the grass runway . . .' It somersaulted three times and finished upside down. Fifty-one people, including the crew, were hanging from the 'roof' strapped in their seats. 'But there was no panic.' One mother held her eighteen-months-old baby in her arms. A man recalled that he could smell petrol and 'it was a miracle that it did not catch fire.' Yet many people remained *calmly* hanging upside down until the pilot and stewardess who had unstrapped themselves and let themselves drop came to their help. One passenger recognised it: 'Everyone was too stunned to panic.'

After a fire breaks out, the danger ought to appear an even more immediate threat, but people become even more inert — their own worst enemies. This is a secondary hazard which has been isolated after careful investigation so that crews can be trained to be prepared to deal with it.

'Meticulous interviewing of survivors and especially crew even in non-fatal accidents is the way to learn about human behaviour in emergencies so that emergency drill and evacuation routine can be adapted to it,' said Edward Slattery of the NTSB. 'After that much-disputed DC–6 crash at Rikers Island (Northeast Airlines, New York, 20.1.1957) there was fire but it spread slowly and there was so little damage to the fuselage that passengers could leave it without difficulty. And yet out of 102 people twenty died from burns and asphyxia. Our men were there practically within minutes and found that several died strapped in their seats. Others just sort of stood idly waiting for death without opening a removable window clearly marked as emergency exit and still in perfect condition after the fire — but never opened.

'Occasionally, some passengers would suddenly recover from the accident shock and there may be a rush for the exits, but usually it's the other way round. I shall never forget the stewardesses whom we interviewed after one of those non-fatal accidents: they were on the verge of collapse. This is what happened: a Viscount was taking off and knocked off the tail of a landing DC–6. The engines and gas tanks of the Viscount were ruptured; with fuel flowing freely, fire was imminent; the DC-6 tipped on its nose; there was not a broken toe; stewardesses tried to get the passengers out — but nobody moved.

'The stairs of the Viscount opened normally. The stewardess begged them, screamed at them, fought them, but nobody was ready to leave the aircraft. A man struggled to find his briefcase first. Some women complained it was too cold outside to be made to leave without their coats. A man stopped at the bottom of the stairs and standing in the middle of a growing pool of fuel, wanted to light a cigarette before he would move on.

'Similar scenes were going on in the meantime aboard the DC-6. The stewardess was crying in her helplessness and knowing that hell may break loose at any moment. But people were just slow. A fat woman got herself trapped in the doorway when she resisted a three-foot jump from the rear of the aircraft. The stewardess had to trip her behind the knees to make her sit down and then people below pulled the woman out by force.

'One of the most important cases of negative panic occurred on July 11, 1961, when a United Airlines DC-8 had to make an emergency landing. It was an important case because it started off a series of inquiries into improving ways of evacuation.

'That plane had some hydraulic malfunction and made the landing at Denver. People knew some two hundred miles out that there would be an unscheduled landing. On touch-down, the aircraft veered off the runway because of asymmetric thrust of the engines, collided with a truck (killing the driver) and with the concrete edge of a new runway, then caught fire. It was still a minor accident without serious injuries and the fire spread slowly. But people wouldn't get out. And, even worse, those who were ready to escape didn't know how.'

Investigation revealed that a rear exit was blocked by the collision damage. Another in the first class cabin was used only by a dozen people because nobody else knew about it. Some rushed forward — then turned to go against the tide. Smoke was filling the aircraft slowly but fire was not yet a threat. There were six minutes to get out, enough time for some seventy people to go through the one exit known to all — but sixteen of the 120 on board never made it.

'The investigation sought to explain why these passengers were unable to escape the aircraft since none appeared to have suffered serious injuries in the accident' (William J. Reals and Richard E. Danielson in 'Flight Fatalities Studied', *Journal of the Kansas Medical Society*, August, 1963). No definite pattern of injuries was found except that all the bodies were burned extensively and there was 'cherry red discoloration of tissue associated with carbon monoxide poisoning'. The results also indicated the victims were alive in the heat and smoke for a while and were then asphyxiated. The 'burns all were post mortem'.

The pathologists' work confirmed the technical and other findings and helped to promote not only a higher degree of safety (better crew training for emergencies, clearer marking of exits, more stringent requirements for evacuation facilities) but also greater specialisation of medical aircrash detection. Until 1960 only the Armed Forces Institute of Pathology helped American aircrash investigators. Then, after a DC–6 bomb-on-board case, some civilian pathologists were appointed as FAA consultants but only the airline cases were properly dealt with. (In 1961 all the 124 victims of five domestic airline accidents were seen by pathologists.) But soon there must also be a better understanding of 'general aviation' accidents. Especially in America, general aviation, light aircraft, business aircraft, etc., is expanding fast in its volume as well as in latest types of jet equipment and also in the threat it represents to airliners by the collision hazard from congestion in the air. Yet, as was pointed out by CAB and the above authors, in 1961 only a very few of the 760 fatalities caused by 426 fatal general aviation accidents were seen by pathologists. One reason for this is that in many American states coroners are elected. They may guard their popularity by complying with religious objections to post mortems.

After the Denver crash, in addition to new CAB and FAA readiness (better prepared pathologists with investigation kits, knowledge of team techniques and legal problems, and easier means of obtaining facilities), coroners, hospitals and medical practitioners were told up and down the country how to help investigations. Human factor specialists, led by Bernard Doyle, then of CAB, gave lectures and the result was that, when only two months later a Constellation crashed near Hinsdale, Illinois, killing seventy-three passengers and the crew of five, medical investigators were ready in all the Chicago area. With such a tremendous toll (at that time the biggest on record) they had to form three teams of pathologists and flight surgeons who examined all the injuries and concluded — supporting the rest of the investigation — that there had been no in-flight fire because all aboard must have been killed by the impact before the considerable burns were inflicted.

The more thorough investigations of fires on the ground and escape problems in the post-war years have brought about some very considerable improvements — and, quite rightly, have also encouraged the ever-increasing note of criticism of the already improved methods. By 1965, enough was known by the American and British flight safety authorities to demand that the emergency evacuation of all passengers should not take more than two minutes. (Half as stringent regulations would have saved the sixteen people aboard the DC–8 at Denver.) And the healthy tendency of free-flowing criticism, study and discussion has continued.

A pilot complained that still too many people were trapped and burnt to death and demanded that 'we must have the maximum number of doors possible, as opposed to the minimum you can get away with' whatever the cost. But the possible maximum, at the present state of the art, is far from ideal. Those investigators who deal with the giant jig-saw puzzles know only too well that the ideal solution, a door for each row of seats, would weaken the structure danger-ously — or increase the weight to the point where passengers could no longer be carried at all.

Once again, based on investigation and findings, numer-ous international studies were carried out to review cabin exit design and evacuation procedures with a special view to the larger number of passengers and new types of seating arrangements in the future. The latest move has come from the FAA. Its studies had shown that in the six years to 1967 279 Americans had died just because of fire and smoke after impact. The safety rules were therefore revised to lessen the risk of fire and speed evacuation — at an estimated cost of $2,000 million.

(It seems odd that no airline has ever shown its passengers actually how to open doors and removable windows — one objection being that someone might try to jump out; and no airline has yet asked its passengers to count the number of rows between their seats and the nearest two exits although this might help them to find their way in darkness since, in survivable accidents, the seats often remain attached to the floor.)

The new safety measures already pay attention to future safety and evacuation problems which will be very con-siderable when a negative panic or a positive one involving a stampede starts among 890 passengers aboard, say, a Lock-heed Jumbo. Those new big aircraft will be able to take advantage of their size by carrying extra safety equipment which will represent a smaller percentage of overall weight than the same equipment would in today's jets, and by having more and more evenly-spaced exits. But their height when standing on the ground, for instance, is a disadvantage when it comes to evacuation. Better use will therefore have to be made of improved and much more reliable chutes which now frequently fail to open properly. (Present aircraft have main escape hatches near the wings, in the centre section, partly because of structural reasons, partly because of equal accessibility to most people, and also because the wings can be used as stepping off points — but very often it is just there where the fire blazes most fiercely).

The faster, ninety-second evacuation must be practised with unrehearsed participants who represent all ages. During crew training, people are marked as 'invalid' and 'seven months pregnant', and American crews have smoke and sharp grinding metallic noises piped in to increase realism, but investigators complain that no airline training programme could ever include the use of panicky passengers who would not move or would run and fight the cabin staff; and also that stewardesses spend between a sixth and an eighth of their training on emergency procedure studies including first aid, and spend the rest of their training time learning things like diets, cocktail mixing, beauty care, route geography and correct ways to address titled passengers.

And, finally, aviation will have to face the problem that worries investigators, including pathologists, constantly: how to predict with certainty that, when accident findings are turned into recommendations, the new safer rules or designs will not have an adverse effect on existing safety levels.

Walter Tye, chief technical officer of the ARB, summarised the hazard in a lecture at a BALPA symposium in 1966:

'At present, in fatal accidents, about eighty-five per cent of the occupants are killed … In less serious accidents, crashworthiness provisions are apparently giving good protection. Thus it will be important . . . to ensure that the (new) features do not result in previously non-fatal accidents becoming fatal.'

CHAPTER SEVEN

WHAT THEY THOUGHT THEY SAW

Ask yourself four questions about your watch without looking at it: (1) what words are printed on it? (make, anti-magnetic, number of jewels, etc.); (2) do figures, dots, or some other symbols mark the hours and quarters? (3) is the second hand mounted centrally or in a separate little circle? and (4) can the figure 6 be seen in full?

If you get all your answers right, you may be one of the very few people who are useful witnesses to an aircrash detective.

To print the mental photograph of an accident, to sort out the shattered, twisted, distorted fragments of memory, and to separate observations an accident witness *knows* he has seen from those he *thinks* he has seen is a fascinating exercise.

The most usual 'observation' witnesses report is that the 'aircraft fell like a flaming torch'. As we have seen, fire in the air occurs infrequently and this 'observation' is usually due to the shock that confuses the order of mental records and to the subconscious association of a post-crash flash with the sight of a hurtling aircraft.

The more time witnesses have to think and talk about what they have seen, the less accurate their memories become. When a large jet* carried out a manoeuvre close to

* Most cases in this chapter will not be identified so that unnecessary embarrassment of well-meaning witnesses is avoided.

the ground prior to landing, it was seen by many people. Seconds later it crashed and there was a raging fire accompanied by thick columns of smoke billowing about the site. The same evening, before the witnesses could be interviewed, a highly respected, prominent citizen of the local community gave a very vivid and dramatic description of the crash on television. He spoke about the smoke and flames coming from the aircraft — before the impact. Next morning, the witnesses with only one exception gave an almost identical account to the investigators. When cross-examined, none of them could give any details — for instance, about the part of the aircraft which burned in the air. The one different witness report came from a man who had no television set in his home. Ultimately, it was proved that there had been no fire in the air and it appeared most likely that the witnesses had been confused by the very impressive, well-meaning television interview.

'Investigators must evaluate every word of the witness because there are numerous pitfalls. And an over-valued or a too easily dismissed witness may cause considerable delays in getting at the truth,' said George Kelly, a senior AIB inspector.

There are people who volunteer information simply because they would like to get into the act. An English village squire just 'had to be on the list of witnesses in order to maintain his reputation of knowing everything best'. Two elderly German women in Bavaria offered information to the local police about the last thirty seconds before an accident, and by saying that they had seen 'a normal approach into a field', they increased the mystery for a while because, in fact, the aircraft must have been spinning out of the sky. Most probably, the two women *heard* the aircraft come down and, on seeing the wreckage, became convinced they had *seen* it.

Others are afraid to say what they have seen. They are

cautious when it comes to signing anything, worried that they might be letting themselves in for something like being sued or becoming an accessory in the prosecution of somebody else.

Investigators seem to agree that the best witnesses are boys in their early teens. They notice and report what they have seen without trying to adjudicate. When Joseph Fluet investigated an American case, he talked to a witness who mentioned that he had been out for a walk with his son when he had seen the accident. Fluet insisted on interviewing the boy, too, whose story turned out to be completely different from his father's. The man protested that the boy was 'just a kid' and so could not be reliable. He interpreted what he had seen, focused on certain points and omitted others — and was nettled when the boy's observations finally turned out to be accurate.

Women tend to embellish the drama — men like to appear experts and form opinions. An American once refused to sign his statement until it included his original words 'I then heard the pilot give it the gun'. He agreed he meant the application of power but thought that 'this is the expression that you guys use so why can't I use it?' Frequently, male witnesses also persist in using 'starboard' and 'portside' instead of right and left although, as Lennart Bergström, the Swedish investigator, said, 'in the excitement of seeing an accident these basic points tend to get confused anyway'.

Very often, the investigator can spot lies and mistakes by the simple exercise of establishing the exact position of each witness at a particular moment. Then the acid test is: could the witness see at that spot at that time all he claims to have seen?

'Well-meaning old ladies are the worst of all,' said Eric Newton. 'But we cannot afford to ignore any report. When we interview them, however, we often get statements like "when I saw that aeroplane I knew immediately that it would crash". How did she know? "I just felt it in my bones." Not a very useful clue, I must say.

'When a woman reported to the police minutes after a crash that she had seen the aircraft wavering up and down violently, our investigator in charge rushed to see her. The report implied some control problem in the air prior to landing and so it looked as though she might have been able to give us an important lead in the investigation.

'He found that her window faced the route taken by incoming aircraft and he knew that at that particular time there had been no other aircraft in the vicinity. To take her statement he sat in the armchair where she had sat knitting, at the time. While she was describing what she had seen, he heard the engines of another aircraft. He looked up, just as the woman must have done, and to his horror, he saw another aircraft "wavering up and down violently".

'It was, of course, a flaw in the undulating glass, through which all aircraft appeared to be out of control.'

In June, 1956, a TWA Super-Constellation collided in the air with a United Airlines DC–7 over the Grand Canyon, Arizona. It was hard to find witnesses, but at last two came forward. One was a man who reported that he had seen the collision while driving his truck at more than 70mph. His description of the weather that day was completely wrong but, nevertheless, the investigators went with him to the spot where he thought he must have been at the time. It was found that even from a stationary car it would have been impossible to see the collision — some fifteen miles away and hidden by hills.

The other witness, a woman, was a passenger in the car driven by her husband. She gave a detailed description of the markings and configuration of both aircraft at the moment of collision. Did she discuss the case with her husband or anybody else? No, never, with anybody. That roused the crash detective's suspicion at once: it must be a unique character who witnesses a disaster like this and lets it go without a word about it to anyone! The witness was driven to the 'vantage point for the observation' and it turned out to be some seventy miles from the crash site. Even on the best day for visibility, it was impossible to see without powerful binoculars the details described by her.

Yet the most unlikely witness accounts are nevertheless meticulously checked partly because they may hold the lead to an unsuspected cause of a crash, partly because they may help to corroborate further evidence — the fact that several witnesses in a key position did *not* see an approaching aircraft helped to prove that it was not at the very spot at the time, perhaps because it had taken the wrong air corridor — and partly because when the incomplete and inaccurate mental pictures are joined in a 'film', the truth may evolve.

The precisely charted position of witnesses, verified by a compass setting so that it shows which way each faced when making an observation, can not only help to establish information like the exact route of a Vickers Varsity to the crash site in March, 1963, but may also lead to the deduction of more elusive facts like the altitude of an aircraft at a certain stage. In one American crash, for instance, several witnesses were asked to estimate the height where the aircraft had made a particular manoeuvre. The estimates varied between 800 and 10,000 feet.

In the Varsity case, the investigators computed the available witness evidence. A mile and a half away from the house, into which the plane crashed, witnesses saw the undercarriage being lowered — below a certain height, houses would have obstructed the vision of those witnesses; above a certain height the witnesses, during their normal activities, would not have noticed the undercarriage or even

149

the aircraft itself. At another point during the descent, witnesses saw the port propeller revolve slowly and the starboard one rotate normally. That again imposed certain limitations on the estimated altitude. When two witnesses, fairly close to one another, reported wildly differing altitudes, the indication was that either the aircraft had dropped suddenly or one witness was wrong. The latter was proved to be the case because the descent appeared to be gradual at that stage and from a drop like that described the pilot could not have recovered the aircraft and fly it as far as the actual crash site.

When an aircraft lost a wing in a dive, most witnesses underneath it got the picture the wrong way round. This was because as soon as the wing detached itself the aircraft rolled upside down so quickly that the wing, not rotating with the fuselage, appeared to fall from the other side. This was confirmed by witnesses who had seen it all from further behind.

With experience, crash detectives learn to recognise these mistake patterns, so that they can turn even optical illusions to their advantage.

In 1952 investigators were taught an unforgettable lesson: not to trust even a hundred thousand witnesses completely.

One hundred thousand was the approximate number of spectators at the Farnborough Air Show that year when sonic booms, the present social menace especially during the night, still used to be the spine-chilling attraction of the day. The boom was then produced by diving an aircraft through the sound barrier. Great artists of the air timed their dive so that the boom should come near the ground when its force and clarity would thrill the spectators most, although that left the pilots precious little time to pull out of the dive.

John Derry, one of the world's best test pilots, daredevils and showmen, who flew a de Havilland 110 fighter,

150

the first two-seater to exceed Mach 1, delighted the crowd with the bang that was described in those days as 'magnificent'. Then he was ready to perform some aerobatics and lined up for a run in towards the main enclosure which was tightly packed with spectators. Derry and his observer were about halfway through that run in when, suddenly the aircraft seemed to come to a halt, and a second later, only tiny fragments and massive pieces of wreckage were gliding through the air. In one larger part Derry and his observer fell to their deaths. A one-ton engine flew into a hillside covered completely by spectators who never had a chance to move even a step out of its way. It killed thirty people. In all, there were some sixty people seriously injured, too.

There has never before or since been an accident witnessed by so many people, including devoted aviation enthusiasts and eminent experts. Sir Arnold Hall, Director of RAE, appealed to them all for statements. There was a tremendous response. The thousands of letters had to be dealt with by a special department, and hundreds of witnesses were interviewed. Yet there was only *one letter* which was of some use and there were fewer than half a dozen people who captured to some extent the true picture of events. Most witnesses 'got the split-second time-sequence of disintegration [as finally proved by the research] backwards, filled in bits with imagination, and preferred theories to reports' (*Sunday Times*, March 11, 1962).

'Fred Jones was away at the time,' Sir Vernon Brown, then head of the AIB, recalls, 'and we brought him back because we wanted the best man for the job.' His long investigation traced the disaster sequence back to compression buckles on the starboard wing. Tension must have developed along the sharp ridge of the buckle which split near the leading edge. The wreckage proved that the failure would lead to the kind of disintegration which, in fact, followed. But was this really the starting-point of the sequence? Jones staked his reputation on marking the spot where, in his opinion, the strength of the wing would give way every time under similar load conditions.

With the speed of Derry's flight and other factors known, the manufacturers ran a series of wing load tests almost to destruction. It was a sad victory for Jones: on the top of the wing, near the leading edge, within two inches from the predicted spot, the buckle appeared. If another DH 110 had flown a replica of the Derry flight, an identical type of disaster would have been inevitable.

Scores of aviators dispute the findings to this day. Their main argument is that they themselves saw it happen. They observed the disaster from the best vantage positions — some even through binoculars — and they 'remember quite clearly' that several fragments detached themselves from the tail *before* the aircraft reared up and therefore not the wing but the tail must have been the prime cause of the accident.

Several crash detectives admitted that it is almost impossible for them to argue with witnesses because 'no man is willing to believe you rather than his own eyes' or even his memory of what he believes to have seen. When two yacht-loads of aviation experts went on a cruise on Lake Washington on their day off from a meeting at Boeing, Seattle, 'Tex' Johnson, chief test pilot, flew a prototype aircraft at low altitude above them. He went into a slow roll, passed them, returned and rolled the aircraft once again. Afterwards the witnesses were asked which way he had rolled the aircraft. The answers were no better than those which would come from people who had not even seen the flight: most said the first roll had been to the left and the other to the right, some thought it had been the other way round, some remembered two left rolls, and a few saw the facts — two right rolls.

Yet it occasionally pays to pursue witnesses. On March 14, 1957, Whisky Echo (G-ALWE), a Viscount, made one of those uneventful, scheduled 'hops' from Amsterdam to Manchester. Fifteen passengers finished their lunch some 4,000 feet up and the pilot began to talk to Ringway Airport. Passing Oldham Beacon at 13.41, he started his pre-landing drills that include lowering of the flaps — the wing 'extensions' at the trailing edge which are housed in the wing during the flight but come out to varying degrees during take-off and landing to give extra lift or drag respectively.

Whisky Echo came down, through the clouds, towards the runway and was noticed by airport staff some four miles away. With seatbelts fastened, the passengers and the crew of five were soon only a mile from touchdown on the runway. But then, Whisky Echo began to veer to the right, banking as it did so. To witnesses it might have seemed a controlled manoeuvre. A few seconds later, the bank and turn became much too sharp to be intentional. Two airport controllers saw that a crash was inevitable — and both reacted by raising the crash alarm even in the seconds before Whisky Echo disappeared from their view.

During these twenty seconds or so five other people watched Whisky Echo from the ground. One of them heard the engine become louder. Another, an ex-RAF pilot, thought the aircraft had side-slipped and saw the rudder move and correct the position. A third man, N. E. Pettigrew, having lunched at home, was walking back to work when he saw the plane directly from astern and noticed something odd about the flaps. He had only time to take a mental photograph for immediately after that, in what seemed to him no more than five seconds, he had more dramatic events to watch.

In an uncontrollable bank, the right wing tip of Whisky Echo touched the ground, and cut a curving furrow in the earth. Bit by bit, half the wing was smashed and scattered. Only then came the crash into houses some eighty-five yards away. The time was 13.46.

All aboard were killed. A mother and baby in the house that had received the main blow died with them. The house collapsed on top of most of the wreckage. Fierce fire broke out in about twenty places. A gas pipe began to leak.

Hugh Gordon-Burge, then an AIB inspector, flew into Ringway 130 minutes later and took charge of the investigation. The police had already drawn up a list of witnesses. Among them was a Mr. Pettigrew who, allegedly, 'saw that something happened to the flaps on the wing'. Experience had taught Gordon-Burge to be somewhat sceptical about witnesses. But from the apparent circumstances of the crash, he thought this witness would have to be the first on his list of elimination.

He spent some time at the smouldering wreckage where firemen were still at work, then examined the furrow already partially obliterated by a tractor, and decided the best he could do for the time being was to see Pettigrew.

'I went to his home and had tea with him and his wife,' Gordon-Burge said. The first few minutes of such an interview are crucial: the crash detective, like his criminologist colleague, must size up the witness for reliability. A quiet, well-balanced, non-dramatising engineer, Pettigrew held a glider pilot licence and used to be in the junior air corps and a flight observer at the RAE. Gordon-Burge had a better than ususal impression: 'He was not an expert aviator, but he knew what he was talking about. He was not the type who would theorise or have a bee in his bonnet about a particular aspect of aviation which he would try to pursue.

'His statement was consistent with the marks I had seen on the ground and, although I could not retrace his route to work and check his reported position of observation until

154

the following day, I was sure he had, in fact, seen all he talked about.

'He saw that the starboard flaps appeared to rise above the wing. Instead of forming a line, the flaps produced a sort of roof-like effect. As he spoke I knew that yes, this could start the turn and bank ... but why didn't the pilot correct this by using the aileron? I didn't ask this: Pettigrew mentioned it himself. He saw that those strangely behaving flaps started the turn. He also looked at the ailerons: but to his surprise — and now to mine — they didn't move.'

Both these points were important evidence: if Pettigrew was right, the flaps might have caused the accident; the ailerons were smaller than the flaps and so it seemed less likely that he would have noticed their movement than that of the flaps; but if he was right, there could be additional danger to all Viscounts.

Gordon-Burge recognised how urgent it was to act on this lead. His technical investigators, men from BEA, Vickers and other organisations arrived one after another. There was a brief meeting in the hotel nearby at about 9 p.m. They agreed that evidence might soon be destroyed: the firemen had tried to do as little damage as possible but had to use grappling irons to free the bodies and stop the gas leakage, and in the morning a Civil Defence gang would have to start moving the rubble.

The investigators got to the site at about 11 p.m. and began shifting the wreckage with their bare hands in the rain. Unfortunately, the starboard flaps they were searching for lay smashed against the wall under a mountain of rubble which alone supported now the house next door. They laid out the salvaged parts in a road within the police cordon. They worked until about five in the morning, went to the airport nearby, snatched a couple of hours of sleep in the lounge, and were back at the site to supervise every move made in the course of clearing up the mess.

They had to keep their eyes wide open — but their vigilance did pay off. They found one half of a 9/16 inch diameter bolt which came from an important place in a starboard flap unit and *showed signs of fatigue.* (The other half was sought by mine-detectors but was never recovered.)

It took a full-scale investigation and a Public Inquiry to prove Pettrigrew right about the flaps and even about the locked ailerons. (Originally it was believed that the ailerons could not be affected.) It also took fifty weeks to prove him right in an official report. But luckily, the investigators did not wait. On the first morning, at the first sign of material evidence, they put more reliance on his words. At that stage, there could have been a million other primary causes of the accident. Within twenty-four hours, nevertheless, corrective action was initiated.

Gordon-Burge commented: 'I have no doubt that the cause of that accident would have been discovered in any case. But it would have not been found as soon as that without the witness.'

One important aspect of interviewing a witness is not to ask leading questions or to prompt a reply. The USAF investigators' manual gives specific warnings about this because as soon as the crash detective asks 'Was the altitude 800 feet?' instead of 'What was the altitude?' the witness tries subconsciously to detect the answer in the interviewer's voice — and *tries to give a pleasing answer.*

This zeal to please is retained by willing witnesses even when questioned with one of the most unorthodox methods — under the influence of drugs.

The drug is sodium amytal, a sedative used for operations. Despite press reports to the contrary, investigators are anxious to point out that it is not a 'truth serum' because they claim the patient, kept between the conscious and unconscious all the time, must be willing to co-operate and can, in fact, withhold any information he would want to retain in the state of full consciousness.

The technique, narcosynthesis, is widely used in medical practice to help patients remember and part with suppressed or forgotten memories. Aircrash investigators used it for the first time after an American Constellation aircraft had crashed on Canton Island in the Pacific in April, 1962.

The cause of the accident was found by ordinary investigating methods: the reversal of a propeller, probably undetected by the crew, led to a swerve to the right from which the aircraft could not recover. The crash killed all on board except Dr. John Miller, riding in the 'jump seat' for supernumerary crew. This doctor was knocked out and regained consciousness in a shark-infested lagoon. He suffered from shock and retrograde amnesia which prevented him from recalling events before and during the crash. He remembered the pilot shouting '... frozen' but did not know what the vitally important word was. He remembered the pilot had then 'reached far to the left', across the pedestal, but had no recollection of what the pilot wanted to do there.

Investigators felt it was imperative to learn everything about crew behaviour and action during the emergency so that, if necessary, better instructions and training could save the lives of others who might have to face a similar situation. Dr. Miller's agreement was sought to the experiment which is 'an invasion of privacy'. In a medically supervised interview, under narcosynthesis, he suddenly remembered many of the seemingly forgotten details.

He recalled the pilot shouting 'controls frozen' and also 'ailerons frozen' as the swerve to the right had begun. Then he remembered the crew's reaction to the emergency. His memory indicated the crew had not recognised the real cause of the uncontrolled movement of the aircraft: they thought the aileron and rudder boost system, the equivalent of a car's power steering, had failed — and the pilot disconnected it by reaching 'far to the left' to pull these control levers to the 'off' position.

Since then, allegedly, there have been only two more cases when investigators used the drug. A light plane had hit the rock face of a mountain killing the pilot. A woman passenger survived but, mercifully, she did not remember even the flight. She was just as determined as the investigators to clear up the mystery that surrounded the cause of the tragedy. She submitted voluntarily to narcosynthesis — and it all came back to her.

Her detailed description of the pilot's words and actions helped to establish all the circumstances of the accident. Throughout her interrogation great care was taken not to carry her memory beyond the point of crash and so avoid her reliving the painful experience of post-crash events.

It is claimed, although NTSB would not confirm it, that when a Lockheed Electra crash (Ardmore, Oklahoma, 1966) was investigated, the drug was used to help some volunteering survivors remember the crash — did 'the aircraft nose over or dive, did they feel any negative "g"?' — but they had no subconscious memory for they had all been asleep when the accident had happened.

Such experiments convinced crash detectives that under the influence of the drug the witness would still try to please the interviewer. The very fact that the witness volunteers for such questioning demonstrates his willingness to help. Therefore it is not surprising that in two-way communication with the interviewer, the witness is influenced by the contents and manner of the questions and tries to answer in the way that seems most helpful.

This hazard, created by benevolent unreliability, is eliminated by another method of probing the subconscious memory: hypnosis. It is a highly controversial subject in accident investigation, and crash detectives prefer not to get involved.

As far as it can be established, it has been used only once in America. The pilot of a helicopter survived a crash in 1965, but could not remember anything that had happened between a few hours before take-off and well after the accident. (*Daily Telegraph*, July 6, 1965.) He was willing to help investigators who were convinced that the mental pictures of his various instruments and readings were hidden in his mind. A medical adviser likened it to 'looking at my watch and registering the time often subconsciously. If somebody asked me a second after I had looked at my watch what the time was, I would have to look again.'

This 'looking' once again was what the hypnosis, conducted by a Los Angeles psychiatrist, apparently did for this pilot. They could elicit details from him about the sequence of events, circumstances, his own actions, long-forgotten information like the engine and rotor rpm.

What amazed investigators was that he would not be hurried in any way. They were not very interested in irrelevant details of events long before or at the beginning of the flight. But he refused to be rushed to the final moments. He was really reliving it all, tried to stick to the same speed of events, insisted on going through details, and it took him almost as long to come to the crash in hypnosis as it had taken in real life.

When they tried to hurry him, he refused to look at what must have appeared to him as the future, argued with suggestions and stubbornly stuck to the facts as only he knew them.

Although hypnosis in this case turned the pilot into a very useful source of information, it is unlikely that the technique will ever become a widespread, regular weapon of crash investigators. This is partly because few passengers have anything even in their subconscious that can help to solve an accident puzzle, and partly because crew survivors, unless suffering from loss of memory, are willing almost without exception to part with every scrap of fact known to them. And if they want to withhold something that may incriminate them, they will refuse to undergo hypnosis.

Throughout this research investigators seemed to be full of praise for pilots — that is to say they wholeheartedly believed that the crew would never knowingly mislead them. But the truth, as known to the crew, may be different from the facts. When a pilot makes a genuine mistake, his intentions are good and afterwards he still believes sincerely that he did not err. That is why crash detectives find it one of their most painful duties to prove pilots wrong.

Perhaps the least enviable of these duties fell upon the men who were charged with the investigation of a DC–4 accident in September 1955.

The aircraft, on a military charter flight with cargo from California to Japan, reached Honolulu and then set out on one of the longest over-water routes above the Pacific. Some six hours later, the crew radioed that they were losing height rapidly due to vapour-lock in the fuel lines which were starving three of the four engines to death. A few more hasty messages ... estimated position ... loss of altitude ... only 500 feet above the water ... then silence. A search was mounted immediately. Ships in the comparative vicinity turned towards the estimated spot where the DC–4 had supposedly crashed into the sea.

There were three pilots and two navigators on board. One navigator was trapped in the cabin and went down with the heavily-loaded, fast-sinking aircraft. Two men were trapped in their seats but were released by the other two, and the four managed to escape through the hatch in the roof. They had no time to launch a raft and the four had only three life jackets.

It was a warm clear evening but the crew of the first aircraft on the scene failed to notice them or their cell batteries which were soon exhausted. At dawn, several aircraft arrived there — and passed without locating the survivors. (Small reflection mirrors were not standard emergency equipment at that time.)

While the search went on frantically, the men in the water fought for their lives simultaneously against two merciless killers — fatigue and sharks.

To combat both enemies they kept close to one another. The shark repellent from the life jackets made no impression on the monsters circling around them, waiting for the first man to drop out. Then the sharks grew impatient and attacked. Noise and slapping the water frightened them away for a while, but then they returned. Robert Hightower, a twenty-two-year-old pilot, was bitten by a shark several times before he managed to kill it with a knife.

All the men were bleeding profusely when the second night in the sea began. When the sun came up for the second time, only the captain and Hightower were alive. And the two were separated by attacking sharks.

Forty-four hours after the crash, it was early afternoon when a ship spotted them. While the captain was hauled into a launch, Hightower became the sharks' target. A man in the boat had to shoot one of them to rescue the young pilot.

The wreckage was at the bottom of the sea and so the investigation had to depend on the pilots' report. In case other DC-4s would be in danger, the interview was urgent and it took place some three weeks later — the earliest moment when the exhausted men could be asked to recall their own actions and the dreadful events.

Based on the men's account, a series of test flights was conducted, then the survivors had to be told the grim truth: the accident had been due to pilot error. The captain had not used the right method of fuel management and, under mounting stress, tried to correct mistakes with other erroneous decisions. Really corrective action had come too late.

There had been no vapour lock. The captain had to be contradicted — not in his fair and frank witness report, but only in his wrong diagnosis and conclusions.

Among investigators the consensus of opinion seems to be that pilots and crew genuinely want to assist the investigations for two reasons: mainly because they want to know and learn from accident causes, and also because they know they would be found out anyway. 'This is why we pay so much attention to what they have to say,' remarked one crash detective, and added that 'we have now, for instance, a test flight accident the investigation result of which is still pending. Everything seems to point to a non-technical cause. There is no evidence of any malfunction, but the pilot says his propeller would not feather whatever he tried to do during the flight. Our attitude is that he wouldn't say that unless he had some good reason. Therefore we're still trying to find some technical proof to support his statement.'

Not surprisingly, incidents are a different problem. Many government and airline officials confirmed that most of their information about in-flight incidents must come from pilots who, understandably, are not particularly keen on reporting their own mistakes — like near-misses — and getting the rap.

Yet even with incidents, there was only one investigator who could recall a single case when, in his firm opinion, the pilot had lied deliberately with the collusion of his crew. As details of the case have never been published, it must not be identified.

Flying over Germany, a charter aircraft went out of control. With the passengers being thrown about, it went into a tremendous dive, pulled out dangerously, began to climb too steeply so that it stalled and then began another dive from which recovery and safe landing amounted to a miracle.

The recovery from the dive overstressed the aircraft. The

wing surfaces were so wrinkled that it left a very narrow margin of safety before the wings would have been torn off.

According to the captain and the crew, there was a supernumerary pilot on board to watch the operation and familiarise himself with that particular type of aircraft. This was normal practice and the captain had the right to demonstrate various problems the new officer might have to face in the future.

The pilot said: 'At one stage, I pulled a fuse out of the inverter to simulate failure and wanted to show the new man, standing behind my seat, what to do in an emergency like that, but I lost control.'

If this was true, the captain made a serious mistake to start with. The inverter supplies the current to some vital flying instruments. If it fails, a warning light comes on and the drill calls for immediate activation of a stand-by inverter otherwise the instruments will give completely false readings. The captain is permitted to give such demonstrations — but never at night when he must rely entirely on his instruments. So that would have been a mistake in itself.

But the investigator suspected this was not the full story. For an experienced pilot, knowing what failure to expect — he himself had simulated it, after all — would never lose control to such an extent. The investigator asked him again if he himself was in the 'driving seat'. The answer was 'yes'. The supernumerary confirmed that he had been standing behind the pilot. The first officer excused himself by saying that he had been too busy with the radio to know what was going on but he expressed his belief that the captain had been flying the aircraft.

Under cross-examination the captain hesitated, asked for more time to think about it and finally declared that he had nothing more to add.

The investigator said: 'I was convinced that they were lying because this was a very grave affair. The captain is

163

permitted to give demonstrations within limits, but all airlines must strictly prohibit training by handing over the controls on passenger-carrying flights. We had no proof and so we only warned the airline. Since then, I've heard a thing or two which have confirmed my suspicion. I have no doubt the captain's intentions were perfectly honest: he wanted to give a colleague experience. I'm an ex-pilot. I understand his motive. But he should have understood that his "good intentions" might have killed a plane-load of people.'

On reflection, the investigator added yet another intriguing thought: 'Had there been a fatal accident and had any of the crew survived it, I'm sure they'd have told the truth. I don't think that any pilot could ever bear the heavy conscience a successful but deliberately falsified self-defence would give him. For that would make him a murderer — and not just a man who erred.'

CHAPTER EIGHT

TELL-TALE DEVICE

THERE was tremendous commotion at the small airport near Casper, Wyoming, after a UAL aircraft had reported it would make an unscheduled landing there with a body on board.

March 29, 1967, was one of those dreaded days when clear air turbulence, CAT — the abbreviation that fits the potential killer lurking in blue skies — struck. A man unbuckled his seatbelt to change seats. He was thrown up in the air — or rather, the plane fell from under his feet. As he dropped back, he struck the seat and the stewardess found him dead.

Airport staff, in their excitement, told the press: *fresh* air turbulence had been encountered. But that was not the only mistake of the day. A newspaper report claimed that the aircraft had lost 8,000 feet in altitude unexpectedly and the implication was that the sudden drop had killed the passenger. An accusing finger pointed at the pilot even though the autopsy proved that death had not been due to the blow but to heart failure, and even though the pilot told a very different story denying that the drop had been sudden and unreported.

He claimed he had encountered light-to-moderate turbulence, instructed his passengers to fasten their seatbelts and requested by radio a new altitude level. Having received authorisation, he descended towards his new, presumably safer, flight path even when he encountered sudden severe turbulence.

The record of his radioed request proved that the descent had been authorised. But how could he prove beyond any doubt that the drop came after, not before, that radio message?

This pilot was lucky: the *witness machine* absolved him completely. The flight data recorder showed the big drop clearly, and when its time scale was superimposed on the actual local time, it became indisputable that the radio message preceded the loss of altitude.

From the earliest days of aviation when witness unreliability became proverbial, crash detectives yearned for some witness machine that would give them dependable data about tragic events at some god-forsaken spot at the dead of night. There were various attempts at recording the performance of some known trouble-makers, like engines, but the results were treated somewhat lackadaisically with a mixture of amazement and disbelief.

When on December 24, 1924, for instance, a DH 34 — a one-engined, eleven-seater biplane — crashed at Croydon

165

airport resulting 'in the loss of lives of all passengers, seven in number, and of the pilot', it came to the investigators' attention that the engine had given some 'rough performance' during flights in the pre-crash week.

'On December 18, the aircraft with Mr. W. G. R. Hinchliffe as pilot flew to Amsterdam in very good time,' says the official report published in 1925. 'The record of the engine revolutions given by the tell-tale device, which was a new instrument supplied in *October or November* [author's italics], was particularly good.' In view of various complaints by pilots the engine was repeatedly examined but its performance was found satisfactory, confirming the 'tell-tale record'.

After the crash, the recording was consulted once again. It gave account of the *previous* flights except the last half hour's. It could 'no longer be read' which was 'not due to deliberate erasure but has been caused by this portion having been exposed to considerable friction in the handling which the chart has had'.

Thus this early case foreshadowed all the problems modern crash investigators have to face: the reliability of the recording must be established; its contradictions with accounts by pilots and others must be solved; as it does not give the full answer to accident puzzles, data have to be carefully sifted and correlated with the rest of the investigation; it must be preserved from the extreme forces of destruction.

And yet, many experts expected recorders to serve investigators like a crystal ball, giving the cause of an accident in a second. In 1962 the British Cairns Report on Aviation Safety still expressed the hope that recorders would speed up investigations. A year later, the *Manchester Guardian* (September 24) claimed that recorders would be 'a step forward from grubbing around a mountain-side among distorted wreckage for tiny clues to a possible mechanical

failure . . .' Unfortunately, none of these hopes has materialised.

Recorders, sometimes referred to as 'crash recorders' although they do not record the crash itself, are best known as
'the little black boxes', an expression used by pilots meaning
something new and a bit of a dark horse rather than a description — for the recorders are painted in bright colours
like fluorescent flame orange so that they should be easier to
find.

There are several types in use. Most apply either mechanical technique (a sharply pointed stylus engraves markings
on metal foil) or electro-magnetic recording on stainless
steel wire or tape.* But they all tap various instrument circuits and record a number of parameters according to
national requirements.

In America, after two experimental and abortive attempts
(1941–1944 and 1947–1948), the installation of flight recorders became mandatory to all aircraft over 12,500 lb.
operated in air-carrier service above 25,000 feet altitude
after July 1958. Including the time scale, the basis of all recordings, American recorders have had to record five parameters ever since: the other four being *airspeed*, *altitude*,
direction (magnetic heading), and *vertical acceleration*.
('Time' may mean local time or the time elapsed from the
beginning of recording or from take-off.)

It was typical of the progressive use of recorders that as
other countries began to adopt similar measures, each made

* Each type has certain technical or commercial advantages and
disadvantages. Some weigh less, some are more expandable and
therefore forward-looking, or less complicated and therefore less
fault-prone, or less destructible, or more quickly readable than
others. As all this is still highly debatable, the various national
regulations do not prescribe the type of recorder used — they insist
only on the recording of certain minimum information. International
settlement of this argument could greatly advance investigation, for
the crash detective could then specialise in the use of recorders to a
much higher degree.

more and more channels compulsory. The Canadian Department of Transport requires the recording of sixteen parameters including data about the engine performance, auto-pilot, primary control systems and air temperature. The FAA is now going even beyond that: for large turbine aircraft they propose to increase the number of recorded parameters to twenty-five.

Crash detectives agree that the more detailed and more accurate the information they get the better. But there are plenty of drawbacks. One is the inevitable hold-up in the investigation. Prater Hogue, the Boeing investigator, and many others already complain that the read-out takes too long. As the number of parameters increases, the recorders must become more and more sophisticated, requiring a great deal of extra checking, verification of data that reached the recorder, recorder performance control, accuracy tests of the recording itself and of the play-back. When the obtained data has to be digested by a computer, the feeding method and the computer performance, too, have to be checked. All this may lead to a finally more precise and better substantiated explanation of a disaster — but the delay may slow down corrective action to safeguard other aircraft from similar mishaps.

Ed Patton, a big chummy man, head of the NTSB flight recorder laboratory, who takes great pride in his work (and in his baby, the reading machine), firmly supports the increased number of parameters.

'There can be no doubt about it,' he said, 'that flight data recording is one of the greatest steps forward in accident investigation.'

A new type of British recorder, which will be expandable merely by plugging in extra units, will have some sixty channels. Using only six of these, a ninety-minute flight will produce an aggregate of symbols equivalent to a book about one-fifth longer than this one. Another type has 270 channels, but the makers claim that the computerised playback machine can select and supply the required relevant information within a few minutes.

A further problem is that the extra parameters increase the investment required from the airlines — and that is very considerable even now. 'You can go on and on with more channels, all may be useful on certain occasions,' Gordon-Burge said. 'If the recorders give you the angle of elevators, you want to know what the pilot was doing with the control column. If a change in the attitude of the aircraft is recorded, you need another parameter to tell you whether it was pilot-induced or externally-induced; if pilot-induced, did he get the sort of response he wanted; if not, what force did he apply: did he treat it too gently or too harshly? And the more data we get, the more work-load investigators will have to put up with. But the accuracy of the results would still justify it.'

Farnborough surveyed a series of earlier accidents to see how much help recorders could have given the investigators at the time. They found that the general usefulness of extra parameters went up until twelve were being recorded. Beyond that, on a cost-effectiveness basis, the cost and complexity of installation increased, the reliability of the recorder decreased, and the usefulness of each extra channel would justify its existence only in one accident in every five years. Nevertheless, the complexity of modern accident investigation has made it imperative to increase the recorded information. From January 1, 1975, most British passenger aircraft (according to maximum take-off weight) will have to carry recorders capable of providing information about the flight path and attitude of the aeroplane at any given moment, the selection of high lift devices and airbrakes, the position of primary flying control and pitch trim surfaces, cockpit warnings about engine fire and engine shut-down, cabin pressurisation, presence of smoke and

169

hydraulic/pneumatic power supply, outside air temperature, instrument landing system deviations, the use made of the automatic flight control system, radio altitude, and the level of essential AC electricity supply. (An excellent evaluation of Aircraft Accident Data Recording Systems by R. G. Feltham was published by H.M. Stationery Office in 1973.)

In America, out of 181 accidents between 1959 and 1965, flight recorders gave vital information in 125 cases and also improved accident investigations, especially those involving encounters with turbulence. On this basis, each extra channel would pay for itself in the end whatever the initial cost, and undoubtedly, this is what matters.

Recorders play their most important role in cases where the wreckage can provide only a minimum amount of proof, where the operation of the aircraft is suspected and the explanation is based on only secondary deductions, and where hitherto only shaky witness accounts — or even guesswork — were available.

On July 1, 1965, a B707 of Continental Airline landed at Kansas City.* It ran off a wet runway and cracked up at a dyke. Although all tanks were broken and fuel flowed freely for some six hours, all crew and passengers escaped with only a few suffering minor injuries.

The first suspicion, as usual in such cases, fell on the pilot: he might have come down too fast. This is a charge which can never be confirmed or denied with any accuracy by witnesses. In this case, the investigation proved that the mishap had not been his fault. But without the evidence of the recorder, the vague suspicion of 'speeding' might have overshadowed his whole career.

In a serious, still *sub judice,* incident the recorder will probably help to pinpoint the most elusive evidence: icing. Checking the recorder, investigators found that although it was in perfect order and the data supplied by it appeared to

* More details of the case appear on page 283.

be indisputable, there was a strange gap in the engraved graph of speed. It looked as if at one point a fault had developed in the recorder which, at a later stage of the flight, righted itself. But then it was noted that the beginning of the gap coincided with the recording of a climb in the flight, and that the speed recording started again when the aircraft had descended. The implication was that the air pressure instrument that measures speed could operate only *below* a certain altitude on that day. This could be explained only by ice formation that stops the air flow to the instrument — and so to the recorder, too. Meteorological reports have already confirmed this theory.

A memorable case, when only the contradiction between man and machine could reveal the truth, occurred during the investigation into the crash of a British naval aircraft. The pilot had ejected and was taken to hospital where he was seen by an AIB investigating officer. According to the pilot, during a test flight, ground control wanted to identify him among several other blips on the radar screen. The usual method was to ask him to make a port turn for this purpose. As he turned, the aircraft began to roll. To stop the roll he took corrective action by applying the opposite stick. Yet the roll rate increased despite more and more correction. Both his instrument and his senses told him that. The aircraft seemed to be out of control and, naturally, he chose to eject.

The flight recorder was examined: yes, there was a roll, but only from the moment of corrective action and it stopped at the point where the pilot ejected (recorded as a sudden brief slowdown of the flight). This meant that the pilot himself caused the roll! After ejection, the aircraft righted itself, then settled into a 'normal' sink condition until it crashed. The instrument that shows the attitude of the aircraft, referred to by the pilot, revealed no sign of malfunction.

The fault was then traced to a big 'junction box', full of plugs and sockets, where an open circuit could have developed causing the attitude presentation instrument to show a false picture of the aircraft as if it were a constant roll.

Without a recorder, the pilot's word would have been accepted for the constant roll leaving behind a mystery and a worrying suspicion about the aircraft. Without the pilot, the recorder could not have explained the crash or the pilot's motive for ejection. The contradiction of man and machine revealed that there was nothing wrong with the aircraft; the junction box probably sent the wrong signals to a faultless instrument which, in turn, misled the pilot who, on top of that, was cheated by his senses into spatial disorientation, a loss of direction, and mistaken belief of bodily attitude in space.

Spatial disorientation is a strange, comparatively new hazard to passenger-carrying aircraft pilots and only a few years ago it was thought to be unlikely to affect other than military fliers. The developments in all-weather flights, landings on instruments with critically low visibility or even in fog, changed these views rapidly. But spatial disorientation as a causal factor could be no more than a logical conclusion, after the elimination of other explanations, because there was no direct evidence of the pilot's action immediately before the crash.

Flight data recorders cannot show directly the presence of this phenomenon in the cockpit. But by charting the flight, they can show the course followed and, if mechanical faults and insanity are ruled out, they lead to a well-substantiated reconstruction of events even in the most involved cases, like that of the BEA Vanguard G—APEE (Double Echo) accident investigation which may well become a text book case for students of crash detection.

Double Echo took off from Edinburgh, Turnhouse, at

23.17 on October 26, 1965. Captain N. Shackell, a very experienced, forty-three-year-old pilot with some 12,000 hours in the air, had bad weather reports telling him about fog and low visibility at London Heathrow, his destination. His answer to that was to take enough fuel on board for six hours' flying, although his journey would take only sixty-five minutes. The tremendous surplus gave him a free hand; he would be able to keep circling near London waiting for weather improvement, or divert to his pre-selected alternates — Manchester and Gatwick — or return to Turnhouse or hold and only then fly to another airport where, if necessary, he could still go into a stack and wait for clearance.

No improvement in visibility waited for him at London. There were two available runways, 28 R and 28 L, and he chose the first for an attempted landing because it was equipped with a full Instrument Landing System (ILS). He was entitled to make the attempt because the Runway Visual Range (RVR) had been given to him as 350 metres, the airline's minimum visibility for landing. (In retrospect, the investigation criticised this as too low.)

Double Echo came in along the normal glide path, but at twenty-three minutes past midnight the Captain reported he was overshooting, which is a perfectly safe, routine exercise executed at a safe height in cases of the slightest doubt about the accuracy of the landing. If at a certain predetermined point the pilot does not see the runway lights he must overshoot according to the rules.

Some eight years earlier, BEA had devised and introduced a kind of 'insurance policy' for low visibility landings and overshooting. This was the so-called Monitored Approach, a system which would rule out unreliable 'reflexes' in moments of uncertainty, go a long way towards a human automatic pilot, and create a situation in which practically no single mistake — only a combination of adverse circumstances — could become dangerous. This practice in

Vanguards went yet another step forward. It took advantage of having three pilots on board, so that the instrument approach would be carried out by the second pilot (First Officer I. Cochrane on Double Echo); the Captain would seek visual reference (the sight of the runway lights) and be ready to take over control and land; while the third pilot (First Officer D. Swanson) would monitor the second pilot's activities by watching the Captain's instrument panel from behind him. Unless the Captain had already taken over control having descended to a certain height, the third pilot would call 'overshooting' for which another predetermined drill was in force.

After this first attempt, it was, as always, up to the Captain to hold, make another attempt, divert or even return to his point of departure. (Crash detectives and other experts hold rather strong views about the number of attempts to be made and we shall deal with this when we come to the 'pilot error' category. But the pilot is certainly entitled to make as many attempts as he finds prudent in the particular circumstances.)

Having received further weather reports, the Captain now decided to make another attempt on the other available runway where visibility was promised to be better. Some ten minutes after the first 'overshooting', he came in again along the glide path. The radar controller noticed that Double Echo was in a not entirely correct position at half a mile from runway and decided to instruct the Captain to overshoot, when he realised that the aircraft was already in an overshoot procedure.

At thirty-five minutes past midnight, the Captain radioed: 'Double Echo overshoot — we didn't see anything that time.' To him it seemed so 'very patchy' from above that he decided to wait for half an hour or so and see what happened. The aircraft began circling at the Garston holding point.

At 00.46 Echo Delta, another Vanguard arrived. It also chose 28 R for an attempt and landed without difficulty. Double Echo was told about this at 00.52. Although the weather had not improved at all, the news might have encouraged Captain Shackell to have another go. On his way from the stack to Heathrow, he heard that Echo Hotel, a third Vanguard, had tried to land on 28 R but had been forced to overshoot because of bad visibility.

At 01.18, Double Echo began its third attempt. Four minutes later, it was three quarters of a mile from touchdown and on the centre line. Yet twenty-two seconds later — probably because the lights were still not visible — the Captain reported they were overshooting once again. It was seen on radar as it began to climb away — and then as it went into a steep dive. It hit the runway 28 R at some 2,600 feet from the threshold. The time was approximately 01.23.

Despite the fog, fire engines were on the scene in two minutes, but all the three pilots, two stewardesses, one steward and thirty passengers on board had been killed on impact.

The investigation began along the many usual lines. But the basic question was: what went wrong in the last twenty seconds or so of a procedure that had begun as a perfectly normal overshoot?

As soon as the crash had occurred, the radar controller made a sketch of what he had seen on the screen — but that was only like 'a simple map of a town's underground system for tourists' compared to the 'ordnance survey map', the real reconstruction of the flight which came from the *red box*, a flight data recorder put on board for proving purpose well in advance of the date of compulsory installation.

Under the chairmanship of William Tench, then a Principal Inspector of AIB, a flight recorder working group was assembled comprising experts from many related fields of aviation — professional engineers, aerodynamicists, mathematicians and physiologists. The arduous process of the read-out produced endlessly long dull columns of figures that represented the landing attempts and the last hundred seconds of the fiight. Each of these seconds was expressed by a set of thirteen figures. The indicated altitude, air speed and course of the aircraft were recorded once every second; the pitch attitude and normal acceleration were each recorded five times every second.

The figures printed out in the correct sequence look like a meticulous book-keeper's account. But they spell out the tragedy.

The final ten seconds begin at 00276 seconds, when the aircraft flew at a magnetic heading that did not alter substantially, and when, at a height of 370 feet, its air speed was 135·6 knots. During that second, while accelerating, the pitch attitude of Double Echo increased from 5·6 to 7·7 degrees. The records of pitch, speed and altitude were increasing for another second and a half. Then a strange picture takes shape: the nose of the aircraft begins to point farther and farther down — the record of the pitch attitude moves gradually into the negative, showing that the aircraft has started to descend — while the altitude record is still increasing!

The climax in the dramatic record comes at 00281 seconds — five seconds from disaster. The aircraft accelerates rapidly. Its nose is pushed farther down severely. From the recorded safety of 455 feet up it is hurtling now towards the runway.

00285 ... the last second begins. Recorded altitude: 105 feet. Air speed: 179·9 knots. The record indicates that the pilots now know they are heading for disaster: four fifths of a second away from the crash, Double Echo flies 34·8 degrees nose down; then there is a meaningful change — the nose begins to lift ... minus 33·4 degrees from the horizon-

tal, minus 30·9, minus 27·4 . . . the last second is completed
. . . just two more recorded values: pitch attitude minus
24·26 and a sudden change in acceleration in the ultimate
one fifth of a second.

This is the record. But the drama was drawn out over a
longer period. There is always a certain delay before the
instruments report changes in the flight. The recording, too,
is thus delayed. There is also another source of delay: it
takes time before the pilot recognises events, more time
before he reacts to it, and even more precious time before
the controls makes the aircraft submit to the pilot's will. On
the basis of the recording, these delays, recording errors and
distortions, and the true story of those final seconds are cal-
culable.

The interpretation of the recording was followed by a
great variety of tests in which the theoretically reconstructed
events in the cockpit of Double Echo were re-enacted
aboard other Vanguards. All that the rest of the investigation network produced confirmed the conclusions, eliminated other possible explanations, and — summed up in the
final report of the Public Inquiry — attempted to reveal not
only what had happened but also why it all had happened.

The first result of the investigation was the recognition
that the Captain had been misled: the Runway Visual
Range given to him was incorrect. He was told he would see
350 metres ahead, the minimum below which he would have
never attempted landing, whereas, in fact, the range was fifty
metres less.

But that alone could not have made disaster inevitable. It
was just one factor, followed by a series of mistakes and
coinciding adverse circumstances which all seemed to have
joined forces in searching for the tiny loophole in the overshooting drill. The result was a break-down of the Monitored Approach system. The overshoot began rather
violently — perhaps F/O Cochrane was too anxious to

avoid the critical height. The Captain's duty at that moment was done to the letter, the overshooting drill was such that 'it was apt to cause unnecessary distraction at a critical moment, when it was essential that all three pilots should have their attention devoted to the flight instruments.' The Captain then made a minor mistake in his job. This increased the First Officer's difficulties at a time when he was just placing too much reliance on the somewhat misleading pressure instruments.

Nine seconds before impact the First Officer tried to gather more speed at the expense of some of his rate of climb which, according to the particular instruments the three tired pilots must have watched, still appeared perfectly adequate even six seconds before impact when he put the aircraft nose even farther down.

At four seconds before disaster the instrument still must have told him — falsely — about 'a substantial rate of climb'. and the altimeter about a gain of height, as shown by the recorder read-out, when Double Echo was, in fact, already descending. Their own senses did not help them either: spatial disorientation had probably played its part.

Yet the crash was still not completely inevitable. The artificial horizon — despite its minor short-comings which have been overcome since then — could have told them the truth. But apparently, due to the above distraction, none of the pilots looked at or at least reacted to that instrument. And so at that crucial time, the monitoring system broke down, 'F/O Cochrane's over-dependence on his pressure instruments went unchecked, and by the time that anyone realised what was going wrong, it was too late'.

The Attorney General's final question to the Public Inquiry was 'What was or were the cause or causes of the accident?' The Report answers: 'Probably a combination of events . . . Namely pilot error due to eleven causes. These are given in the following order:

'(i) Low visibility. (ii) Tiredness'. (The pilots were well within the officially permitted limits of duty and rest times, but they were at the end of a long, tiring day which already included two, inevitably alerting or even tension-creating, overshoots.)

'(iii) Anxiety. (iv) Disorientation. (v) Lack of experience of overshooting in fog. (vi) Over-reliance on pressure instruments. (vii) Position error in pressure instruments.

'(viii) Lacunae in training. (ix) Unsatisfactory overshoot procedure.' These two were perhaps the most tragic and most disputed causal factors because they sound as if they could have been foreseen and — together with the over-reliance on certain instruments — could have been forestalled fully by better training. But this was not quite the case. The training of airline pilots is a constantly improving process — the need of such improvement is only reemphasised by incidents and accidents which reveal shortcomings. Training has gone a long way towards turning men into machines. It can go even further, but flying will never exclude completely the human element. Even with the fully automatic landing system, already in existence, people cannot be dispensed with. People have the right to overrule the machine — even the machine cannot be relied on to remain faultless for ever.

As for the 'unsatisfactory overshoot procedure' itself, the investigation revealed another combination of tragic circumstances which suggested that if only Double Echo had got into a similar situation a few weeks or perhaps just days later, the crash might never have happened.

Only three weeks before the Double Echo disaster, the monitored approach and overshoot system functioned smoothly. On October 6, a Vanguard flew from London to Edinburgh, tried to land in bad visibility and had to overshoot. Flying the aircraft, F/O Peter Bugge, the second pilot, got into difficulties, lost height considerably without knowing it until the third pilot called his attention to it, climbed away too steeply, then over-corrected — but got away with a fright.

For the benefit of those who like to generalise and say that 'pilots are reckless by nature' and that 'they have not learned that there are old pilots and there are bold pilots but no old bold pilots', let us quote from the letter Peter Bugge wrote six days later to R. E. Gillman, Senior Training Captain, Vanguards: '... I had previously considered myself an average, competent instrument pilot upon whom other members of the crew could rely. However, after the overshoot in question it became apparent to me that I was far from competent to perform this manoeuvre with safety and accuracy ...' He had thought about it and found some possible explanations: he was out of practice, had never been compelled to overshoot in actual flight, and he was tired. Moreover, he saw dangers in the overshoot drill. When his Captain retracted the flaps — correctly — Bugge faced unexpected difficulties. He suggested changes in the drill.

Captain Gillman found this letter 'an extraordinary coincidence' coming just after the subject had been discussed by him and others. He was in the process of suggesting changes in training and drill much along the lines taken by the letter.

The uncanny coincidence did not end there. Thirteen days from D-day for Double Echo, another Vanguard flew from Edinburgh to London. Fog, holding, weather improvement, ILS approach, no visual reference, 'overshoot' call at two hundred feet — and before they knew what had happened they were down to a hundred feet. The next thing the Captain realised was that the third pilot 'was calling into his ear "Climb, climb". He instinctively pulled back on the control column' and saw at the same time that they were already down to forty feet. A just slightly slower reaction would have ended in the crash that was now to become the fate of Double Echo.

Unfortunately, but quite understandably, the matter was not considered to be of particular urgency — until the crash. Then, within a few hours, the drill was altered.

The final two of the eleven causal factors were '(x) Indifferent flap-selector mechanism design' which pilots had been warned about confidentially some eighteen months earlier, and which was made safer after the crash investigation had shown that this design had, in fact, made it easy for the Captain to err and thus contribute to the accident by '(xi) Wrong flap-selection'.

The report paid great tribute to the service rendered by the flight data recorder. Among its recommendations the report suggested that recorders should 'include a parameter for elevator angles'. Further useful information for the investigators would have emerged from knowing what the pilots had said in the cockpit during the final minutes of the drama. This might have revealed not only what they intended to do, but also what they knew about their predicament at the various stages of the flight — factors which are, as yet, only logical conclusions.

To get these facts right was one of the main reasons why *voice recorders* in the cockpit had been made compulsory first in the United States and Australia. Other countries must follow suit although pilots are often, at least in the beginning, reluctant to put up with the 'airborne bug' or 'spy in the sky' or 'Big Brother' listening and recording all communications between the aircraft and the outside world, and also all the conversation of crew members in the cockpit.

The pilots' reluctance is understandable: nobody likes to have his chat and private views recorded and made available to his employers. But the fact is that these recorders are not an invasion of their privacy. The recordings must be used for nothing else but to observe and refine piloting techniques, and, of course, to help accident investigations by replacing dependable deductions with even more reliable direct factual information.

Ed Patton's NTSB section has already gone even beyond that. They evolved a new technique to correlate the spoken words with the flight data recording. When the two read-outs are superimposed one on another, they can co-ordinate the intentions of the crew with the actual events — the response they got from the aircraft. They also utilise the 'noises' in the sound recording: the 'click' of switches, the 'bang' of the landing gear when it is folding up or the roar of the engines when full power is applied, are all food for the fact-hungry investigator.

In a recent case such correlation has provided water-tight evidence. An aircraft, involved in an accident, was destroyed but its recorders remained intact. Calculations based on the flight recording showed at what point in space the aircraft must have been at a certain moment. It was an area where air traffic control imposed a constant speed limit. Yet at that point, the recording revealed, the speed of the aircraft had exceeded the speed limit considerably. This extra speed might well have contributed heavily to the cause of the accident.

Now all sorts of arguments could have arisen about that accusation. Perhaps the instruments cheated the pilot who thus did not know his real air-speed. Perhaps the flight recording was faulty. The 'spy in the sky', the voice recorder, gave the answer: it had recorded the sound of an *overspeed warning horn*. When the two recordings were superimposed one on another, the exact moment of the warning horn and the speeding record coincided. So there had been overspeeding – and the pilot had been warned.

A cockpit voice recorder might have provided this kind of crucial, indisputable evidence helping to bring about a more precise and satisfactory conclusion of the Trident (near

Staines) accident investigation in 1972. There were rumours of animosity, disputes, crude jokes and unpleasant exchanges on the flight deck — all implying that perhaps not a hundred per cent attention was paid to flying. If the captain had a heart attack, was it noted? What was the reaction? Who gave what orders? The final accident report commented: 'The investigator is still left in the dark as to what was passing between the crew members by way of orders, comment or exclamation. Had we been furnished with that sort of information, it might well have established why the droop lever was moved forward, the identity of the person who moved it, reactions of the crew thereafter and as a consequence the underlying causes of the crash.' The investigators found that the installation of cockpit voice recorders was overdue. From then on it still took another two years to introduce a new regulation, but since January 1975 virtually all major British passenger aircraft must carry a 4-channel voice recorder. In questions of safety, privacy will have to take the back-seat.

The protection of all this valuable information is not easy. When investigators emphasise that recorders have become specially important because of the more complex instrumentation and more complete crash destruction of modern big aircraft than that of their predecessors, they also stress how the massive impact and severe post-crash fire often imperil recorders, too.

Therefore the box is usually placed in the aft section of the fuselage where it is best protected in most crashes. The casing of the recorder is required to be tough — in the United States, for instance, it must withstand an impact shock that is a hundred times bigger than gravity (g) and must resist heat even if the exposure to or envelopment in 1100°C. flames lasts for thirty minutes.

Early mishaps — and even very recent cases — have demonstrated sufficiently the importance of such protection.

When in 1961 (September 17, O'Hare, Chicago) a Lockheed Electra of Northwest Airlines crashed, 'parts of the flight recorder were found strewn along the entire wreckage path' because it had been installed near the nose of the aircraft and the high impact loads destroyed the magazine and fragmented the recording foil which thus provided no useful information.

When the Pan American 707 Clipper 214 crashed at Elkton, Maryland, in 1963, the recorder was completely crushed. Only fragments of the aluminium foil were found, but it was imperative to do something even with those. For there were strange circumstances: the aircraft, with eighty-one passengers on board, was 'stacked' over New Castle, Delaware, waiting for a storm to pass. At 20.40 the 707 was ready to land and ground control promised 'to pull you away as soon as I can'. 'Roger, no hurry,' answered the pilot patiently — only to shout a few seconds later: 'Mayday ... mayday ... mayday ... Clipper 214 out of control ... here we go ...'

A DC–8, stacked a thousand feet above the 707, saw it 'going down in flames'. The 707 had been struck by lightning. But, as mentioned before, nobody used to believe that lightning could destroy a jet by causing a fuel-air mixture explosion in the tanks.

Ed Patton and his men worked several hundred hours to reassemble the recording foil. When the jigsaw puzzle took shape under the microscope, 5,000 'data points' became readable. These helped to prove the flight-path, and the approximate time the aircraft could have remained aloft after the reported moment of lightning strike.

To eject flight recorders, perhaps automatically, would be another way of preservation, but a strong argument against this is that ejection would need some explosive charge which, in turn, might cause accidents.

If an aircraft breaks up in the air or if it falls into water, the recovery of the well-protected recorder may run into immense difficulties. (The Boeing 727 that sank to the bottom of Lake Michigan also took the recorder to its grave.) And a Boeing expert has already warned that if a supersonic airliner broke up in the air over America, the recorder would have to be searched for in five or six adjoining states because of the initial height and speed of its plunge.

To overcome this, *sonic detection devices* — like the one in an expensive golf ball — have been developed. These and flashlights are actuated automatically on impact or on coming into contact with water, and emit signals on a preselected frequency. A new British invention uses a soda water type compressed air bubble which, when the aircraft is under water, reacts to the outside pressure and ejects the floatable recorder.

Yet all this tremendous advance in crash detection by flight data recording is only the very beginning of the Brave New World of aviation that is already a reality. The idea is to enlarge the concept of recording, *monitor perhaps several hundred aspects of aircraft operation in flight, transmit the data to computers on the ground for analysis, inform the pilot about the findings and recommend suitable measures against developing hazards.*

Some U.S. Air Force fighter squadrons already use the method. If, despite the system, a mishap occurs, all the recorded data will be found in safety — on the ground *before* the crash. Status or operation monitoring has already been used for testing new types. (When a BAC One-eleven crashed during a test flight, 68 of the 270 channels of the 'maintenance recorder' on board were used — and these provided accurate information without which the investigation would have been much more difficult and much less factual.)

The main obstacle to the general installation of such a continuous, detailed monitoring system is, of course, the astronomical capital investment it requires. For the sake of safety alone no airline could afford it — the prevention of the few accidents they have these days would not keep them out of the bankruptcy court. This may seem a cynical attitude, but we must remember that airlines — at least, most airlines — do not live on charity. Fortunately, the monitoring system will soon have such overwhelming economic advantages that its installation will become a financial must.

At the moment, maintenance is extremely expensive because it keeps those fast-aging giants on the ground. (TWA, for instance, makes 'service checks' after every 35 hours of flight, a more general check after 200 hours, an even bigger check after 700 hours, a complete overhaul after every 7,000 hours; engines, too, are checked periodically and are completely overhauled after a maximum of 6,000 hours when the job takes 2,300 man-hours in fifteen days — if all goes well — and may cost $30,000. Aircraft maintenance has been likened to carrying out a visual inspection of a car every time it is taken out of the garage and to changing all tyres of a car after every 750 miles.) With the aid of the vast number of monitored parameters maintenance will be done when it is really needed — well before a fault can fully develop and, significantly from a financial standpoint, sometimes well after the limit of a part's *expected* life. This will also save valuable time in fault detection because the maintenance base will be ready for a particular repair job and the necessary spare parts can be delivered before the aircraft has landed.

Airport problems will also force the airlines to speed up their operations. Today, if some minor fault is discovered, the aircraft may be delayed a few hours. If this happens to a couple of aircraft, the busy airport lounge may be crowded by an extra two hundred passengers waiting for take-off. With the Jumbos in full service, two delayed aircraft may put in an extra thousand people — and paralyse the entire airport.

The system will also be used for safety and economy in many other ways. American Airlines, the first — and at the moment still the only — civilian airline to install similar monitoring equipment, has carried out experiments for three years, including the use of a development model aboard a 'BAC 400 Astrojet' for a year. At the end of 1967, twenty such systems, called Astrolog, were installed at the cost of two million dollars. The equipment of their entire fleet will cost seventeen million dollars — but it is expected to save ten million dollars a year through improved flight and maintenance control and reduced losses through cancellations. (The Astrolog will monitor forty-seven parameters, such as air-speed, and forty-four 'events' such as whether the auxiliary power unit is working or not. But the investment would not be enough to pay for telemetry, the relaying of information to ground during the flight. The recordings will be taken from the aircraft after each day's flight and examined by computers which will produce the findings at high speed.)

Apart from technical safety and maintenance information, American Airlines expects to benefit greatly, both financially and in safety, from the computer reports about the 'end product' — the way the aircraft is flown. Instead of just periodical retraining and supervision, the pilots' performance will be evaluated and their 'product' will be analysed for each flight. This will facilitate the review of training programmes, flying techniques and drill. It will also help to warn pilots about developing particular undesirable habits and thus probably reduce the chance of human error to a great extent.

From here to warning the pilot *during* the flight is only one costly step away. The equipment, with up to 270 channels and four voice tracks, is ready. One day, most accidents will be spotted in their embryonic incident or even would-be incident stage, and most of the investigation will be an armchair job — for a computer.

CHAPTER NINE

THE COST OF ONE DELAY — 234 LIVES

THIRTY people were on board the United Airlines Boeing 727 when it flew from New York to Chicago on the night of August 16, 1965. Just before it was due to land, it crashed into Lake Michigan. There was speculation that a bomb might have caused the accident. FBI agents pounced upon the records to see if any passenger had taken out a large sum of insurance for the flight. But it was one of those rare occasions when most people wished the killer really were found to be a bomb. For however tragic, sabotage would have caused no more ripples on the calm surface of aviation than the crash had momentarily stirred on the waters of the lake.

A top-brass airline executive's reaction was typical: 'Well, here we go,' he mumbled on hearing the news, 'I give no more than a month for another two to fall.'

There seemed to be something menacingly mysterious about the 727 and the other members of the 'second generation' jets which had swept-back wings and 'T'-shaped tails. Their engines were rear-mounted — and when they began to crash, people talked about the 'sting in the tail'. They were created for short and medium range operations to provide a jet-conscious society with 'up-and-down' jet service. These were also designed to operate from smaller airfields, shorter runways, where the giants could not get in. The way to do it was to 'sink' them in rather than 'slide' them in gently. And sink they could — and did.

The question was: could their high sink rate be controlled? Thorough tests by manufacturers, airlines and governments showed that the answer was 'yes'. But were they right? Did any of the basic, hazardous characteristics go undetected? Did they really just *sink* fast or, with the weight of their engines aft, did they simply *drop* out of the sky?

It was thought that in the hands of well-trained pilots they would give no trouble, but experts dreaded the day when these aircraft got into less experienced hands.

They seemed to be proved right when the Trident made a good start. So did, later, the DC–9.

But even in the best hands, the BAC One-eleven had stalling problems. At slow speeds, when the airflow was insufficient to hold it up, the aircraft reared up, pressed its belly instead of its nose against the volume of air it ought to ride – and dropped. Perhaps mercifully, the prototype crashed in 1963, during tests. Some people still blame the authorities for 'over-testing' it. The accident report says that the stalling tests ought to have been 'more cautiously approached'. The accident led to a complete cure of the problem, but it was typical of the public mood that, three years later, many people simply refused to accept that another crash of the type was due to completely different causes.

The 727 came into service in February 1964. It became tremendously popular with the public overnight. Pilots viewed it with some suspicion: it flew only ten per cent behind the speed of sound, but could slow down with expanding wing surfaces to the speed of a propeller-driven aircraft.

Seventeen months later, about a month before the first accident, a Lloyd's aviation insurance underwriter's words sounded unduly sceptical: 'The pilots' initial suspicion was a good safety valve. It showed they were learning. Earlier, when they changed over from propeller aircraft to jets, they pooh-poohed re-education courses, regarding the jet as "just another machine".

'The trouble is that familiarity breeds contempt. Whereas structural problems tend to come out soon in service, handling problems tend to come out much later because at the beginning a suspicious pilot would never give the aircraft a chance for mischief. So later, when we have a crash — whether it's due to man or machine, a design mistake, uncontrollability by an average pilot in serve conditions, over-confidence, or careless regard for meticulous flying technique — it helps to keep the rest of the crews on their toes.

'Sometimes, perversely, it needs some tragic blow to get through to some of the pilots ... and even to some airlines.'

The Chicago crash was such a blow — but the message could not be read. It had sunk to the bottom of the lake with the wreckage. CAB spent some one hundred thousand dollars on the recovery, but the wreckage gave very little to go on and the flight recorder has not been found. Even today, they cannot yet publish a report.

The guessing game continued. The airline executive was glad to be proved wrong: the month was up, September ended, and no more 727's crashed. October gave some ground for optimism: almost 300 of the type were already in service. But the pessimists visualised an exaggerated doomsday when most of them might fall out of the sky in one go.

November 8, 1965, was a quiet day for Thomas Saunders although he was the CAB Washington duty officer, investigator in charge of the GO team. After his shift of regular office hours he returned home. At about the same time, American Airlines Flight 383, a Boeing 727, left New

York's LaGuardia Airport for Greater Cincinnati Airport with a crew of six and fifty-six passengers on board.

At a quarter to seven in the evening, Flight 383 radioed the estimated time of arrival at Cincinnati as 19.05. As the aircraft approached and Captain David Teelin began to talk to the Cincinnati Tower, the weather deteriorated rapidly. Captain Teelin sat in the co-pilot's seat from where he had to observe the work of Captain William O'Neill, a Captain for eight years and now in the final process of becoming a 727 Captain, too. O'Neill was now completing his seventh 727 flight — all under Teelin's observation.

At seven o'clock it began to rain, the tower told 383. Eleven seconds later the tower asked if they could still see the runway. (They were to make a visual landing.) 'Ah just barely we'll ah pick up the ILS here.' Seventy-nine seconds after seven: 'American 383. Approach lights, flashers and runway lights are all high intensity.' 'Okay,' said Teelin three seconds later.

At about the same time, a man on the ground noticed four bright landing lights coming towards him. Then he saw 'the aircraft bank rapidly to the left, crash into the hillside and burst into flame.' It took about ten seconds.

In the same ten seconds, an AA pilot, a non-revenue passenger in the first-class, most forward window seat of Flight 383, watched the apparently rapid descent. When he looked out next time, 'it seemed like we were very low . . . I then sat there unconcerned . . .' Then he felt the left turn, the bank, heard some noise — and 'we made contact with the ground, with quite a large bang, and it seemed like the destruction of the airplane.' While two passengers and a stewardess were thrown clear, he was stunned by debris piling on him. With flames behind him he extricated himself quickly and moved forward. He 'stepped out of the front of the aircraft which was completely missing'. Then came an explosion, and a few seconds later the rain.

Nineteen minutes later, Saunders received a telephone call. His team was alerted and two FAA aircraft were prepared. At 11 p.m. the first, at midnight the second, aircraft touched down at Cincinnati.

By 11.45, an investigation command post had been set up at a nearby motel and while telephones were being installed, a sub-command post was established at the wreckage site. The Kentucky State Police had already surrounded the area.

Apart from the four, there were no other survivors. Witnesses were rounded up, the story of the flight was studied, information came in about the background and the training record of the crew, the radio communications record was urgently transcribed — the team swung into action. At daybreak, there was a quick survey of the accident site. At 8.30 in the morning, Saunders called the first organisational meeting to set up the specialist groups and establish contact with his converging army of men: there were seventy-four people from CAB, FAA, the airline, the manufacturers, pilots' and engineers' assocations, National Aeronautics and Space Administration, the county coroner's office and the Armed Forces Institute of Pathology. Even UAL sent two representatives because the Lake Michigan crash was theirs and they were naturally interested.

In all, there were six CAB headquarters men, seven co-ordinators and ten specialist groups. (Twenty-three per cent of them from CAB, more than half of them from non-governmental organisations; the seventy-four people's salary and living expenses — excluding transport-ation — came to $175,000 during the 'field phase'.)

'At the time I had heard rumours about the type and how easily a T-tail and its char could "bloody the nose" of an aircraft,' Saunders recalled. 'I had a good look at the bird from all angles, but now it was different: I had to get at the truth, the full truth, because not only a single type and its passengers' lives were at stake — the giant Lockheed, for instance, was also to have a T tail.'

Prater Hogue, the Boeing co-ordinator on the scene, had confidence in the aircraft. Now he was worried: was there some hidden, still unknown characteristic? 'The company attitude was to let the chips fall as they may. If the accident had anything to do with the design, it's better to find out now than after another crash.'

Ed Slattery, too, had plenty on his plate. As the Board Public Information Officer, he worked flat out at Cincinnati. 'I was inundated with press enquiries from all over the world.'

In possession of the preliminary findings, within forty-eight hours of the crash, the investigators at Cincinnati made an important decision: they proposed to form a new, special group to examine the performance characteristics of the aeroplane (could it do what it was designed for?) and to see if the pilots were ready to cope with those apparently different characteristics (was their training for the task good enough?).

'On the 11th, at nine in the morning, I phoned Bobbie Allen, then Director of the Bureau of Safety in Washington,' said Saunders. 'Our recommendation was approved in principle, but I couldn't get him on the phone. Tried it later again, but had to phone him in the evening, at home, to read him the proposal. He was watching television and had to turn down the sound a little before I could begin to read. But I never got far with it. He suddenly interrupted "Wait, there's something on". A local TV station had apparently beaten our communications network — something had happened at Salt Lake City.'

Like Saunders only seventy-three hours earlier, George (Dick) Baker, the duty officer, was already at home. 'It was about eight in the evening, with my wife and three boys we were at the end of our dinner, when the call came through: a

UAL 727 had crashed on the airport at Salt Lake City and was on fire. It happened some ten minutes earlier.* Eighty-five passengers and a crew of six on board.

'Two hours later my GO team was assembled, as pre-arranged, at Hangar 6, Washington National Airport. By government aircraft, we got to the scene some five and a half hours later and set up our headquarters in the Holiday Inn nearby during the night.'

By dawn, the usual hordes of investigators had converged on Salt Lake City. Some, like Ed Slattery and Prater Hogue, had flown direct from Cincinnati. National and foreign government and public pressure on them increased every minute. 'Ground the killer' was the cry up and down the country. It grew into an emotionally highly-charged issue.

'Our job was to get the facts,' said Baker. 'At seven in the morning we formed the groups, although I never seemed to be able to get off the phone. Washington was watching us all, co-ordinating Michigan, Cincinnati and us, asking for information, giving clues, instructions, and calling attention to points overlooked or raised elsewhere. Each night we all had a meeting and I also talked daily to the other 727 investigators in charge.

'The man in charge is like a "grand manager" or a "house mother". The most difficult stage of the job is to assemble all the available information quickly — and to keep all the men at top performance. That in itself is a two-fronted fight: the meetings are important because everybody must know what's going on, nobody should work in a vacuum; but the danger in this method is that when we get something that seems to be a positive lead — say, a system is sus-

* The above times were all Eastern Standard. The crash at Salt Lake City occurred at 17.25 local Mountain Standard time, which is two hours behind Eastern. Therefore Salt Lake City gave the news when by their time it was only 18.00.

pected — other groups may lose a little interest because "systems" are in the spotlight. It's my job to see to it that determination fizzles out nowhere, for after all, systems may turn out not to be all that important.'

And 'positive leads' they had galore at Salt Lake City.

Like the other two, the accident happened in the landing stage. The weather seemed to have played no part in it. The fast sink rate was a prime suspect in this case, too. According to the official report, 'Impact occurred 335 feet short of the runway threshold, the main gear sheared,' the aircraft burst into flames at once and slid some 3,000 feet on its nose gear and belly. Despite the devastating fire, 'this was a survivable accident'. Of ninety-one people on board, fifty managed to escape although two of them died in hospital a few days later. Why couldn't the rest escape?

Temporarily, this accident commanded the greatest attention not only because it was the latest of the three, but also because for the first time the investigators had a *live crew* to consult. Second Officer (flight engineer) Ronald Christensen was only ambulatory so he was interviewed first. Shortly before impact, he said, First Officer Spicer started to apply power which would have arrested the rather fast sink of the aircraft, but Captain Kehmeier brushed his hand away and told him 'not yet'. He thought that the Captain had not increased engine power until about seven or eight seconds before impact. Was this a lead? Was it all the captain's fault?

The hospital then authorised an interview with First Officer Spicer. He thought it was between 90 and 120 seconds prior to impact when he attempted to apply power. (He was flying the aircraft under the direction of the captain — which is regarded as the captain flying the aircraft through the co-pilot.) It was long after that, *between five and ten seconds but no more than fifteen seconds* before impact, that the captain applied full power.

Eventually, the hospital permitted the investigators to talk to the captain. He confirmed the statements of the other two, that he had stopped the application of power at first, but he thought that the timing was different: in his opinion, full power was finally applied *at least thirty seconds* before impact, at an altitude of about 1,000 feet. Then why couldn't the engines slow down the descent in time? The Captain said the engines did not respond with proper acceleration to the selected revolutions per minute.

This was yet another 'positive lead', for although the Captain's testimony contradicted the two officers, two stewardesses, survivors and witnesses — who, according to the final report, stated that the engines 'did spool up prior to impact' — great importance was attached to the Captain's words. The engines took their place on the list of prime suspects.

The jigsaw men came into the spotlight. They found that foreign material had been ingested at impact by the No. 1 engine causing serious damage — a clue which showed that the engine had produced substantial thrust at the time of the crash. That discredited the Captain's explanation. The other two engines had ingested less foreign material. They had been sent to San Franciso, where UAL had put them on test beds to run. The indication was that the engine response should have been normal!

While the various lines of enquiries were continued, a concerted effort was made to discover why so many people had been killed in this survivable accident. The escape story of each survivor was pieced together. From these and from the technical evidence, the sequence aboard the crashed, burning airliner evolved. It appeared that 'all emergency exits were available and used'. But at the main loading door there was a tragic delay: passengers from the cabin crowded the area and the pressure there was such that the stewardess could not open it. While the injured Captain and First

Officer managed to escape through sliding windows of the cockpit, the Second Officer went back to help the struggling stewardess. He managed to open the door and inflate the slide, and then directed the evacuation there. (It is impossible to guess how many additional lives might have been saved by avoiding the delay. But after the investigation, the stewardesses recommended that they should be seated 'near emergency exits for all take-offs and landings' and UAL made this a standard procedure.)

The overwing emergency windows were opened by passengers. So was the galley door on the right side between rows 8 and 9, but there the escape slide was not actuated until a stewardess, a passenger on the flight but now already outside the aircraft, instructed a man (also already outside) to activate it.

Throughout this time, unknown to escaping passengers and scores of rescue squads, three people fought for their lives in the rear of the aircraft. The stewardess, who had opened the aft passenger entry door, found that the ventral stairway was blocked. (She did not know that the main gear had been sheared and the plane was sitting on its rear.) Two male passengers who were with her in the stairwell tried to help her but they could not open the stairway more than about six inches. Through that gap, it was impossible to escape.

They ran back towards the cabin but now the flames and smoke beat them back. They were trapped.

The three retreated from the approaching flames as far as possible and huddled together. She knew they were at the airport, she knew that already firemen must have long been on the scene, and yet her yelling and pounding on the fuselage brought no help.

Some *twenty minutes* had passed since the inferno began. In her desperation, she pressed herself against the gap and pushed her arm outside. At last, some three minutes later, her arm was noticed. Firemen passed a hose through the gap into the stairwell, and one man sprayed the area to contain the flames.

It took approximately another five minutes before the three could be rescued 'through the large hole which had burned through the aft cabin wall on the right side'.

The detailed reconstruction of the escape story was only a side issue of the investigation, but it certainly furthered the study of better evacuation methods and the conclusion based on it had some ominous significance. For there is hardly disguised criticism implied when the investigators recall the earlier CAB study of U.S. accidents involving fire that 'lists various recommendations which, if implemented, would enhance passenger protection, survival and reduction of injuries'. (The pathologists examined the bodies and discovered no impact-caused injuries that would have prevented the escape of those passengers who died from suffocation during the fire.)

The reconstruction of events in the cabin was also closely related to other 'side issues' of the investigation which led to further 'technological fall-out'.

One of these was that the emergency lighting system failed to illuminate the emergency exits when they were needed most. On November 30, nineteen days after the accident, a new method to operate the system was recommended to FAA. The same day, the CAB sent an even more important letter to FAA: this concerned *the cause of the fire*.

'It puzzled us from the very beginning why so immediate and so intense a fire occurred,' said Dick Baker. 'After all, this was not much more than a really bad, heavy landing and the fuselage belly structure had not collapsed. The answer was provided by the technical investigation. The fuel lines ran from the wing tanks to the rear-mounted engines under the belly, and were protected only by the fuselage sidewalls. When the right main landing gear was sheared, it crashed

198

through the sidewall and broke the fuel lines. Sparks from runway contact might have caused a fire. But probably, there was an even greater source: electrical leads ran in the vicinity of the fuel lines and these were also torn at the same time.

'The re-routing, better protection and maximum separation of these fuel lines and electrical leads seemed to be urgent and imperative because quite frequently, a low approach over dykes or other obstructions could break the landing gear and cause an *incident* — but with the current design, such incidents could cause a devastating fire and become *accidents*.'

The CAB letter, in agreement with FAA and Boeing investigators, called attention to this serious problem. It also raised an even wider, and graver, issue: 'We recommend that *all other similarly configured aircraft* (e.g. DC–9, Lear Jet, Caravelle, BAC 111, Jet Commander) be the subjects of a study to determine' if their designs represented a potentially similar fire trap. (Author's italics.)

Another sixteen days later, CAB sent a third letter to FAA. It said: 'Preliminary information indicates that the interior furnishings contributed greatly to the spread of fire and the emission of heavy black smoke, both of which contributed to the fatalities.' The letter referred to a just completed FAA study of this subject and suggested that if it had not yet been done, FAA should examine a special problem: apparently, when various materials, used in aircraft interiors, burned together, the toxicity of the *mixture* of gases would be worse than that produced by the burning materials individually.

On January 13, 1967, William F. McKee, Administrator of FAA, gave detailed answers to the three letters. FAA experts had already studied the recommendations 'and are pleased to report that we have had many of them under consideration for some time'.

The location of the fuel lines still appeared to be the best possible (their re-location might create new hazards) but they would be strengthened. The electrical leads would be re-routed to achieve greater separation and they would be better protected, too. The landing gear would also be improved. The emergency lighting system was studied both in 727s and other aircraft. The flammability and smoke characteristics of interior materials had long been studied and were the subject of current research. Other rear-engined aircraft, too, were being examined from the relevant points of view.

Not without a refined touch of venom, the FAA letter demonstrated an example of inter-departmental rivalry by concluding: 'In summary, may I state the Agency is acutely aware of the need to continuously seek improved crash-worthiness standards ... It is extremely gratifying to me to know that the actions which the Agency either has had under consideration, or now is contemplating, have your support.'

Thus there were already some positive results in the problem areas highlighted by the crash detectives. But the main question — what had caused the tragic series of three crashes? — was still far from being answered. The frustrating and inevitable delay in pinpointing the killer of thirty people in the Michigan accident had already caused another 101 deaths at Cincinnati and Salt Lake City.

At Lake Michigan the search for the wreckage continued.

At Cincinnati, after the slow progress made in the first few days, some pieces of the puzzle began to take shape: the impact on the trees was measured, the attitude of the aircraft at the time of the crash into the hillside was estimated — and then Washington gave Saunders the flight recorder read out on the telephone. The fast descent appeared clearly suspicious — the pilots would not have wanted it that way. Was it possible that they *could not* do anything about it or that when they did try to arrest the sink rate they were too low?

The specialist group, which had been set up literally in the same moments as the Salt Lake City accident occurred, was taking now a most critical look at the design, performance and controllability of the 727. It found — like the early Boeing tests and the FAA airworthiness trials — that the aircraft was 'highly versatile and responsive', and that it did what it had been designed for: produced a high rate of climb and descent. Would it take such a steep path on its own initiative? The group and the various research organisations gave that question a negative answer, but recognised that the 727 responded more readily to smaller control efforts than those applied on other types.

A well-trained pilot would be aware of that characteristic and would not take any liberties with the aircraft — but this thought begged another question: how well were the pilots trained for the 727?

The group was therefore expanded and also charged with the examination of crew training and current 727 piloting techniques. It soon emerged that the training ought to have been more strenuous. Perhaps the most important finding was that the pilots had been *warned* not to operate outside the carefully prescribed 'normal flight envelope' — in other words at a faster than desirable sink rate — but were not required to train for and demonstrate their ability to handle the plane in a manoeuvre outside that safety envelope at high sink-rate close to the ground.

The Air Line Pilots' Association (ALPA) and the Allied Pilots' Association (APA), representing most American pilots who flew 727s, carried out a survey to establish the 'line pilot' viewpoint based on the experience of the best possible test: day-to-day routine operation of an aircraft. The 'pilots were generally pleased with the flight characteristics' of the 727, and 'had experienced no major difficulties' in flying it.

S—AD—L

In December 1965, some six weeks after the third crash, the airlines operating 727s — in consultation with FAA — made some changes in training and flying procedures. As the causes of the accidents were still unknown, this was purely a preventive measure against a *possible* hazard.

In the light of all this information, special significance was attached to background details, now being compiled, about Captain Kehmeier who had survived the Salt Lake City crash. It showed he had become a captain in 1944 and progressed well until November 1960, when he began transition training for jets. After some examination and flight difficulties, a flight standards observer noted: 'A review of Captain Kehmeier's record still indicates unsatisfactory performance in the areas of command, judgment, Standard Operating Procedures, landing technique and smoothness and co-ordination. On the basis of the above I recommend Captain Kehmeier's DC–8 transition training be terminated.'

In February 1961 he was returned to DC–6 aircraft 'on which he was rated average to above average'.

He entered the jet programme once again in May 1962, now training for Boeing 720s. His progress was erratic. As recalled by an FAA inspector for the benefit of the investigation, he gave the impression that he could fly the aircraft well but 'would deviate from accepted procedures and tolerances' and would have to repeat some manoeuvres to achieve a satisfactory grade. Finally, he obtained his 720 rating. About his work in 1963, his Flight Manager reported on December 31 that he 'has done a creditable job during the period'.

Yet two days later, he failed to pass an instrument proficiency check because of mistakes like being 'slow to add power' during a manoeuvre. Another two days later, he passed the same check.

A year later, in January 1965, he began training for 727s

and in February he was licensed to fly the type. That was on record. The FAA inspector, when talking to the investigators, could only 'recall a few items' about that check flight. 'The main outstanding thing in my mind was that he could fly the aeroplane but it was necessary several times to remind him to stay on altitude or airspeed.'

In September 1965, his 'en route proficiency check' graded his performance 'above average'. In November came the crash.

This, together with his crewmen's reports, flight recorder data and other findings, certainly loaded the dice against Captain Kehmeier. But if this was to be regarded as a 'positive lead' to the cause of the accident, then it also pointed a finger at the training and piloting standards maintained by the FAA and the airline. Many pilots make mistakes or even fail flight tests and evoke unfavourable comments. But, fortunately, it is not the pilots' duty to evaluate their mistakes and issue ratings. If the black marks in Captain Kehmeier's record were now to be regarded as omens that lined the road to disaster, why had they not been recognised as such at the time of their occurrence?

The issue of pilot training came to the fore yet again as the public enquiries were being prepared.

In January 1966, the voices of 'ground the aircraft with sting in the tail' campaigners were still strong. Although the majority of expert views were against them, their case gained an unwanted impetus on February 4.

On that day, at 17.55 Japanese time, All-Nippon Airways Flight 8302, a Boeing 727, took off from Sapporo, on Hokkaido, Japan's northernmost island. The plane carried 126 Japanese passengers, most of them visitors to the local snow festival, and a crew of seven. They were scheduled to land at Tokyo International Airport at 19.05. Flying at 12,000 feet, the pilot was instructed to begin his descent at 18.56. Soon after that, the instruction was to 'maintain

10,000', pilot acknowledged 'Roger' — the language of the air is English — and then to 'contact Tokyo tower approaching'. At 18.59, the 727 was flying at ten thousand feet.

A JAL Convair 880 was coming in over Tokyo Bay, ready to land, and the 727 was told about it. 'Do you have aircraft in sight? Over.' There was a ten-second silence during which, presumably, the crew tried to spot the Convair. Then the pilot began to give a negative answer — and went off the air in the middle of the sentence. The tower called him more and more frantically. Only *two* minutes before he had been at ten thousand feet! But by that time the aircraft was in the Bay. The toll was 133 lives — the worst single airliner disaster in history to that date.*

Despite the bitter cold, an armada of boats began to search the bay immediately and hundreds of relatives crowded the shore, but their hopes soon vanished. Duishi Narabayashi, perhaps the best Japanese crash detective, was put in charge of the case. Not surprisingly, stall or that fast sink rate were the most obvious suspects, but very prudently, the Japanese were determined not to be influenced by the pending American cases. An American team left for Japan without delay although Boeing, for instance, were now beginning to run short of specialists for the job.

The international uproar that followed was inevitable. Pro-727 experts felt obliged to question the plane's controllability. Politicians urged governments to ground the type. Henry Gonzalez, a Democratic member of the American House of Representatives, made the same demands in the light of four crashes and the loss of 264 lives: 'The fact that each of the four crashes occurred under similar circumstances. as the planes were preparing to land, makes it even

* The reconstruction of this investigation was greatly helped by the excellent documentary film which — made by Yoshitino Hovii for NHK, the Japanese TV network — won the Italia Prize in 1966.

more imperative that the Government act immediately before additional lives have been lost.' In Britain, R. J. Maxwell-Hyslop, a Conservative M.P., suggested that 727s should not be allowed to land in Britain until it was known whether accidents had been caused by defects in the aircraft or in its handling technique. The concern was understandable: almost three hundred 727s were already in service and another two hundred had been ordered.

The FAA, under tremendous pressure, had to face an agonising dilemma: they had great faith in their own original tests of airworthiness — it would have been crooked to license the aircraft without firm conviction — but their critics had raised scores of questions to which they had not yet had the full answers. For February 18, they now called a conference with eighteen American and foreign airlines operating the aircraft. There was suspicion that this might be a prelude to grounding the 727s. But they only started an exchange of views and safety suggestions, which, by early March, led to new safety measures. Training for 727s was made to be much more strenuous than before, more practice was required from pilots in command before allowing their co-pilots to take over for landings and take-offs. The procedure was changed: during the landing approach, co-pilots would have to call out altitude and other data at regular intervals. It was recommended that a newly developed Boeing device, giving aural warnings of altitude in the last critical stages of descent, be fitted.

These were preventive measures based largely on the recent findings of investigations, but the Agency, in recommending their implementation, now committed itself although those findings had not yet yielded the explanations of the accidents.

From Tokyo came disturbing news which caused minor tremors in the shaky ground American investigators then stood on. As the wreckage was salvaged, the positions of the engine fire extinguisher levers were examined and it appeared that the No. 3 engine extinguisher might have been activated. The meter registering engine power showed that No. 3 gave an abnormally small output. The indication: engine fire in flight. Frogmen stirred up the muddy seabed in an effort to find the tail section with the engines. At last it was found on February 15 — but No. 3 was not there. It was found three days later and the jigsaw men had a field-day. They found there had been no fire. The clues had been misleading. But why did the engine fall off?

As the two American crash investigations reached the Public Inquiry stage, the Japanese found one of the three broken bolts that had once secured No. 3 engine to the tail. The sheared surface looked unusual — although the pattern was indiscernible, failure might have been due to metal *fatigue*. It was at midnight that Narabayashi drove thirty miles to the house of Professor Yamana, an outstanding structures expert, one of the massive specialist team on the case.

Yes, it was probably fatigue, was his verdict. If so, when the bolt failed, the engine would have worked itself loose, the power output would have fallen, the pilots would have perhaps interpreted it as fire in the engine which, in the meantime, would have broken the other two bolts and fallen off. Some scratches on the fuselage, reconstructed in a hangar, seemed to confirm this theory. Teleprinters all over the world typed out the ominous warning: fatigue.

But in the American cases there was no sign of fatigue. Boeing found nothing to support the view. And finally, after long arguments and research, even the Japanese metallurgists found there was no fatigue.

The Tokyo investigators worked on the handling aspects, too. There was a two-minute gap between the pilot's reported altitude of ten thousand feet and the last, unfinished sentence. Was it fatal to descend at 5,000 feet per minute? The crash detectives, serving as guinea pigs, repeated the manoeuvre in another 727 above the crash site giving themselves an extra 2,000 feet height for safety. The aircraft, they found, would have given no trouble even at such a high sink rate — as long as the pilot knew what he was doing and how near he had got to the ground.

One theory was that the experienced, very meticulous pilot, who had shortly before the crash been rewarded for his 5,000 flying hours without a single incident, had his attention diverted in the final ten seconds by scanning the sky for the Convair.

Another theory involved the limitations of the human eye. In the absence of indisputable evidence from the wreckage or from survivors, these theories have remained only logical explanations. But in any case, it seems likely that the crew paid insufficient attention to instruments, especially the altimeter, during descent.

The new FAA recommendations would have been a safeguard against this hazard.

Completing the job in record time, the CAB published its final report on the Salt Lake City accident on June 7, 1966. It contradicted Captain Kehmeier, showing that there could not have been more delay in engine response than could be expected from jet engines. It concluded that the rate of descent had been three times faster than that recommended by UAL for landing approaches. In the Captain's training records it found indications of 'a tendency to deviate from acceptable standards and tolerances'. Finally, accepting that 'the captain stopped the first officer's initial attempt to apply power', the Board stated that 'the probable cause of this accident was the failure of the Captain to take timely action to arrest an excessive descent rate during the landing approach'.

This patently was a clear-cut 'pilot error' report which — as usual, especially in this category of findings — came under heavy criticism immediately. The crash detectives were attacked for discrediting the report of the only surviving captain, thereby making him a scapegoat, for using parts of his record deliberately to put him in a bad light, for whitewashing FAA, the 'sister agency', and everybody else at the man's expense. These all raised some important points.

One is that to take a severely critical view of all governmental attitudes and actions is not only often desirable, but also very popular — especially if these criticisms help to defend the individual.

Another is that however popular, it is not always expedient to run down accident reports because casting doubt without evidence on the findings will not enhance the progress of aviation safety. Captain Kehmeier reiterated his argument in a letter published in a book* but there has been no appeal against the report although the pilots' associations are always ready for a good fight for their members even if they have no more than a toehold on legal grounds.

A third point is that crash detectives do not try to *blame* anybody or anything for an accident. They seek an explanation so that other accidents could be avoided. Although their reports are used frequently by lawyers as blueprints for subsequent legal action, it often happens that the courts disagree with the reported findings when apportioning blame. It simply does not pay the investigator to try to 'sell' a false cause as explanation because (a) he never signs the report — some top brass, like the British Chief Inspector of Accidents or the five members of the Civil Aeronautics Board, do that, and if he misled them, they would never give him promotion; (b) today so many experts are involved that anti-pilot investigators would soon be found out, and come under fire for professional incompetence; and (c) their unsubtantiated evidence would be exposed when the next crash came.

* *Airline Safety is a Myth*, see Bibliography.

It would, of course, be possible to expose their interest in false findings by accusing them of corruption. Had there been any ground for that, many interested parties who were targets of their accusations would undoubtedly have done so. As it happens there is no room for such direct corruption in the set-up, because even if a case were successful, the wealthy or influential dodger — like the manufacturer, airline or FAA would still have to take subsequent corrective action, and in so doing would be exposed. As indeed, when crash detectives had made genuine professional mistakes, repeated accidents proved them wrong.

Finally, the critics in these cases — not for the first or last time — *displayed an inability to read between the lines.* It is perfectly true that, proportionately, the report over-emphasises and almost revels in the flaws in the captain's record. But it is equally true that having produced apparently indisputable evidence of the captain's fatal mistake, his background and career tend to *lessen* his responsibility. For this, in fact, implies that although with current training standards it was possible to fly the aircraft well, and that although the current checking standards made it possible to judge pilots' suitability, there was room for improvement in both areas. As always, this was wisdom in retrospect which, while argued in public, had been admitted partially and indirectly by the FAA and the airlines through the new regulations issued three months before the publication of the report.

The Cincinnati report came out only in October 1966. This, too, exonerated the aircraft and was a 'pilot error' report and thus came under similar criticism as had been voiced on the Salt Lake City report. It was not, however, such a clear-cut case. Weather deterioration played a part and investigators found that a delayed or an instrument approach would have been 'more prudent judgment' of the situation than flying under visual rules. Although they saw similarities to the Salt Lake City accident in some elements 'relative to pilot/crew judgment', the basic difference appeared to be that, while at Salt Lake City the mistake was in the execution of a *planned* fast descent, at Cincinnati the mistake was the late or non-recognition of coming in too low too soon. As there were no crew survivors and the flight recorder plus wreckage evidence ruled out every other explanation, the tests and logical conclusions led to this verdict:

'The Board determines that the probable cause of this accident was the failure of the crew to properly monitor the altimeters during a visual approach into deteriorating visibility conditions.'

Among the 'recommendations', the report raised a new point (new in the 727 story), which called for improved instrument data presentation to ease the strain the increasingly complex duties impose on the pilot. The fully disciplined monitored approach is one solution of the problem, the altimeter that gives warnings at lower altitudes is another.

In this case, lawyers and critics had an even better chance to argue that test conditions are not identical with the actual flight, that fact-finding by elimination is good enough only in philosophy, and that logical conclusions are no more proof than the 'observations' reported by a spiritualist medium. Therefore, the real test of the aircraft and of the findings was yet to come. This inspired Thomas Saunders to say:

'The revised training standards were the most important result of these investigations. This is the candle we lit, I believe. But we still cross our fingers, and sometimes, at night, I wonder: did we do everything possible? Only time can tell.'

Early in 1968, some two years after the last in the series of 727 disasters, when some 500 were already in constant use, an insurers' crash expert of international renown told a test pilots' conference: 'Six 727s have been lost in all. That's about 300,000 hours of flight per wreckage ... which is excellent. Much better than average.'

A month after that, a Formosan 727 crashed into a field near Taipei as it came in to land. Of sixty-three people aboard, ten were killed and forty suffered injuries. On January 5, 1969, another 727 (Ariana Airline of Afghanistan) crashed in bad visibility, near Gatwick, killing fifty people. There were some other 727 crashes (such as the TWA, near Washington, in 1974) but the type accumulates flying hours so fast that the statistical record is better than ever.

CHAPTER TEN

MEN OR SUPERMEN

THE expression 'pilot error' is the H-bomb of aircrash investigation. It is the most explosive, potentially most destructive, verdict, not only because a surviving crew's future or a dead pilot's reputation are so blatantly hinged upon it, but also because the absence of *facts* often allows it to become an emotionally charged issue. Many investigators accuse the pilots' associations of always starting with the premise that the pilot did not and would not make any mistake. (Pilots would be perfectly within their rights to take this standpoint: it is their duty to defend a colleague and insist on his innocence until he has been proved guilty.) Pilots, on the other hand, claim that crash detectives make them prime suspects much too readily. Unfortunately, this accusation is a cross investigators have to shoulder partly because it is a left-over from the past when their predecessors indeed had such an attitude, partly because there is still some truth in the accusation in substance, partly because 'pilot error' still turns out to be the cause of many accidents, and partly because the human factor is the darkest spot in the spectrum where investigators must still place more reliance on logic than on tangible evidence.

Typical of this latter point is the fact that the American CAB (NTSB), the organisation with the world's finest human and financial resources in this field, has been forced to alter its findings only twice in thirty years — and both cases were originally in the pilot error category. They had to alter their findings partially in another two cases — and these, too, had first seemed to be pilot errors.

Various experts have long urged an increased research effort in this direction. The Guggenheim Aviation Safety Center at Cornell University, Los Angeles, has always placed the 'human factors' problem high in its list of priorities, and its Survey of Research Projects in 1966, for instance, stated that 'there appears to be a need for more research to determine why a carefully trained, highly motivated crew in a vehicle with most advanced equipment and adequate ground support, fails to execute the proper technique at a critical portion of the flight. Variation in aircrew discipline and efficiency caused by environmental and social factors, along with improved monitoring, should be considered. This should be approached as a research project, and not in any case as a disciplinary investigation.'

In this respect, advanced flight data recorders, like the 'Astrolog', will help specialists to gather factual data on invisible hazards like individual bad habits or more general dangerous malpractices due to insufficient training. While an industrial research programme found that in machine shops an unsafe act was committed, on an average, about three hundred times before resulting in one injury,* we have

* H. W. Heinrich, *Industrial Accident Prevention*, quoted by the Guggenheim Center.

no such figures for flying an aircraft. Therefore frequently, when a pilot has erred, we do not even know the exact circumstances of his falling into what may have been a ready-made trap.

In 1962 a Flight Safety Foundation bulletin mentioned an example of the type of problem investigators must sort out. An inspection lamp was left on top of a pair of steps in a factory. A man knocked it off accidentally. It fell on a tin, broke up and set fire to the inflammable fluid in the tin. The man who knocked off the lamp (the pilot) caused the fire. But who put him in this accident-prone position? The man who left the lamp in an insecure place or the one who had originally removed a protective shield from the lamp or the man who failed to report that the shield had been removed or the one who used it in an unsafe condition or the one who issued it for such use or the supervisor who failed to notice the hazard? And the list of possible 'suspects' is still incomplete. For the inflammable fluid should not have been there. Its illegal presence could be pinned on a number of other people, and it could be argued that without that fluid there would have been no fire even if a man knocked the lamp off inadvertently.

To explain the case and to share out the responsibility, all the factors must be known including the reason *why* each participant acted in the way he did.

The fact that 'why' is being asked more and more often is the sign of the biggest advance in the investigation of pilot error cases. 'The record shows a tendency to blame the pilot,' said Joseph O. Fluet, Chief of the NTSB Central Investigation Division. 'This is partly because inevitably, pilots make many true errors. But also because in the past, we had many strongly opinionated investigators who would say "Oh yes, it was a mistake, when I was an airline pilot I myself made the same mistake, he just didn't get away with it". But they did not question why they or the more unfortunate pilot had made the mistake in the first place. By asking "why?" the over-simplified "pilot error" case will grow into the thorough investigation of the more comprehensive "human factor" issue.'

In the same way as anthropologists discover traces of the human past still surviving in some corners of the world, one finds that the more ancient — more superficial, if you like — methods of crash investigation still survive. It is an alarming fact, too. For there is an enormous market for the latest, most sophisticated planes in countries where the post-mortem of a flight has not yet advanced much beyond the 'what goes up, must come down' principle. And these are not necessarily those countries which are regarded as underdeveloped in other respects.

Dr. Harald Widmer, Switzerland's former Chief Investigator, exemplified this attitude when he remarked about an accident: 'It was quite clear from the beginning that it was a navigational error.' (In this case, one should not forget that, as seen in the third chapter, he is one of the few who know enough about the achievements of investigation to recognise the amateurism in several European and many Asian and African countries, and one of the even fewer who have the moral courage to admit the fact.)

The accident he spoke about happened on May 15, 1960. It was a DC–4 of Balair, a Swiss charter company, which crashed into Mount Marra in the Sudan killing its crew of seven (three pilots, two flight engineers and two navigators) and five company employees travelling as passengers. The completely tangled, burnt mass of metal that was left of the aircraft gave only a few clues: the DC–4 had apparently struck the slope at cruising speed. The cockpit was so entirely destroyed that 'no coherent piece of it could be found' and so to ascertain instrument readings or radio settings was out of the question. The time of the crash was established as 19.57 with the aid of a witness who had seen a flash at about eight o'clock (GMT) in the evening, and also by examining the only not completely burnt crew-watch. (The hands were missing but bright marks on the dial were accepted as their 'shadows' imprinted by the impact and fire.)

The investigation board was appointed by the Sudanese government and the three members (a civil aviation official, Dr. Widmer and a flight captain of Balair) reached the scene of the accident after a seven hours' jeep ride and several hours' climb. Their calculation showed that the aircraft had come to a spot where it should not have been according to the flight plan, and that the crew must have been mistaken about their true position.

The accident report reveals that the mistake was made long before the crash. Navigation was done by the stars and the crew radioed two estimated position reports based on an 'astrofix', which must have been inaccurate. (Had they been at the reported spot at the time, they would have needed to fly at a speed beyond the capability of the aircraft to get to the crash site by 19.57.) Because of this mistake, the crew did not realise that they were a few degrees off the planned track, and that they were flying almost twenty per cent faster than they apparently imagined. The investigators concluded that at the time of the crash the crew 'were perhaps not excessively concerned about their position' because they were waiting to come over the El Fasher radio beacon in about four minutes when they would begin to climb well above Mount Marra.

What the investigation never seemed to ask — and what the report does not attempt to answer — is *why* the first navigational mistake had been made. Not that they could have expected to come to some really startling conclusion about such a well-tried old type of aircraft (this airframe was fourteen years old) but they might have made some rather useful discoveries about the operational aspects.

One was what the report did not mention, but Dr. Widmer did in a discussion, that the aircraft had done a great deal of service over Africa, taken savage beatings in sandstorms, and that the astrodome, the window to the sky, was badly scratched. When a navigator must 'shoot a star', a scratched astrodome will not make his job any easier. Dr. Widmer thinks that this man might have based his 'fix' on the wrong star.

Another pointer to a problem appears briefly in the report. It was a dark night and clouds obscured 'a good fraction of the heaven'; the crew thus 'may not have been aware that they flew, at least during the last two or three minutes' very close to the ground. Did their altimeter fail to warn them? Or did they fail to look at it? How many of the three pilots were on duty, anyway? Is it possible that one flew the aircraft and two were resting at the time?

These questions were not even raised by the report — let alone answered — although the latter two are very closely related to another menace to air-crews: fatigue.

The operation began in Geneva the *previous evening*. The crew's duty time counts from at least an hour and, in the case of a long flight like this, from ninety minutes before take-off. So this crew was on duty from about 19.00 the previous day. With two technical landings — which, with the strain and extra duties of landings and take-offs, are an additional work-load rather than rest — they flew sixty-five passengers to Jiddah, in Saudi Arabia, where they landed at 11.23 the following morning. Less than two hours later, they took off again for Khartoum in the Sudan, where they landed at 15.50, almost three hours behind schedule.

The Balair plan for them was to fly on with an empty plane to Dakar, where Mecca pilgrims were waiting for transport. But the plan envisaged their departure for Dakar only after a *twelve-hour rest*. 'For reasons unknown, the pilot in command decided to take no rest at Khartoum but to proceed directly to Niamey and Dakar after refuelling.' This, with the take-off at 17.26, meant that by the end of the flight they would have been *on duty for some thirty-six hours*.

The Swiss officially permissible duty time for crews was then rather excessive anyway, but this flight would have gone well beyond even that. (In Britain, the statutory duty period limit has recently been reduced for propeller aircraft with three pilots and a bunk on board and further reduction of duty time for each sector, counted in landings, flown.) The DC–4 carried no bunk and so the crew on this flight must have rested on empty passenger seats. Thus the pilot's decision to fly on from Khartoum, together with the existing government regulations, were evidently questionable, but the report did not question them. At the time of the crash the crew had been on duty for more than twenty-four hours with five take-offs and four landings, when errors in navigation or otherwise would be more likely to happen than earlier on.

And finally, the report did not establish how much the El Fasher radio beacon could have contributed to the accident. The investigators found that its signals were rather weak. They developed a theory of the coincidence of navigational error and bad reception lulling the crew into false security about their position and about the reliability of their radio compass.

To put this accident report into perspective — even an optimistic perspective – is a disturbing exercise. It makes one wonder how many reports are drawn up on similar assumptions today, and how many 'pilot error' or 'human error' findings of the past could be criticised in the light of present knowledge.

One of the problems that has always taxed crash detectives' experience and ingenuity to the limit and caused some of the most vicious controversies between them and pilots involves the use of instruments.

The pilots themselves have a strange love–hate relationship with their instruments. In the early days of aviation, pilots were taught to distrust and disregard their instruments, judge air speed 'by the whistle of the wind', pitch 'by the seat of their pants', danger of stalling 'by the feel of the controls', bank 'by a good look at the horizon', for their few instruments already installed were hard to read and even less reliable than their senses. After the first non-stop transatlantic flight in 1919, Captain Alcock reported: 'The fog was very dense ... we looped the loop, I do believe, and did some very comic stunts, for I had no sense of the horizon.'

Although instruments have greatly improved since then, and pilots have been trained to trust them almost implicitly, many aviators have retained an innate mistrust and say, even in print, that 'I want to see where I am going'. This, of course, does not help the pilot's case particularly after landing accidents, when the investigator can only explain the disaster by deciding that 'the pilot must have caught a glimpse of the runway lights, sort of abandoned his instruments and tried to taxi in on the "I can see where I'm going" principle'. Such conclusions lead to arguments which much too often seem to prove that aviation has not progressed satisfactorily in this respect since the 1930's when, allegedly, Henry Ford said that flying was made up of ninety per cent pilot and ten per cent aircraft.*

Facing a vastly complex situation, crash detectives must sort out and examine three essential factors: (1) pilot behaviour, (2) instrument behaviour, and, the most intriguing of all, (3) the interplay of the two.

(1) This is what you may call the case of ordinary, simple human error where, it appears, the motives are much too obscure even to attempt an answer. One aircraft, for in-

* D. R. Whitnah: *Safer Skyways*, p. 124. See Bibliography.

stance, disappeared flying over the Sahara. A massive air-search was mounted, but there was no trace of the aircraft or its fifty passengers. It was only several hours later that they were spotted — but only by chance, because the aircraft lay intact in the desert several hundred miles away from its planned route. It turned out that the pilot had lost his way because when setting his compass to his 'true north', he had moved the variation setter to 60° instead of 6°. He then flew on until he began to run out of fuel and so had to make an emergency landing in the desert.

'If only all suspected pilot error cases were as clear-cut as that,' sighed Norman Head, a Principal Inspector of AIB, 'our job would be much simpler.' In one case, for instance, he received some criticism for *not* blaming the pilot for an accident. 'But I had no choice,' he said. 'As an ex-pilot, I appreciate the captain's problem landing in suddenly deteriorating weather when his windscreen wipers proved inadequate to cope with the heavy rain. He had no chance to switch — physically or mentally — from visual to instrument flight. If the job becomes too difficult for a normal human being, is it fair to condemn the pilot for not proving himself a superman?'

Or you could take the case of the BUA Viscount, which, on October 30, 1961, during 'a missed ILS approach in poor visibility' struck the ground alongside the Frankfurt runway. It was badly damaged but only two of the sixteen occupants were injured. The accident report, signed by Hans J. Reichel, Flug-kapitan, German Chief Inspector of Accidents, found that 'the accident was caused by the fact that the Commander in the ILS approach flew below critical height'. Pilot error? Yes. But how did it come about?

Captain Denis Woolfe certainly watched his speed and altitude, but also his other instruments carefully — up to a certain point. Where, how high above the ground, this point was cannot be determined exactly, but the accident and the report contradict his statement by putting him nearer the ground than he claimed to be. Then he saw that the needle of his ILS instrument moved ... it meant the aircraft was not on the centre line to the runway any more. He was warned on radio too. Seven seconds later, the men precision-monitoring his approach on radar warned him again that he was drifting even farther away from the centre line. He corrected the drift when 'almost immediately the First Officer called out "the runway is below us" ... I took it for granted that the First Officer had seen the runway lights.' (Part of the captain's statement published in the report.)

This, however, was not the case. The report recognised that probably 'a contributing factor was that at the critical moment the assistance given by the co-pilot to the Commander was erroneous and misleading'. Even if the Captain had been watching his instruments until then, he now admittedly 'looked up from the instruments and out and down'. But all he could see 'was a glow'. There was *less* visibility than given earlier to the pilot. This decrease in the Runway Visual Range had never been reported to the flight although it would have been an additional warning to the pilot. (After the accident, 'measures to remedy this deficiency have been ... taken by the German Meteorological Service'.) So now the Captain was looking for the runway lights more and more desperately. He and his co-pilot, First Officer Ronald Riches, even missed the overshoot call from the ground — 'Pull up go around' — some two minutes *before* the crash.

Yet even now, during these final moments of the drama, not all was lost. 'Apart from the fact that he flew below the critical height,' the report concluded, 'the Commander had the choice between the reading on his ILS needle which had previously shown him to be left of the runway centre line and the warnings of the radar control, on the one hand: and the remark called out to him by his co-pilot on the other. He decided to go by the latter.'

'Where are the lights?' he called out to his co-pilot — 'and then we struck the ground'. And even then, on the ground, from no more than sixty metres away, the maximum intensity runway lights could still not be seen.

(2) Faulty instruments have not only caused many accidents but often also led to suspected pilot error. The reason is simple: if a particular instrument is known to function well and there is no reason to presume that a certain case was an exception to the rule, the temptation is great to find an explanation in the pilot's role in the events. If he 'abandoned' his instruments or overruled them by 'flying by the seat of his pants', the result could be the same as produced by the malfunction of an instrument misleading the pilot.

A special difficulty in these cases is that usually the instrument itself is found too badly damaged. Had this been the case in a BEA Comet crash on December 21, 1961, Captain Kenneth Ruddlesdin might have easily gone on record as the man who was foolish enough to climb too steeply on take-off and take with him twenty-six people to death while injuring another seven.

In a private conversation some participants of the investigation confessed that they were 'ready to pre-judge the case and write it off as yet another pilot error accident'. Fortunately, this view was not to prevail. One can only hope that what other crash detectives said about it would become a typical attitude everywhere. Bertram Morris of AIB summed it up: 'At the beginning we had no evidence against the "yet another stupid human error" theory. We just refused even to suppose as yet that an experienced crew — a Senior Captain and two Senior First Officers — would ever make an elementary mistake like this.

'The Comet made an apparently normal take-off from Ankara's Esenboga Airport at night — then suddenly began to climb excessively at almost twice the normal angle. A stall was inevitable, and as they were only at about 450 feet above the ground, recovery was impossible. The aircraft fell out of the sky at an almost flat attitude. Wreckage examination gave us no indication of the cause. Why would the pilot knowingly put himself in such a dangerous position when there was no special strain or confusion in the cockpit? "Knowingly" was the key word. Did he know the angle of his climb?'

The pitch indicator had already been found and sent to Farnborough for examination. Fred Jones opened it — and stopped work on it almost immediately so that more specialists could be present when he proceeded with a more detailed scrutiny of a promising clue: one of three small screws was sticking out, obstructing the movement of the pitch pointer beyond an equivalent aircraft pitch attitude of $7\frac{1}{2}°$. This meant that although the aircraft had reached the excessive 45° pitch attitude by the time it stalled, the instrument would still have told the pilot that the pitch was not more than $7\frac{1}{2}°$, which was far from enough. Naturally, he would use the elevator to steepen the climb. The elevator would do the job properly, but the instrument would not tell the pilot about it. The maximum ten seconds available to him would not be enough to recognise the fault — he, like the investigators later would probably suspect his elevator rather than the pitch indicator. In those few seconds he might have had a sudden *sensation* of steep climbing but he was too well trained to let the seat of his pants overrule instruments so easily.

Some criticism and dispute about Fred Jones's first examination of the instrument led to the creation of a new tool for the investigator. It is the 'endoscope', a probe telescope, the kind which had already been used by the medical profession (for instance, the gastroscope) enabling a doctor to examine some inside parts of the body without the surgeon cutting it open. 'The French used such equipment first.' John Forsyth of the Accident Section explained, 'but they had too little light and too much heat from a special lighting system. We use quartz rods which let ninety per cent of our *outside cold light* through. It enables us to see the inside of an instrument or suspected cracks inside a wing — and even photograph them – without any further damage to the evidence which would be caused by first cutting or dismantling pieces of wreckage.'

Among all the cases of faulty instruments, one gave American crash detectives their most painful experience. 'It was a shameful experience, too,' commented an NTSB official confidentially. 'One we all would like to forget but, I hope, never will.'

It is the case of the Martin 404, TWA, which took off from Albuquerque, New Mexico, soon after seven in the morning, on February 19, 1955, and crashed into Sandia Mountain some eight minutes later, killing all its sixteen occupants. The great puzzle was: why had it flown towards the mountain at all when the captain's approved flight plan would have led it in a completely different direction, far away from the mountain?

After eight months of arduous investigation, CAB drew some shattering conclusions. It was no ordinary 'pilot error' report: it claimed that the deviation from the planned route, the short-cut towards the mountain, and the lower than prescribed altitude for the mountain course were *intentional* — which made it sound like 'suicide by Captain Ivan Spong killing another fifteen people'. Putting all this in an even worse light were the findings that there was no evidence of instrument failure, and that even if there had been any malfunction, the visibility was good enough to enable the pilot to see the mountain and recognise the hazard for 'all the captain had to do was look outside to determine that he was not following the airway'.

The 'killer's widow' was besieged by malicious telephone calls. Captain Spong's adopted little son was taunted by schoolmates, and as a result developed an ulcer.

The most odious aspect in the report was that it simply failed to recognise — and so examine — clues in the evidence the investigators themselves had gathered. They did not see that the captain's private and professional background practically ruled out motives of suicide and the likelihood of even minor — not to mention such criminal — mistakes. They did not or, for some reason, chose not to notice the contradictions in the witnesses' evidence about the weather, and relied on an Air Force officer's testimony which, after some misinterpretation, seemed to prove that the visibility had been good when, in fact, it had not been so. And finally, apart from some minor points, they did not take into account the warning, given by several incidents, that the fluxgate compass, a much more reliable instrument than the ordinary magnetic compass, could occasionally and temporarily malfunction and give just the sort of false information that would take a pilot off his course and, from Albuquerque, right into the Sandia range.

To investigate all this, to reveal the flaws in the report, and to take CAB at its word that the cause is never more than 'probable' because no case is ever closed fully, was left to J. L. de Celles, a TWA captain. He had had the frightening experience of fluxgate compass errors, studied the problem and called the attention of TWA to it shortly *before* Captain Spong's accident. The Airline Pilots' Association and TWA backed him all the way. (The company's contribution was perhaps specially remarkable because no airline likes to see its accidents continuously in the headlines. Yet TWA, which began to investigate de Celles's theory at once, and soon modified all its compasses, gave every possible assistance to keep the investigation going and to make the CAB reopen the case.)

De Celles and his colleagues did the job with an almost religious fervour. They amassed evidence from their own researches, collection of fluxgate compass malfunction reports, and tests. At last, the CAB was ready to listen and re-examine the evidence — but found that it was not convincing enough. All that had been achieved was an 'amended' report which left out the word 'intentional', and with that the implication of suicide, but reiterated the rest of the conclusions. Thirty months had passed since the accident, but the fight went on. If the CAB appeared to be stubborn, it was understandable. Not only because no professional likes to be caught out by a 'part-time' investigator, but also because even if they had blundered, they sincerely believed that they had not.

No less stubborn was their opposition. De Celles, ALPA and TWA had come a long way from just 'feeling in their bones' that Captain Spong could not have made such a blatant error. Further research, test flights and, perhaps above all, the critical examination of the original record compiled by the official investigators gave them their principal weapons. Once again, when they could promise new evidence, the CAB was ready to play fair and re-examine the closed case. But now the evidence was overwhelming: five years and four months after the accident the *third* CAB report cleared the dead pilot's memory.

(3) The one-sided love–hate replationship between pilots and instruments and the constant interplay of the two which in retrospect, especially when the pilot is dead and the instrument squashed, have turned many an aircrash investigation into a dramatic 'whodunit'. When an accident happens, crash detectives must answer this basic question: did the instrument give the wrong information or did the pilot get it wrong?

The instrument which has posed this question perhaps most frequently is the *altimeter*. Because of its known shortcomings and possible malfunctions, it has been the subject of continuous development studies and has also been improved following discoveries by accident investigations. Some of the hazards in its operation pilots have been trained to live with. Its work depends on barometric pressure and therefore it is exposed, for instance, to the 'air pressure instrument disease' — a vital few seconds' delay in giving the correct reading (for instance in the case of the 'Double Echo' crash at London Airport, mentioned in Chapter 8).

Unfortunately, the radio altimeters, which send bouncing signals to the ground and give more reliable instantaneous readings, are less widely used even though naval helicopters, for example, can safely hover with the aid of this instrument as near as thirty feet above the sea. (It was with considerable pride that Lufthansa advertised in 1967 the introduction of an additional radar altimeter, which bounces a radar beam off the ground, for its whole fleet because of the higher degree of instant accuracy achieved.) Although various devices have been created to facilitate the pilots' work and supply them with more accurate information, there is here considerable room for improvement.

Like altimeter malfunctions, some of the mistakes pilots can make with this instrument are relatively straightforward. Although the mathematical chances ever to have it reproduced must be next to nil, and although investigators did not need much ingenuity to solve what happened, it is worth recalling the flight of the BOAC Comet, that approached Nairobi airport on February 2, 1964. With sixty-two passengers and a crew of seven, it was making an instrument approach (ILS) at night.

The First Officer, flying the aircraft, suddenly saw that his ILS instrument indicated he was *too low*. He looked at his altimeter which told him he was flying *too high*. While the Captain was running through the check list for landing – the undercarriage was already lowered – the First Officer looked out and saw the ground lights 'almost fused into a continuous line' in the distance. It meant he was *too low*. He began to arrest the descent when they hit something. It was the ground on which they ran for about three seconds. With remarkable presence of mind, the Captain applied full power and the First Officer lifted the plane off the ground. They climbed to 8,000 feet again but before they could start another approach, worrying that their landing gear might have been damaged, the First Officer had yet another tremendous shock: he realised that his altimeter, due to his mistake when setting it, had shown 3,000 feet altitude at *ground level*.

When a car runs at 50 mph and another overtakes it at 60 mph, the speed of the second car can be expressed in two ways: its true speed is 60 mph and its relative speed, measured against the progress of the other car, is 10 mph. For altimeters, there are two settings. Depending on the barometric pressure, radioed to pilots before each approach to land, the sub-scale of an altimeter can be set so that the instrument will give the relative altitude to the airport and will read approximately zero when the aircraft lands (QFE) or it can be set so that the altimeter will show the true altitude above mean sea level and will coincide with the published elevation of the airport above mean sea level when landing (QNH). (If an aerodrome is a thousand feet above mean sea level, an altimeter will show 'zero' with QFE setting, and '1,000 ft' with QNH on touch-down.) En route, all aircraft use the standard 1,013 millibars setting to avoid collision.

In the Comet, the landing procedure was that one pilot would set his altimeter for QFE, and the other pilot would wind his altimeter sub-scale on QNH. Thus the difference shown by the two altimeters would spell out the height of the aerodrome and any malfunction of one of the instruments could be detected at a glance. In this particular case, it

227

was the Captain who used QNH but, due to various co-inciding factors, he failed to check his First Officer's altimeter setting properly.

Meanwhile, the First Officer made the sort of error which is, as the East African accident inspector's report acknowledged, 'difficult, if not impossible, to prevent' and 'to which humans are liable'. When on the radio he heard that his QFE setting should be 839 millibars, he began to wind it on his altimeter — but, moving the sub-scale down from the standard 1,013 mbs, he stopped at 938 mbs which, according to his statement, gave him 'a visual appreciation of 839'.

The recorded conversation with the control tower shows that the QFE 839 setting was repeated several times in the last fifteen minutes before the accidental and near-disastrous touch-down — and each time the First Officer read a mental mirror-like picture of his actual figures 938.

'It was a singularly unfortunate set of circumstances,' said John Boulding, the forty-seven-year-old BOAC Chief Inspector of Accidents. 'Should the last figure have been anything but nine in the critical moments, nothing would have happened. Had it been 8 — the reversal would still have been 838. Had it been 7, it would have been impossible to wind the sub-scale that far down, but even if it were possible, 738 would have meant a mistake the other way round: a 3,000 ft altitude when the pilot thought he would already be on the ground. Had there been any change as usual in barometric pressure during the descent, the need of re-setting the sub-scale would have made the pilot recognise the error.

'As always, our own company investigation was completed well before the publication of the official report. And because this accident inspectorate is completely independent within the firm and has direct access to the chairman and secretary of the Corporation — our reports go direct to the Chairman and Divisional heads – preventive action was implemented without delay. Due to some earlier problems with altimeters, the company had already done a great deal of research and re-thinking in this field, and so now quick action could be taken: we introduced a third, stand-by altimeter in the cockpit and a new cross-checking procedure that was to rule out any kind of confusion in checking these different settings.'

The most important of these problems referred to by John Boulding was, of course, the one that still worries all airlines and investigators: *pilots may misread their altimeters.*

Laymen can perhaps appreciate this hazard more easily than pilots who are trained to take in and mentally photograph almost at a single glance the arresting, baffling or even alarming array of scores of instrument dials, warning lights, counters, indicators and switches. To make flying easier, the number of instruments has been multiplied several times in the past two decades and, in order to have room for them all on the 'dashboard', they have been subjected to drastic miniaturisation. In 1965 a senior captain told the British Airline Pilots' Association's symposium that 'the smallness of some of these instruments has reached almost the ridiculous stage, where they cannot be read with accuracy at a glance'.

Even though modern airliners have more simplified 'dashboards' now than before, the captain, aided by new attention-calling warning systems, still has to watch something like sixteen instruments in front of him, eighteen dial faces in the centre section between him and his co-pilot, six in the roof panel, five counters, etc. This means that the presentation of the new, better instruments has not yet overcome the limitations of the human eyes which can *see* a large area but can *read* only what is in about a 25° field of sight in the middle. Therefore the pilot must scan his instrument panel regularly, a time-consuming process especially in moments of strain. Although he is trained to know where to look exactly even for less frequently required information, he has a decreasing amount of time for each instrument and it has become essential 'to reduce both the demand on the pilot and the risk of confusion, oversight or mis-interpretation'.*

In the late 1940's, the traditional altimeter, which spelled out height by three circling pointers, came under scrutiny, but the studies on improvement were inconclusive and, in order to avoid inevitable accidents during the transitional period to a not much better design, nothing was done about them. The problem was again critically accentuated by the introduction of pressurised aircraft which cruised at higher altitudes, produced a higher rate of climb and descent, and so required a more concerted effort from the pilot in a shorter space of time. In these circumstances there arose some of the trickiest cases for crash detectives.

By the late 1940's, a crucial international situation had developed. Britain, for instance, had more than her fair share of such accidents. In 1958 alone, there were three cases of misread altimeters. When dealing with them, inves-tigators had to eliminate other possible causes through wreckage and operation examination, and then relate the pilot's actions (such as how much he extended the flaps) and the mode of the crash to what the pilot must have intended or tried to do. To use a crude example, if an aircraft, pre-pared for touch-down, struck the ground in a fairly steep nose-down attitude, it might be probable, other circum-stances permitting, that the pilot had thought he had still a fair way to descend.

One of the above three cases involved a Viscount oper-ated by Central African Airways of Rhodesia, near Benina airport, Libya, on August 9. The crash killed thirty-six and injured eighteen people. Two interesting points of this investigation appear in the foreword of the final report, for

* *Aviation Safety,* 1962, p. 29. See Bibliography.

the Libyan Minister of Communication admits that 'in the absence of a suitably established accident investigation organisation' in Libya, they had to request assistance from AIB London (H. Gordon-Burge) and ultimately delegate the inquiry to Rhodesia, the State of Registry of the aircraft; of the two Rhodesian members of the board, one was the Chief Operations Officer and the other the Chief Inspector of Aircraft – neither of them a full-time investigator.

The cause was found to be a descent below correct height during the landing approach, and the probable reason for that had been the misreading of the altimeter. All this was made most likely by the very short lapse of time between the pilot's radioed altitude report and the moment of the crash. As this would have implied a dangerously excessive rate of descent (denied by aviation experts among the survivors and also by the pilot's great experience), the validity of the altitude report had to be doubted.

Why would the pilot misread his altimeter? In addition to his usual chores and strain of landing, his efficiency might have been lowered to some extent by 'slight pains in his stomach, for which he was given some kaolin' and by some fatigue — the crew had been more than '19 hours without sleep, of which 12 hours 44 minutes had been spent on duty', including nine and a half hours' flight time. (The Rhodesian law then limited pilots' flight time to twelve hours in any twenty-four consecutive hours.) Straight pilot error, it would seem, but the altimeter, too, was given some critical thoughts.

The instrument had two lighting systems. Its red light might cause 'a shadow to be cast over the upper part of the altimeter, thus detracting from the ease of reading'. Its ultra-violet lighting, if used, would eliminate this difficulty. The altimeter made mistakes easy because the pilot, while watching all pointers, would probably have to concentrate on the most relevant one at the time. After entering cloud at some

231

2,000 feet, he would be more concerned with the pointer marking the *hundreds* of feet of descent than with the 1,000 feet hand. Therefore, after a misreading of the latter pointer, he would watch the hundreds and might fail to notice the error. The final piece of logical evidence was that if, in fact, the pilot's last altitude report was 1,000 feet above his actual height, his normal rate of descent would take him to the crash site by the time of impact.

Similarly, this time element was most important in the third such accident of 1958, which became one of the few famous cases of investigators' luck.

On December 24, a Britannia aircraft was on a test flight. The ground was fogbound with clouds in layers above so that during the climbs and descents the highly professional crew did not expect to get any visual ground reference. The Britannia hit a power grid and crashed into the ground at Hurn, near Bournemouth. The site and wreckage examination showed that it had come down in a normal shallow descent angle, undercarriage was up, flaps in descent configuration.

'Because of its last altitude reports, we know that it should have been well above the ground and that a misreading of the altimeter would be a distinct possibility but to prove that we would have to know the *exact* time of the crash,' said Group Captain P. G. Tweedie, then Chief Inspector of Accidents. 'My boys were still working at the site when, by a stroke of luck, the proof came to them: men arrived to repair the grid and reported that the impact had not only blacked out houses in the area, but also *stopped the electric clocks* by depriving them of power.'

Cases like these drew increased attention to altimeters. Yet basically nothing was found to be wrong with them. They could be read safely and accurately – in normal flight circumstances. But these hardly exist. In most misreading cases there were additional factors: weather deterioration,

232

radio tuning problems, troublesome passengers, fatigue, slight indisposition, etc., when the situation called for supermen — not merely well-trained, conscientious pilots. One altimeter, for instance, was found to have needed 'another good look' when showing 6,150 feet or else it could easily be misread as 16,150 feet, because one pointer masked another. (It in fact led one aircraft into a mountain peak at 6,100 feet.)

Apart from direct research and tests, statistical accident investigation helped a great deal to spotlight the problem. In 1967 an RAF Directorate of Flight Safety spokesman recalled: 'During the routine study of special occurrence reports it was observed that there had been a number of instances of pilots misreading the altimeter. Further investigation revealed that, in the greater proportion of these cases, a particular type of altimeter was involved. From research carried out it became evident that, although the altimeter in question had a good record of accuracy and reliability, pilots had found it necessary to apply a greater degree of concentration than usual when interpreting the indications of the instrument. Consultation with the instrument manufacturer has resulted in the production of a new design in which instrument interpretation has been simplified, and the accuracy and reliability have been maintained.

'We expect that with the introduction into service of this improved type there will be far fewer occurrences of this instrument being misread by pilots.'

Most such research projects found that the three-pointer altimeter should be replaced by a one-pointer type which had a digital counter* and perhaps even a 'warning flag' that appeared whenever the aircraft descended below a predetermined safe height. The new types gave pilots seven seconds longer to correct a height error than the old design,

* UK Altimeter Committee report — see Bibliography.

but, unfortunately, the implementation of researchers' and crash detectives' findings is usually a slow process. Altimeters, which reduced the risk of misinterpretation to 1·04 per cent of all readings, had been perfected in the late 1950's and yet, as a speaker stated at the conference of Industrial Safety Officers at Llandudno, aircraft were still produced in 1966 with altimeters of an 11·7 per cent misreadability risk.

The good investigator is not satisfied with 'misreadability' as an explanation. He wants to know *why* the pilot misread the instrument – he wants to solve the 'human factor' puzzle.

On January 19, 1960, a Turkish taxi-driver got into a sudden snow-storm. He stopped, got out of the cab to look at the windscreen wipers which could not cope with the snow — and became an important witness to the weather at the time of the death of forty-two people aboard an SAS Caravelle.

To help the Turkish investigation, a team of fourteen Swedish and Danish specialists went to Ankara to participate in what turned out to be one of the most fruitful altimeter enquiries ever. Having examined the wreckage and the impact points on the ground, they related apparent pilot action to routine duties and the flow of information from the ground. After flight tests with Sud Aviation, the manufacturer, and experiments with a large-scale model hanging on adjustable strings to reproduce the exact attitude of the Caravelle in flight, they came up with the probable cause of the accident — and a staggering list of sixteen remedial recommendations.

The probable cause was determined as inadvertent descent below minimum height, due to a combination of a number of adverse conditions, during approach to Esenboga Airport.

It appeared most likely that the pilots thought they had a

thousand feet more than their real altitude. The mistake was the equivalent of one revolution of the altimeter pointer. There were three altimeters on board: two old-type three-pointers and a new drum-type. Because the Captain had only limited experience of this recently introduced instrument, one recommendation was to give crews special training in reading techniques whenever there was some innovation in the 'dashboard'. Although the possibility of misreading was known to them, the investigators refused to accept that a reliable crew would make such mistakes in ordinary circumstances under ordinary strain. And in this respect a wealth of information awaited them.

They found that the *normal* rate of descent used by the Captain was too fast because, among other reasons, the normal cockpit duties had to be performed by a strenuous effort, very quickly. On this flight, however, there were additional minor difficulties none of which alone could have caused the accident or even the altimeter misreading. There was a new type of vertical speed indicator which might have given the pilot not used to it the impression of a slower than actual descent. The ILS system was just being installed at Esenboga Airport but, by not noticing a warning flag, the crew might have tried to use the non-existing glide path. (A few days later, another Caravelle crew did precisely that.)

Then, in capsuled time, there was more extra work-load for the crew. They were coming down fast, reporting the correct altitude of 6,500 feet, when suddenly, due to a wind direction change on the ground, they received an instruction on the radio to 'circle' and not to go 'straight in' any more. They had to replan the approach, check the circling minima on the chart — and get on with the rest of their checklist while entering heavy snow-storms. That was when the altimeter was probably misread.

Here is a rough summary of what the Captain and his co-pilot must have been doing in their last two minutes, reconstructed partly on the basis of evidence in the wreckage:

CAPTAIN: 18.44 — coming to outer marker beacon, check altimeter settings, establish minimum final approach speed, change plans and prepare for circling. 18.45 — ice warning and fuel temperature warning systems give alarm, brakes checked, airfoil and engine de-icing to start, speed reduced when flaps extending, possibly a warning of drop in hydraulic pressure and flap extension stopping, aircraft lined up on inbound track. 18.46 — speed still being reduced . . .

CO-PILOT: 18.44 — finishes radio communication, starts tuning for the next, the inner marker; altimeter set and checked, synchroniser off, radar off, part of checklist completed. 18.45 — message from tower, acknowledges message, receives Air Traffic Controller warning, landing gear down, and locked, brakes checked, air conditioning closed, airfoil and engine de-icing set, checklist completed. 18.46 — tuning both receivers to inner marker . . .

If they had misread the altimeter, they hardly had a chance to notice it. Should one call that pilot error?

Judging from the sixteen recommendations, the crash detectives looked well beyond the error. The investigation resulted in several changes in the operation manual, training programme, and 'flight deck management' (splitting duties and using more cross-checking in more time), and also in research and elimination of several possible contributing factors (for instance, modification of the drum altimeter to reduce the risk of misreading).

SAS then added a seventeeth task: to examine the possibility of installing more dependable radio altimeters which give a warning when the aircraft descends to minimum height. (After five years' research, this instrument was perfected and it is now installed in the entire SAS fleet.) The accident happened in 1960. One would have hoped that all operators had learned from it. But in April 1968, when a Boeing 707 crashed at Windhoek, South Africa, 123 people died because yet another pilot had misread by 1,000 feet his drum-type altimeter 57 seconds after take-off. In this case it was possible that he had been distracted by a birdstrike against the windscreen.

The latest instrument developments are promising. The so-called 'head-up display' — the pilot gets his most important information reflected on his wind-screen, therefore without looking down — is particularly promising . . . but not yet widely used. The final answer is, of course, the completely automatic or 'blind' landing, that uses radio altimeters, computers and other devices. In some systems, the pilot has to take over from the machine only for the last one hundred feet which leaves him practically no margin of error. Other systems, already in use on some aircraft of the PanAm fleet, British Airways Tridents and Super VC 10s for instance can do a fully automatic landing in practically no visibility — with the pilot merely monitoring the procedure and looking out for warning flags through which the system reports its own malfunctions. This automation is in the future. But many pilots and some crash detectives still react reservedly to the promise of perfect reliability. Their past experience with instruments explains those doubts even if machines — designed to a ten million to one safety factor — rightly claim a 'more perfect than thou' efficiency.

The most important break-through is expected from the introduction of MLS, the Microwave Landing System, to replace ILS. MLS has numerous advantages: aircraft can approach a runway from any angle within a vast 120° fan of electronic beams — instead of balancing on a single beam — and parallel runways can be used simultaneously. Unlike ILS, MLS can be installed easily at any airport.

CHAPTER ELEVEN

THE CAUSE BEHIND THE CAUSE
BEHIND THE CAUSE

RIDING the 'jungle-cab', a helicopter, a hundred feet above Borneo, listening to the occasional Indonesian bullets whizz past, Lt.-Colonel Burnett, commander of a Gurkha Battalion, commented: 'War is not a very interesting occupation. It consists of long periods of boredom interspersed with short periods of fear.'

Many pilots describe flying in the same way. But unfortunately, it is in those 'short periods of fear' that they have to make their most crucial decisions.

Pilots are well trained to deal with emergencies. They are trained to think clearly under stress, and make decisions sometimes in the fraction of a second. The wealth of stories about pilots who have saved their passengers and their aircraft in extreme against-all-odds conditions is proof of that. 'But as the tension mounts in the cockpit,' said a German investigator, 'it becomes easier to make the wrong assumptions. Even the most careful and non-aggressive driver will take undue risks to overtake others if he's caught in a seemingly endless traffic jam. Similarly, the pilot who always has the ultimate right to make his decision can be tempted to make a foolhardy one. The problem for the accident investigator is where to draw the line between pilot error and the tragic conspiracy of circumstances.'

Take the situation which arose on November 6, 1963, at London Airport. The night was dark, the runway was wet and the airport was fogbound. The Trans-Canada Airlines

DC–8, bound for Montreal with a crew of seven and ninety passengers, had to wait for start up. The weather began to improve on one runway but that was too short for the DC–8 carrying maximum take-off weight. Captain S. R. Found, a forty-six-year-old pilot with a long, perfectly clean record, knew that he was within his rights to wait indefinitely, but nothing seemed to go right. Waiting and waiting for clearance has an exasperating effect on the flightdeck. The pilot knows his aircraft is packed with more and more fidgety passengers. The no smoking sign is on.

At last they were able to move. But the DC–8 needed radar assistance to taxi to the runway in the fog, Then there was a misunderstanding with the tower about the centre lights. More talk about other runways. More taxiing problems. Warnings pouring in over the radio. The cumulative effect of irksome circumstances must have been built up unnoticeably. Then, at last, they were cleared for take-off.

As the aircraft picked up speed on the wet runway, the nose-wheel began to hop and hammer on the centre lights, which was not only distracting but added annoyance to the tension caused by a dozen other sources.

Accelerating all the time, the final seconds before lifting the aircraft are a strain on the crew even in ideal circumstances. Watching their engines, instruments, speed and direction, changing from nose-wheel to rudder steering, they approach the 'point of no return'. This comes with reaching the speed, pre-determined by weather, weight and other factors, at which the aircraft must take off — must, unless something tells the pilot that there is an emergency. Then it is up to him to decide which is the lesser of the two evils: start the flight with a faulty aircraft or abort even if he might not be able to stop before the rapidly approaching end of the runway.

Captain Found was coming to the point of no return when he tried his elevator, but did not get proper response.

He tried more stick force but there was still 'slackness or sloppiness in the control column'. It is always hard to decide how much more force to use because it may 'freeze' a jammed control even more firmly. And there was no time to experiment. To take off with really serious elevator trouble would have been catastrophic. To abandon take-off grew more hazardous every fraction of a second because the DC–8 was already 'at a speed and position . . . which precluded the possibility of bringing the aircraft to a halt in the runway length remaining'. Yet this appeared to be the only sensible course to follow.

The DC–8 overran the runway and when, already badly damaged, it came to rest in a cabbage field, two of its engines were burning fiercely. Only five people were slightly injured, but many of those trying to get away got lost in the fog. The fire and rescue services reached the crash site twenty-three minutes later.

William Tench, now Chief Inspector of AIB, recalled the interview with Captain Found: 'It was quite obvious that I was talking to a man of great sincerity and experience. The sight of the wreckage affected him very badly. He could plainly see the possible salvation or ruin of his career in it — even though the survival of all on board must have been a relief. The wreckage also contained the answer to the major question: did the Captain use his ultimate authority in this emergency in order to save ninety-seven lives by not taking off with a faulty elevator control — or did he endanger ninety-seven lives by making the wrong decision?

'It was not a question to be lightly treated. This man had done good service for many years, but that one crucial second ruined his life with all the value of thousands of right decisions behind it. Because, for once, he had made the wrong decision. Quite frankly, we *hoped* to find a trace of malfunction of the elevator controls. But we couldn't discover anything.'

It could not be measured or determined to what extent the circumstances had influenced the Captain when faced with one of the pilots' basic dilemmas. The circumstances only made his decision more understandable, but did not absolve him. He, too, saw that. He made a statement about accepting responsibility for the misinterpretation of elevator response, and by the time the final report was published — the pilot 'in his mistaken belief' of having defective elevator controls abandoned take-off too late to stop on the runway — he had already resigned from TCA 'for personal reasons and of his own volition'. (In a case like this, an airline may reward the pilot's loyal service by, say, keeping him in a ground job until he is entitled to his pensions or making an *ex gratia* payment, but their responsibility to their passengers usually denies them the right of forgiveness.)

Crash detectives hardly ever stop thinking about cases like this. One explanation of the strange control behaviour in this case might have been the inadvertently incorrect setting of the elevator trim. An explanation may not absolve the pilot but may help to prevent recurrence. The other, still more mysterious, explanation may be found one day in the pilot's reaction to tension — but that is completely individual, depending on the man's sensitivity to stress.

The chief of pilot selection for a major airline said that only about ten percent of the applicants are suitable for training and only about ninety per cent of the selected recruits will become pilots. The selection methods include a varied stress programme to watch performance and behaviour under heavy work-load, to detect decreasing efficiency when more and more earphone instructions are given or the would-be pilot is subjected to distraction by music or a chat during his tests, and to gauge reaction to an emergency like an engine being suddenly cut off. But test conditions will never be perfect, and some people's reactions will always be different from those to real situations. (Stress tests will be more tolerable to those, for instance, who are not really dedicated candidates for becoming airline pilots.)

Training – especially in those splendid modern simulators which can convey very convincing visual, audible and motional aircraft reactions, short only of killing the trainee who erred, and, as Bernard Doyle, Chief of the NTSB Human Factors Group, put it, 'increasing attention to human behaviour in the cockpit' — can certainly improve a man's ability to stand up to tension or even emergencies, but there is always a dark spot left only to be exposed by the hazards of reality. And this dark spot is regularly probed whenever an aircraft is coming in to land, for instance. Pilots are used to this stress. They are familiar even with the increased stress of landing in bad weather at difficult airports (lack of most up-to-date landing aids, a mountainous terrain, etc.), and usually, they can make the right decisions even when the regulations can give them no more than guidance.

But how much the tension mounts in the cockpit after an overshooting or two unsuccessful landing attempts, we do not know exactly. Most second and even third attempts are successful. But studying accidents in which the weather, for instance, was a factor, one finds in the reports with disturbing frequency that the crash had occurred during the second or third landing attempt.

There are no definite rules about the number of attempts that can be made. It is obvious that aviation has not yet come to the point where pilots can be deprived of their ultimate power to break all regulations and overrule even their fully automatic landing equipment. It is equally obvious that in certain circumstances no limitations can ever be imposed: the pilot, after all, must get in somewhere, somehow, and he may be running out of fuel, may have some other emergency on board, may see conditions worsening even at his pre-selected alternative airports. But, as one investigator explained, 'it makes one wonder how pilots subconsciously react to the frustrating memory of three attempts while trying to land the fourth time'.

He was talking about the accident which occurred at Idris Airport in Libya on September 21, 1955, at night. There was a strong wind blowing and visibility was poor. Due to various circumstances and his previous experience at that airport, Captain R. Griffiths made the justifiable decision to land his BOAC Argonaut on runway 11 instead of runway 18 even though the latter had some advantages in length and approach aids. The first time he had to decide to overshoot was at 22.06. On his second attempt he had difficulty in lining up with the runway once again, and four minutes after the first he was forced to overshoot for the second time. He had enough fuel to spend another thirty minutes above Idris before diverting still with safety to Malta.

The third time, with extra ground assistance, the aircraft was better lined up but came in too high and too close to attempt a landing. Within twelve minutes, this was the third overshoot. During the fourth attempt, at 22.23, the aircraft came in too low, struck a line of trees and crashed 1,200 yards short of the runway. A steward, a stewardess and thirteen passengers were killed, five members of the crew and sixteen passengers were injured, and only eleven passengers escaped uninjured. The accident report accepted the Captain's choice of runway but criticised him for not revising the decision, after three failed attempts, in favour of runway 18. It recognised the existence of difficult conditions but gave the opinion that 'the accident was the result of an error of judgment on the part of the Captain who . . . on his fourth attempt allowed his desire to keep the runway lights in view' and so 'failed to make adequate reference to his flight instruments . . .'

This case, like others involving repeated landing attempts, revealed no sign of the fourth approach being inherently more dangerous than the first or the second. But one is left with the inevitable question: knowing the Captain's immaculate record and almost 10,000 hours of flying experience, would it not have been pertinent to strongly advise or even instruct him to think, hold, divert or try the other runway before making his fourth attempt?

Unfortunately, crash detectives cannot offer clear-cut advice from their experience. But it is not without significance that an admittedly haphazard international opinion poll among forty-one professional accident investigators — all former airline pilots or at least holders of pilot licences — produced an overwhelming, thirty-seven to four majority in favour of 'no more than two attempts without a change in circumstances like weather improvement, better visibility'.*

This, by no means fully representative, sample may well serve as a starting-point of much-needed research. 'It seems that the first attempt is always an expert's routine job,' one crash detective said. 'For the second attempt a slight disappointment comes into it: "Oh dear, if only I had come in a little lower, I'd have made it." With additional knowledge and modified information about the prevailing circumstances, there is no reason why he shouldn't have made it the second time. But a second failure ought to be a warning. Two attempts are logical. The third attempt, many pilots admit, is a bit of a challenge. And when landing becomes a contest between man and machine or man and conditions, the pilot lays himself open to making mistakes.'

Another investigator of long experience would not put any limit on the number of attempts. 'If a pilot has already diverted to an alternate airfield, there can be no question: he

* The question the author asked during the interviews was: 'Judging by your flying and investigating experience, how many landing attempts would be advisable in a given situation when at least minimum requirements for landing exist and when the pilot has the choice?'

must get in. Each attempt eats into his fuel reserves. But even at the original destination, he should be free to make any number of attempts as long as there is some improvement each time. It means the pilot is gradually ironing out the difficulties. But he must balance this, of course, against his own naturally deteriorating performance under stress.' This investigator agreed that beyond a certain (as yet inestimable) stress point, the pilot is the least capable of judging the decrease of his own efficiency.

Several of those interviewed referred to the passengers' reactions: 'They hate, of course, to land at an alternate airport several hundred miles from their destination. But coming near the ground twice makes them similarly restless, disappointed or worried. I'd never try it a third time, partly because of my own passengers, and partly because, especially when you must fly on instruments — and this is when the question of a third attempt mostly arises — you become mentally and physically more and more ragged. The third ILS approach is usually less smooth. This is my experience more from incidents than accidents. But if then you hold for, say, thirty minutes, because you have enough fuel even then to divert in case there is no improvement in weather, then you can count it as a fresh start. After holding and in improved conditions, the third attempt counts as a first, and the fourth will be no worse than the second.'

None of these forty-one investigators would automatically regard an accident as being due to pilot error only because it happened during the third or fourth attempt — but all would consider it as more likely that some operational imperfection might be a contributory factor at least. If this is interpreted as a trace of prejudice, it is unfair to these men — the careful selection of suspected areas is not the equivalent of a headlong rush to pre-judge an issue.

During take-off, the question about the advisable number of attempts is asked less frequently, partly at least because several circumstances in aborted take-offs call for immediate inspection, for instance of the brakes. But the basic dilemma is identical. It was summed up in three tragic sentences by a dying French military pilot. He veered off the runway and crashed during his third attempted take-off, but lived for a few more hours and briefly regained consciousness. 'In fourteen years of flying I have never been forced to abandon take-off because of engine failure. Now it happened twice in fifteen minutes. It made me angry, irritable and suspicious, and yet I tried it again, the third time ... why?'

Investigators could not answer him. The cause of the accident was recorded as 'engine failure during take-off' and the cause of the engine failure was traced. But the real answer — why did he try it the third time? — remained an enigma.

Infuriating as this may be, one must recognise that the state of the art, the limitation of current knowledge, often renders the investigator helpless in discovering the psychological — or, very often, technological — trigger behind some human error. That is why 'pilot error' is often an insufficient description of what has happened, and it can even be a gross injustice to an innocent victim caught in hitherto mysterious circumstances.

When the holder of a brand new private pilot licence crashes near his home, favourite pub or girl friend's garden — especially if a letter, saying 'watch the sky' at such and such hour, is found — investigators rightly examine the probability that a foolhardy new pilot tried to do stunts he was not yet ready for. At least on one occasion, two pilots were *known* to have been playing 'chicken' with empty airliners. Although the investigation of the subsequent fairly serious incident could never prove clearly that the game had been responsible, calling the cause a 'pilot error' and 'poor judgment and discipline' was perfectly justifiable.

But in most cases, the problem is much more complex. The DC-8s, for instance, had already established an excellent record in four million flying hours when something completely unexpected occurred. On a training flight, the pilot was required to shut down one engine. He did it probably too fast and with unnecessary force — and pushed the throttle into reverse thrust. Luckily, the instructor diagnosed the symptoms within seconds and, having sufficient height, disaster was averted. Pilot error? On the surface, yes. But although it was a most unlikely manoeuvre to occur in passenger service, Murphy's Law raising its head in the mask of a handling hazard seemed a possibility. Therefore immediate steps were taken to 'design out' the pilots' chance to err.

Talking about the annoyingly frequent mistakes in the cockpit, Benjamin O. Howard, an aviation industry consultant, said that such cases can be treated 'in either of two ways: Bury the dead, clean up the mess and blame the pilots; or, simply fix the airplane so that the pilot cannot make the error. The choice is ours and it's just that simple!'* Critics of the industry and of accident investigation may agree wholeheartedly. When, after several serious crashes and the death of planeloads of passengers, DC-3 and DC-4 aircraft were still permitted to fly for years without a device like a rubber band to ensure the complete release of the gust lock (it protects the rudder and elevators from gusts on the ground by immobilising them), the critics were right to call the lack of the obvious corrective action sickening. When time and time again, in cases of engine malfunction, pilots shut down the wrong engine, in other words the one that alone could have kept them in the air, it should have been obvious much earlier than the existing cockpit lay-out, the

* The Attainment of Greater Safety, 1957. Presented in Aircraft Accident Prevention Course, University of Southern California, January 1967.

position of levers, etc., called for the type of superhuman pilot no designer can count on.

On the other hand, 'wisdom in retrospect' is not born easily. When a new type of aircraft, which has performed well in test conditions, meets several mishaps in its early actual service life, suspicions are easily aroused: something must be wrong with the aircraft, its operation or with the training pilots have had in coping with its peculiarities. But when a type has already given a fair amount of reliable service in the hands of average pilots and sometimes even in emergencies, it is natural that instinctive suspicion moves towards pilot error. The more flying hours a type accumulates, the more likely it becomes that something 'odd' happens, that an unsuspected loophole is exposed, and that a situation arises to show that the design may sometimes call for supermen at the controls. This, occasionally, may become obvious only after several similar cases.

One of these 'classic' cases occurred to a widely used small aircraft.* In a single day, two of them fell into the sea. About the first, the verdict was 'pilot error': he had probably used his fuel contents gauge the wrong way and thus let his engines run dry. As it had never happened before, there was no reason to suspect anything but the human factor. Some salvaged wreckage of the second accident was taken to Farnborough, but nothing conclusive was discovered and the cause remained a mystery. Soon after these, a third aircraft fell out of the sky with suspected double engine failure — a most unlikely cause. After the engines had been exonerated, suspicion fell on possible pilot error and general handling drill, but the investigation considered that the system was subject to possible 'gas locking'. Ultimately, this was named as the cause of the crash and new drill was introduced to eliminate a recurrence. Yet only a month later, in

* Because some of the five cases to be dealt with were not to be named, this whole series has been disidentified.

1960, there was a fourth accident — luckily, in this case, ending with a crash landing that spared the pilot's life and did not destroy the aircraft.

At the time, in London, the AIB was already accumulating data about the three crashes. When the request to participate in the investigation of the fourth came, the investigator sent a cable 'drain tanks, preserve fuel'. That turned out to be a profitable opening move. When he got to the scene, he found that the fuel obtained was from the main tanks — the two reserve tanks had been completely empty. That was odd, as they should have contained a small amount of residual fuel, enough only to preserve the tank bags when not in use . . . and on this particular, not very long flight, they had not been supposed to perform any role. A leak, after the crash, was, of course, a real possibility. The investigator had the reserve tanks refuelled 'to normal, pre-take-off level' (with a small amount of residue). The tanks' integrity was proved beyond doubt. There was no leak. If at the time of the crash there had been fuel in them, it would have been there to be drained afterwards.

In the meantime the type had been grounded. The reason: suspected fuel system — the gassing of fuel at high temperatures. This had been the verdict on the third crash. It was supported by the fact that all four accidents occurred while the aircraft were operating in hot climates.

But a quick calculation on the distance flown by the fourth crashed aircraft and on the missing amount of fuel gave a new lead: the residual fuel in the long-range tanks would have been just about enough for the short flight — if the main tanks had not been used. This indicated *fuel mismanagement*. A repetition of the first crash? Did the pilot open the wrong cock?

The likelihood of an affirmative answer was far from being evidence, especially when the pilot stated that he had selected (opened) the main tank cocks only. (This was no lie.

249

He would not have flown *knowingly* on the small quantity of fuel in the long-range tanks. But did he know what he had done? The cock controls were above and behind the pilot, out of his sight.)

When the investigator saw the wreckage, all tanks — both main and reserve — seemed to have been selected. The cock levers were in the '12 o'clock' (fully open) position. 'Impact damage in the cockpit was such that it was not possible for it to alter the setting of all cocks,' the investigator concluded. 'By then I was quite sure that I had the answer but it was essential to obtain material proof if possible.'

The pilot and people who had had access to the wreckage after impact were questioned. One possibility was that the pilot himself had realised his mistake at some stage and had opened all the cocks to cover up his mistake. Another was that a friend might have done the same for him. One man, who had arrived at the scene soon after the crash, said, 'I made the wreckage safe', but could not remember what he had done to it. The investigators were not terribly interested in these details: 'We were not looking for grounds for some petty disciplinary action. We wanted to make the aircraft safe for pilots who are not expected to be infallible demigods.'

The impact damage in the cockpit was the main source of evidence of conditions existing at the time of the crash. One of the main tank cock controls was slightly buckled — it must have been hit by something. That control, its handle mounted on a plate, is turned sliding above another, a fixed plate from '9 o'clock' (shut) to '12 o'clock' (open) position. Those two plates never touch one another — in normal circumstances. But when one is slightly buckled or otherwise distorted by impact, the two might come into contact. That was the investigator's logic when he dismantled the cock. On both plates, facing one another, there were tiny marks — made possibly during manufacture, assembly

250

maintenance . . . or impact. The enlarged photographs of both plate faces were superimposed one on the other. In the enlargements, the striking similarity of some imprint marks were immediately obvious. When the 'cock' picture was turned above the other, a perfect match could be made — but only in the '9 o'clock' position. It meant that the main tank cock *must have been fully shut* at the time of the accident.

Pilot error was proved, some might say. But with four accidents in hand, the investigation could go beyond that. Although material proof was not available, circumstantial evidence suggested that the first accident almost definitely, the second possibly and the third most probably must have been due to the same error. This conclusion indicated a design loophole.

'The cock controls were repositioned in the entire fleet without delay so that they were now *in sight* of the pilot, and they had to be moved *forward to open* and *rearward to shut* which is more natural to human psychology,' said the investigator whose recurring comment was: 'You look and look, and with a bit of luck, you find the cause,' although he seemed the last man to leave anything to luck. 'When I returned to London, I heard sort of privately about a fifth case which happened just before the grounding: a pilot made the same mistake, selected the wrong cock, but luckily realised the error in time and corrected it. That was a good sign: we were on the right track. But the final proof came only from years of experience — since then, in eight years, touch wood, we've never had another crash like that.'

Benjamin O. Howard estimated in 1957 that mis-use of cockpit controls (these excluding the primary flight and power controls) had caused the deaths of 8,000 Americans. He claimed that cockpit design is based on established average pilot performance without sufficient margin for individual error in certain circumstances, and that this failure 'is responsible for fifteen times as many crashes as result from structural failure'. Further, he charged that we are just shrugging off the responsibility of designing safe controls 'by leaving it up to the pilot to read his check-list and do things right'. Like stopping people from falling down an open lift shaft by merely putting up a sign, 'it just doesn't work and the records prove it. Reduced, it simply means that any aeroplane that requires the use of a check-list for safety is in fact unsafe'.

Some crash detectives made almost identical comments: 'These are very strong words. But they are true. An automated sequence that eliminates the possibility of forgetting something would be more reliable than a check-list. If an electrical circuit prevented the pilot from doing something without accomplishing all his previous duties, it would be safer than merely hoping that the pilot will notice a warning light. Then, of course, the systems would have to be duplicated and triplicated to reduce the chances of malfunction. Since 1957 we've gone a long way towards this — like in automatic landings. But, are the public willing to accept slower operations and considerably higher fares to pay for marginally increased safety?'

There is, for instance, what is known as the 'allowable deficiency' list. It includes minor faults of the aircraft and its equipment, and it is left to the pilot's discretion to take off or not with such faults in the particular circumstances. Except in some extremely odd situation, it is perfectly safe to fly with these faults. But then this is yet another decision to be made — possibly erroneously — by the pilot. And one must remember that in America, the weather radar was on this list until it became most probably responsible for the deaths of thirty-one people near Baltimore, Maryland, on May 12, 1959. (Installation of the equipment was not a federal regulation until 1960.)

There are many so-called pilot error cases which are,

really, mysteries because investigators do not yet know what lurks behind the 'so convincingly obvious' failure of the human factor. *Icing* of control surfaces, the already mentioned 'evidence that melts away', has long been one such grossly misleading cause of mysteries. In these cases, evidence has hardly ever remained available to investigators — short of a miracle.

One exception to the rule was the flight recorder that gave some positive indication. Another was encountered by Sir Vernon Brown, former chief of AIB. A farmhand reported that something had fallen off the aircraft which crashed, seconds later, nearby: 'Whizzed past me 'ead it did, and when I dug it out of ground a large chunk of ice it were.' The man described the ice-block and noted that it had had a groove along one side — just like the negative of the leading edge of the wing. Having excluded all possible causes of the accident except icing or pilot error, the investigators concluded that 'although icing conditions prevailed on that day, had it not been for this lucky piece of evidence the cause of the loss of control of that aircraft might never have been known for certain'.*

Barely a decade ago, it was taken for granted that icing would usually be mistaken for pilot error, and especially so in cases of ice accretion on the airframe and control surfaces because it would re-cast temporarily the shape of, say, a wing and thus deprive the aircraft of its basic ability: flying under control. The fact that it is still tremendously complicated to prove on the ground, after a crash, that icing did exist in the air and did actually bring about disaster, might help to explain — even if not excuse — the second of the two most serious slip-ups by CAB.

Late at night on April 6, 1958, a Capital Airlines Viscount crashed and burned near Tri-City Airport,

* Accident Aftermath, *Aviation and Space Magazine*, September 1962.

Freeland, Michigan, killing the three crew members and all the forty-four passengers. One year and nine days later, the CAB report set out the circumstances and concluded that Captain William Hull, a 'careful and conservative pilot' who had been with the airline for seventeen years and had accumulated as many thousand hours of flying, completed a turn to final approach and then let the aircraft stall, pitch forward and dive into the ground. It was a clear-cut summary of pilot error excused only to some extent by factors like the malfunction of his stall warning system.

A series of stalling tests in Britain and America supported the mainly theoretical evidence. But not all findings were similarly unequivocal. The danger of wing stall would be most acute during the steepest part of the turn and decrease from then on. Yet witnesses testified that the aircraft did complete the turn and did roll level before the 'momentary nose-high attitude', the indication of stall, and the dive came. Impact damage on the nose, wing, leading edge and propellers, together with the wreckage distribution (all in practically one big heap) and with the site examination (a sixty-five-foot high tree just behind the wreckage, thus in the path of the crashing plane, was completely undamaged), indicated that the aircraft had struck the ground almost vertically. This again was strange. After a stall it would be more normal for an aircraft to come down in a flat spin, dropping one wing, and even if the pilot pushed the nose too violently forwards to balance the pitch, it would need more altitude than the Viscount had to reach a vertical dive position.

'My greatest objection to the stall theory was the idea that icing might have caused the crash,' said George van Epps, now chief of the NTSB New York office, who was in charge of the investigation. 'But the trouble was that this was no more than a hunch. And a hunch, however strong, is not proof. The strongest advocate of the icing theory was the pilots' representative from ALPA, Captain Ernest Burmeister. He, as a pilot, once experienced tail icing conditions which made his aircraft pitch forward. He said he could just avert a crash. But these personal experiences are always a bit suspicious whether they are used for or against proving pilot error. I was not the only one who was inclined to believe his story rather than the hypothesis of a stall. But we had no proof. We didn't know enough even to tell the very co-operative manufacturers what sort of new, additional tests to conduct. The main argument against us was the time factor: although icing conditions did exist on the fatal night, the aircraft was supposed to have been exposed to them for an insufficiently short time for ice to have built up. And the switch of the de-icing equipment was in the 'off' position.

'Years went by, but the case never stopped worrying me. The "probable cause" just didn't sound right. Burmeister did even more than think about it. He had a chance to collect information about icing incidents and work on theories which we discussed occasionally, but we couldn't produce anything conclusive enough to get the case reopened. Terrible as it may sound, we had to sit back and wait for another crash.

'It happened on January 29, 1963. A Viscount of Continental Air Lines crashed at Municipal Airport, Kansas City, Missouri. Luckily, there were only eight people on board. I heard about it late in the evening and telephoned Burmeister the same night. He arranged that his company should free him from duty and I picked him up by car. We talked all day and I requested a Washington hearing for him. He presented his case very well, CAB became suspicious of icing, too, but although there were common factors in both accidents and some incidents in between, all the theories seemed to prove no more than that icing *could* happen and *could* cause such accidents.

'But then, at last, we found the vital link in the chain of evidence — thank God, without further loss of life. It was a

255

serious incident and we had a live crew. It changed our argument from "it could happen" to "it did happen". The tests provided the final piece of proof. One question we could never answer: Why was the de-icing switch in the "off" position in the wreckage? It is possible that the pilots had not used it because they had not noticed icing. It was also possible that the equipment had been used but had not done the job quite properly. And it was also possible that preparing for the landing, the pilots switched it off — because it was on the landing check-list.

'Quite frankly, this was the least of our worries. The three main purposes of Burmeister's fight had been achieved: a good pilot's name was exonerated; seven years after the accident, the Tri-City report was revised and a new one was issued saying that the probable cause was an undetected accretion of ice on the horizontal stabiliser which, in conjuction with a specific air-speed and aircraft configuration caused a loss of pitch control, and recovery from this was beyond human capabilities; and finally, steps could be taken against any repetition of this disaster.'

CHAPTER TWELVE

THE ANGRY AIR

IN over 20,000 hours of flying, Captain Stephen Parkinson had never experienced as hard a jolt as the one that shook his DC–8 in August 1963. It triggered off severe buffeting and made him feel as if he were 'sitting on the end of a huge tuning fork that had been struck violently'. It was difficult to understand what had happened: the aircraft, N8607, had taken off from Dulles International Airport, Virginia, and climbed towards clear blue sky between two thunderstorm cells — the nearest of these concentrated meteorological violences being some twenty miles away. But there was no time to ponder over the cause of the pandemonium that broke out in the cockpit at only some five thousand feet above the ground. The instruments ran wild and seemed to disappear in a white blur. The pilots had no idea of attitude, air-speed, altitude, heading or even time — the chaos might have lasted for anything from ten to a hundred seconds. The buffeting continued throughout, shaking the aircraft severely, and the cockpit was filled with 'ripping, tearing, rending, crashing sounds. Briefcases, manuals, ash trays, suitcases, pencils, cigarettes, flashlights flying about like unguided missiles. It sounded and felt as if pods were leaving and the structure disintegrating.

'The objects that were thrashing about the cockpit seemed to momentarily settle on the ceiling which made it impossible to trust one's senses . . .' The pilots had a feeling of being inverted and held only by their stretched seatbelts. They struggled with the controls that now called for all the physical strength they could muster. At last the plane began to roll the right side up. Instruments began to give help. As the aircraft slowed down a little, the air-speed indicator could be read for the first time at 250 knots. As 'the air smoothed out and we gently levelled off', their altimeter gave them the final shock: they had only some 1,400 feet of altitude from disaster.

After landing, passengers were told the aircraft must have hit a tornado. But was it a tornado? Only a month earlier, over O'Neill, Nebraska, another jet, thirty miles away from the nearest storm, had suddenly 'reared up' and gone into a dive in which the tremendous air pressure immobilised the controls. Although the speed was already well above the designed safety limit — in other words, the airframe had the right to fall to pieces — a desperate Captain Deuscher applied even more power, and managed to pull the nose up.

And it happened again on November 9, of the same year. With more than ten thousand hours of flying, First Officer Grant R. Newby was well qualified to fly the Eastern Air Lines DC–8 under Captain Mel French's command. He, too, climbed towards a patch of clear blue sky between two thunderstorm cells over Texas. Then he suddenly felt a bump 'like driving across a railroad track' and the needles of the two air-speed indicators sank to zero. Newby did not hesitate for a second: he pushed the control column forward to force the nose down, and avoid the stall and gather speed which alone could keep the aircraft in the air. To hasten the process, he added nose-down trim. Being at 18,000 feet, it seemed he had room for manoeuvre, but there was no time to think about it twice. Another jolt — and the aircraft was in an apparently uncontrollable high-speed dive. With 124 people on board, the swept-wing aircraft hurtled earthwards and even if the machine could stand the pace, and even if the pilots' combined effort could exert the necessary pulling force on the controls (in some cases it may amount to a 320 pounds pull), the danger was that the opposing forces would break the overstressed aircraft like a matchstick.

When all attempts had failed and the choice lay virtually between a certain crash and probable break-up, the pilots put the engines in reverse thrust, and with this aid they continued the struggle. At last, the giant began to obey them, but the mysterious force that had already made them drop 13,000 feet and was now trying to slam them all to the ground, still resisted them. The clashing forces ripped off one of the four engines and a part of a wing went with it. With perfect airmanship, the pilots made an emergency landing at an Air Force base.

There was no talk about tornadoes. The key to the near-disaster was *turbulence*. It was already achieving the dubious distinction of being the 'dirtiest word in aviation'.

Towards the end of November, when First Officer Newby was being restored to flying status, a DC-8 of Trans-Canadian Air Lines took off from Montreal, received a blow from turbulence, and crashed killing all 118 people aboard. In December, when Newby had one of his routine proficiency checks, a PanAm 707 crashed in a storm near Elkton, Maryland — turbulence was suspected first, but this was the unique accident, already mentioned, which had been caused by lightning. In January when Newby passed his regular FAA medical checks, an American Airlines 707 was tossed about in the air near Alamosa, Colorado, but the pilot managed to retain control.

On February 25, 1964, Newby was at the controls of a DC-8 once again. Captain William Zeng was in command, there were five more crew members and fifty-one passengers. Moderate to severe turbulence existed in the area at two o'clock in the morning when the aircraft took off from New Orleans International Airport. Five minutes and forty seconds later, this Flight 304 disappeared from the controllers' radar screen. It crashed into Lake Pontchartrain, Louisiana. There were no survivors. Twenty-eight months later, turbulence was named as the trigger of the events that ended in disaster.

Although each of these cases was subjected to investigation individually, all seven were seen in perspective as episodes in a long 'investigators' nightmare' — to use an NTSB man's expression — that began with a crash at the Everglades National Park near Miami, Florida, on February 12, 1963, and which led to lasting controversy mainly because so little was known about turbulence at the time. Typical of the attitudes in those days were two comments.*

One came from Bobbie R. Allen, who was to become one of the most successful directors of the CAB crash detectives'

* *Life International*, January 11, 1965.

Safety Bureau: 'If I were trying to write a best-selling novel, I'd put "turbulence" in the title — there seems to be so much interest. We don't know if we have a turbulence problem or not.'

The other comment was equally disturbing because the FAA director Najeeb Halaby, made it: 'I can discern neither a pattern nor a panacea, and so I don't sleep so well nights. This is a terrible admission to make, but I wouldn't know what to do about it if we did prove turbulence was the cause. I guess we think that the system of corrections we've launched will be the answer.'

The problem, of course, was not at all new. Turbulence had been a known hazard but its role was constantly underrated. It was simply regarded as agitated air that goes with rough weather especially in the lower regions and near mountains where pilots have to keep sufficient clearance over the peaks. When the wind is strong this clearance may mean several thousand feet. Japan's Mount Fuji, for instance, has long been known for very violent air turbulence and World War II bomber pilots were advised to keep well away from it. But after a crash it has always been difficult to convict turbulence because it leaves no traces behind and only circumstantial evidence is available to crash detectives. That is why even when turbulence was accepted as the probable cause of an accident, the details of *how* it happened had to remain rather vague.

Take the case of the 'Saint Kevin', Dakota EI–AFL of Aer Lingus. On January 10, 1952, it took off from Northolt Airport en route for Dublin with a crew of three and twenty passengers. An hour later it reported that the expected time of arrival would be 19.51. At 19.12, the captain warned another aircraft: 'You'll find it pretty rough over the hills tonight.' Then he asked Dublin for permission to begin the descent and reported his position. Permission was granted — but possibly, the message never reached the aircraft. For the position report was wrong: when the pilot thought he was clearing the last of the Welsh land and reaching the Irish Sea, he was actually far to the north of the planned course and bringing the Saint Kevin into the leeside of Snowdon. (The leeside of a mountain is always more likely to harbour dangerous turbulence.) The aircraft struck the ground in a soft peat bog about a mile and a half east of Lake Gwynant in Caernarvonshire at a height of about 1,200 feet above mean sea level. The time was approximately 19.15. All people on board must have been killed outright.

While disproving all possible technical causes, the investigation concentrated on the meteorological situation and on the reasons for the pilot's miscalculation about the position. But the public court of inquiry still had to accept *three* possible versions of the actual tragedy:

'(*a*) The Pilot, being in error as to his true position began his descent from 6,500 feet to 4,500 feet and before he realised it ran into an unusually strong downward current in the lee of Snowdon. This downward current took him below the level of the crests of the mountains. In such a current an aircraft could lose 2,000 feet of height before any action for recovery of height could be effective. Once the aircraft reached a level below the crests of the mountains, it would, in the conditions prevailing there at the time, be in a region of most chaotic turbulence from which in the darkness there would be the greatest difficulty in regaining control and recovering height. While the Pilot was making an effort to do this, the aircraft encountered an unusually violent local gust which put the aircraft completely out of control and produced the stresses which broke off the starboard wing and plunged the aircraft into the bog.

'(*b*) The aircraft ran into a region of unusual violent turbulence which dislodged the Pilot from the controls. Before he could recover control of the aircraft the task became impossible, the wing was torn off and the crash followed.

'(c) The . . . turbulence dislodged moveable equipment in the cockpit, which in its turn jammed the controls or injured the Pilot and produced the same result as in (b).'

With the advent of the jet-age, many experts believed that these high-altitude, high-speed machines would fly 'above the weather' — and above turbulence. A heavy death-toll subsequently proved this assumption wrong. For turbulence still caused trouble at altitudes even above 30,000 feet and it was shown that the condition even existed in the rarefied air at 50,000 feet, too.

The magnificent streamlined structure of the jets turned out to be a new potential hazard. One of the most common techniques of flying in turbulence is to reduce air-speed. But with the modern swept-wing aircraft this was a less readily available solution. For the jets, built for much greater speed, became unstable more quickly and risked a stall more easily than earlier and slower propeller-driven aircraft had when using the same technique. Their speed was less forgiving to wrong decisions by the pilots, and once they went into a turbulence-induced dive, they built up speed 'by nature' so fast that there remained much less time to recovery than in earlier types. This tremendous extra hurtling dive imposed additional stresses on the structure. Fortunately, the bigger lift of the jets permitted them to have much stronger structures — some of the above cases and others like the previously described dive of a 707 with the malfunctioning auto-pilot had given ample demonstration of the jets' rugged strength which could endure much higher stresses than even their designers had hoped for — and thus turbulence itself hardly ever caused direct structural failure. But, on the other hand, the clash between the fast dive and the pilot's effort to pull out of it could develop the stresses necessary for tearing an airliner apart.

The investigation of accidents and incidents began to accumulate a great deal of circumstantial evidence and knowledge, but the inevitable basic research was still delayed — mainly because of lack of funds. And this delay continued even when gradually it became evident that the available knowledge about turbulence was extremely limited. It was not known what types of turbulence existed. It was not known how to predict and avoid them. It was only suspected that a turbulence area might be miles or just a few feet wide at various heights. And then yet another mysterious phenomenon appeared among the suspects: although weather radars were well on their way to fulfilling the promise of spotting thunderstorm cells and helping pilots to avoid turbulence, now there was something radar could not see — the invisible potential killer that became known by that most befitting abbreviation, CAT. It stands for *clear air turbulence*, and it may occur in clear blue skies, completely dissociated from thunderstorms.

Increased attention to CAT was part of the 'technological fallout' of the investigations into the two Lockheed Electra catastrophes in 1959 and 1960. These accidents were eventually traced to structural failure of the wing in the air, caused by 'forces generated by undampened propeller whirl mode' (a wobbling vibration that weakened the engine mounting as well as the wing structure); but that only showed how exceedingly misleading similarities existed between the remains of aircraft destroyed by true structural failure and of those that had been sent plummeting by turbulence.

'Every possible cause under the sun had to be suspected when the Northwest Airlines 720B broke up in the air over the Everglades National Park some forty miles from Miami International Airport, Florida on February 12, 1963,' said Martyn V. Clarke, now assistant chief of the NTSB Central Investigation Division. Although turbulence was a possible cause from the beginning because of the stormy weather at the time of the crash, an endless list of other causes had to be eliminated. These included fire in the air,

263

explosion, sabotage, fatigue, structural weakness caused by design or an earlier minor landing accident of that particular aircraft, etc., and therefore, after a meticulous site examination — the wreckage was scattered over a vast fifteen-mile-long area indicating in-flight break-up — one of the biggest reconstructions ever had to be carried out. About ninety-seven per cent of the aircraft was recovered, and transported by helicopter to a U.S. Coast Guard hangar in Miami, where the mock-up was built by April 1.

All this helped to establish at what altitude and in what order the break-up had progressed. This aircraft 'reaction' could then be related to the events in the air revealed by the flight recorder and to the pilot's probable action deduced partly from routine standing instructions for encountering turbulence and partly from the positions of wrecked controls. (The horizontal stabiliser in the tail was, for instance, in the fully nose-down position in this case as well as in the Montreal and New Orleans cases. The setting of the power-operated jackscrew that adjusts the stabiliser could not be altered by the impact and so it disclosed the pilot's action and intention: at some stage, he tried to push the nose down as much as possible.)

The aircraft departed from Miami at 13.35 and crashed killing the forty-three people on board about fifteen minutes later. There was a great deal of thunderstorm activity in the area with anticipated turbulence at the time, and investigators found that in order to avoid turbulence 'circuitous routing was utilised during the climbout'. Dodging thunderstorm cells the pilot reported that he was climbing towards clear air, and that it all looked 'pretty bad' up there. Apparently this was no better than the usual, more direct course and he advised the controller 'you better run the rest of them off the other way then'. He reached 17,500 feet altitude at 13.48 — and it was soon afterwards that the forty seconds of drama began.

It was one of those cases in which the investigation could hardly have gone much beyond the above facts without the vast research carried out by the FAA, NASA, U.S. Weather Bureau, Air Force, Northwest Airlines, and, perhaps above all, Boeing. The various tests, experiments and subsequent analysis proved that 'Clearly, many factors, which individually would not be considered as extreme hazards, were involved in producing this accident. In many ways, this accident is a classic illustration of the *man-machine — evnvironment* [author's italics] casual triangle concept'. The turbulence was not extreme enough to break up the aircraft. The machine itself stood the test well. But once the initial effects of turbulence had made an impact on the flight, the characteristics of the machine readily gave them a helping hand. The pilot — whose training, built on insufficient basic knowledge of the situation, had not warned him to 'swing with the blows' — threw away the last chance of recovery in the available ten seconds or so by acting in the way he had been taught to act and doing his very best according to the state of the art.

The probable pattern of such accidents and incidents now began to take shape. A savage, storm-generated updraft would suddenly shoot the plane towards the sky. The pilot would try to maintain his altitude and push the nose down. With that he would get behind the events and compound the danger when the instruments go haywire and deprive him of true information. Desperate to control the pitch and altitude, and to stop the violent shaking and buffeting which imply to him the imminence of a stall, he would make drastic nose-down adjustments. Carrying this now 'dive-shaped' aircraft, the updraft would hit the 'jet-stream', a narrow, high-velocity wind that circles the earth at altitudes of about 30,000 to 35,000 feet. The jet stream, used by airliners for a free ride that gives them an extra 200 or 250 mph speed, would clash with the energy of the updraft and the deflected energy would produce a tremendous downdraft into which the plane, progressing through the updraft, would enter.

The updraft was tossing the aircraft towards the sky at some *nine thousand feet per minute*. The downdraft, aided by the dive-ready trim of the machine, would draw it towards the earth at the speed of about a *thousand feet per second*. With warning lights flashing, bells ringing, loose items tossing around, crew members would be strap-hanging bodily, struggling to get their 45-pound hands on the wheel and their lead-heavy feet on the rudder pedals.

The vital seconds in which recovery could be attempted are lost. Speed builds up fast to 470 or 480 knots and the on-rushing air practically paralyses the controls. If the pilots, confused by the chaotic conditions in the cockpit and totally unaccustomed to negative 'g' forces of such frightening magnitude, manage however to impose their will on the machine and begin to alter the angle of the dive — the over-stressed structure of the aircraft then often gives way to these superior forces.

There is hardly any time to make a decision — as opposed to acting instinctively — and no chance at all to revise that decision, because in this Northwest accident, for instance, the time gap between the nose over, the beginning of the dive, and the actual crash, *after* disintegration and fire, was only twenty seconds. The time for action at the beginning of the dive was about eight seconds.

One part of the final report, dealing with individual reaction time, clearly answered those who would prefer to choose the easy way out and blame the pilot whenever in doubt. It stated that this pilot, Captain Roy Almquist, was well qualified 'and possessed average or better flying abilities. However, the Board is convinced that a clearer understanding of the "limits" of an "average" pilot must be found in order to insure a safe matching of the man to the machine and the environment. Perhaps statistical methods will have to be applied in prescribing a realistic capability range for the "average" pilot in order to provide the aircraft designer with more meaningful data to use in achieving a safe design that provides for full consideration of all associated human factor elements.'

The investigation and experiments, while finding the cause of a particular accident, spotlighted the areas of necessary further research and established what sort of new flying techniques, introduced by improved training, could break the man-machine-environment vicious triangle when turbulence is encountered. Attention was also called to several hazardous contributing factors. One recommendation was to improve the readability of instruments in such circumstances. Another was the better use of a modified autopilot that could accomplish 'loose' flying better than its master.

The speed of weather information to pilots also received due criticism. The U.S. Weather Bureau sends out regular 'sigmets' — messages, mainly for aircraft in flight, that give warning of potentially hazardous weather conditions. On the day of the accident, Sigmet No. 3 was valid from *09.00 to 13.00*. It 'forecast moderate to severe turbulence in thunderstorms, with a chance of extreme turbulence in heavier thunderstorms'. Turbulence described as 'extreme' is rarely encountered, would toss the aircraft about violently, causing damage, and making the flight 'practically impossible to control'. Captain Almquist received this no longer valid report in the operations office and was probably influenced by it in making his decision to use a circuitous rather than the usual departure route. Sigmet No. 4, valid from 13.00 to 17.00, came in on the teletypewriter at about 13.15 — which was some fifteen minutes late, but still ten minutes before the taxiing time and twenty minutes prior to the take-off time of the flight! But, the investigation revealed, 'the dispatcher for this flight is stationed in Minneapolis' and the 'physical limitations involved' prevented him from advising Almquist about its contents. The most significant change in Sigmet 4 was that it deleted the reference to 'extreme turbulence'. It was impossible to guess what would have happened in the circumstances had Sigmet 4 reached the pilot, but there can be no doubt that he ought to have been told about it.

In 1963, during the series of accidents and incidents involving encounter with turbulence, politicans, of course, made long speeches about the problem. Some just tried to gain popularity, others helped to serve a good cause. Some knew what it was all about, others demanded the grounding of all jets or at least 'these structurally suspect 707s' even though the cases involved various types and DC–8s fractionally more than others. Even their most ludicrous demands and criticisms helped, however, to create a sense of the greatest urgency, so that via a concerted effort, more adequate training and handling techniques, technical improvement and further research projects were initiated. But to acknowledge their effectiveness makes it even more unfortunate that those politicians dropped their interest as soon as at least partial improvement was achieved. Partial, because the turbulence hazard is still far from being overcome. (Perhaps it is enough to mention only the BOAC 707 disaster in March 1966 which killed 124 people after the aircraft disintegrated in severe turbulence over Mount Fuji, causing the airline's first fatal accident after nine years of crash-free operations.) And yet it is, above all, the shortage of funds that delays the initiation of new research projects and the completion of others which try to forecast and learn more about the nature and behaviour of turbulence, detect the presence of CAT by ground-based high-powered radar, or by other devices like the one using infra-red rays.

Helping to obtain more money for such research is not the only point where some politicians could support a good cause as well as cash in on the emotional effect of the mysterious word 'turbulence'. There is another, less important but not insignificant issue in connection with CAT — which would save people from injuries and would not cost a penny.

When an aircraft flies in the vicinity of thunderstorms, pilots are aware of the possibility of a 'bumpy ride' and switch on the sign 'fasten your seatbelts'. (For take-off and landing the fastening of seatbelts is, of course, obligatory, and after take-off the pilot announces when the passengers *may* release them.) About CAT, no such information is available to the pilot. Here are some haphazardly chosen incidents to show what may happen if the pilot is not in a position to give advance warning — or if a passenger does not take such a warning seriously.

When Captain Parkinson suddenly found himself seated 'on the end of a huge tuning fork' in August 1963, behind him in the cabin, a baby slipped from his mother's arms and she, unable to move, had to watch helplessly her 'baby lying on the ceiling, crying'.

After Mel French and Grant Newby had saved their DC–8 from the fatal plunge, one of their passengers, a New Jersey estate agent Robert Monihan, recalled that some passengers had been pinned to the ceiling during the dive. 'I was in mid-step when the aisle went from under my feet and my back hit against the roof. I was glued to that roof like a stamp to an envelope ... Just as suddenly everyone was thrown to the floor but there was no panic.'

In January 1966 two stewardesses and a woman passenger were hurt when a DC–8 of Air Canada flew into severe turbulence before landing at Prestwick Airport. In March 1967 two passengers and two stewardesses were injured when a Qantas 707 was hit by CAT at 34,000 feet en route from Karachi to Calcutta. One passenger was thrown out of his seat with such violence that he suffered a spine fracture.

Two months later, an Air France Caravelle encountered unexpected turbulence and dived 3,000 feet over Turin. Twenty-two of its sixty-one passengers were injured and six of them had to be detained in hospital.

In October 1967 a BAC One-eleven of LASCA Airlines flew into a storm near Grand Cayman Island, in the Caribbean. The pilot flashed the seatbelt signs — but several passengers ignored them. Five minutes later, the aircraft was caught in a downdraft and plunged 10,000 feet from an altitude of 29,000 feet. Those who had not buckled their seatbelts were thrown out of their seats and against the ceiling together with whisky bottles and luggage. A man and a woman were killed, others were injured before the pilots managed to break the dive, level out and land the aircraft.

Crash detectives were apparently among the first to recognise this hazard. Their incident reports gave warnings and many of them told the author that they would never travel without seatbelts on. They would loosen them for comfort but would not unbuckle them while seated. For several years, most airlines stubbornly refused even to consider such advice to passengers. They claimed that the belts would cause slight but unnecessary discomfort, that the advice would frighten away passengers, and that, according to one big American line, there was 'no need to take such a step because these mishaps were extremely infrequent and insignificant.'

After the cases in 1963, the FAA took a different view, especially when it was discovered that between 1960 and 1964, in the United States alone, there had been more than two dozen reported incidents, all of which had been caused by turbulence and had resulted in serious injuries to eighteen stewardesses and passengers. The Agency therefore asked the airlines to devise some voluntary system for advising passengers *to keep their seat-belts on all the time*. The most usual reaction was that pilots were asked to give this advice to passengers verbally on the intercom but make clear that it sort of 'adds to the fun' and that seat-belts give you the status of being an 'experienced traveller'. After a few years of adolescence and euphemisms — 'keep seatbelts on for your *comfort*' — most lines now give frank advice: 'keep the seatbelt loosely fastened whenever you are seated, particularly during night time or when you intend to sleep. This will protect you against unexpected turbulence.'

Stewardesses, moving about most of the time, are inevitably least protected against CAT. But perhaps it would not be an improper suggestion to provide the users of the lavatories aboard with seatbelts, for if turbulence is suddenly encountered they may not be able to get back to their seats in the cabin and follow the pilot's urgent instruction.

And a final word from a crash detective: 'Judging from passengers' reactions to turbulence incidents, even if no more than a single passenger has been slightly injured, I'm sure that these people will frighten away more potential airline passengers with their stories about no panic, heroic silence and expert first aid to the injured, than frank advice and fastened seatbelts ever could.'

CHAPTER THIRTEEN

DANGER ON THE GROUND

AT least half of all aviation accidents happen at or in the close vicinity of airports. This fact in itself spotlights a problem area and although no airport has been named as *the* cause of any accident, it has long puzzled aircrash detectives how much the terminal area and its equipment have contributed to any particular case. The main difficulty is that

there are no international or even national standards.
ICAO, for instance, has issued an avalanche of guidance
and recommendations to achieve some uniformity of standards, but 'only about half of the recommendations have
been taken to heart at the international aerodromes of the
world and much less than half at the others'.* The suitability of location and lengths of runways vary just as much
as the equipment, landing aids and qualification of personnel from the 'almost completely inadequate' to the
'highly sophisticated peppered with infuriatingly petty
shortcomings', as an American investigator put it.

This lack of consistent standards stems from the fact that
airports are owned by all sorts of groups and organisations,
towns, counties, individual American states, and so on.
Most of the control is left in the hands of operators whose
licences burden them with the responsibility for the safety of
operations. This situation has developed into a main source
of frustration for the major airlines' own investigators, three
of whom, while wishing to remain anonymous, stated in separate interviews that 'at least in marginal cases, when the
safety and operations chiefs would advise the airline to cease
using an airfield, the commercial director can overrule our
advice because competitors do use similar aircraft at the
same field or same runway, and we just cannot afford to stop
unless it's an absolute must'. It sounds as if safety were
sacrificed for the sake of business, but it is comforting to
know that such decisions occur only in the marginal cases.

There was, for instance, the problem with the runways at
Barcelona. Pilots of one of the big, international airlines of
Europe landed their Caravelles there regularly but found
that the surface was too dangerous to tyres and pressed the
airline to do something about it. Investigators of a British
company, having looked at the high number of 'blown tyre

* Captain C. C. Jackson: A Long Shot at Air Safety, *Flight International*, December 15, 1966.

272

incidents', supported the pilots, because such incidents had in fact also caused accidents. Although there was a long delay in improving the condition of the runway, the company could not afford to suspend operations even as a warning because other lines continued to land aircraft of similar size there despite the incidents.

Sub-standard airport conditions are often due to lack of funds or ignorance.

Insufficient *firefighting equipment* is one of the most wide-spread negligences affecting airports. Such equipment may make all the difference between life and death to crash-landing passengers, may save the aircraft from complete destruction, may save other lives and property from spreading fire, and ultimately, it may at least preserve vital evidence in the wreckage to facilitate investigation. In 1963 the American Airline Pilots' Association issued a report claiming that more than ninety per cent of the U.S. Airports in airline use still lacked adequate rescue equipment and training. The FAA was powerless to bring strong enough pressure to bear, and Robert J. Serling reported the case of a crashed aircraft burning at a small airport 'while firemen wrestled in vain with a rusted door lock on a garage containing their lone fire truck'.* Ed Slattery of NTSB said that 'all major U.S. airports have good firefighting equipment but even these are often in need of considerable improvement. Smaller cities find airport fire equipment and personnel a big financial burden. The only solution would be to shut such airports down altogether — but that would put a lot of people out of business'.

In June 1967, a CV 240 of Lineas Aereas Paraguayas caught fire on a runway at Ezeiza Airport, Buenos Aires. An attempt was made to operate firefighting equipment but that turned out to be impossible — most probably because of inadequate maintenance. The first vehicle to arrive at the

* *The Probable Cause*, p. 294.

burning aircraft was an ambulance that could take *one* person. Then came another ambulance of the same size. Luckily, Shell, Braniff and Aerolineas Argentinas employees bravely helped all passengers to safety while soldiers tore away a burning wing with the aid of a tractor, towed it to the edge of the runway and extinguished the flames by throwing mud and sand on them with their bare hands!

Although it was an exceptionally disturbing occurrence in itself, it was not wholly unexpected. For publication in this book, a crash detective of one interested party disclosed some confidential details of a long battle fought by the Airline Operators' Committee (AOC) against the various Buenos Aires authorities. It appears from minutes taken at meetings that the problem had been known officially as long ago as 1947. Committees and sub-committees were formed, and endless arguments raised about who should do what, but hardly any improvement had been achieved in twenty years.

Airports are classified on the basis of traffic statistics as agreed by ICAO signatories — including Argentina — and as stated in the relevant ICAO Convention Annex 14. Yet such officially approved statistics did not exist for Ezeiza in 1967, when an airline representative reported to his company his own estimated figures. He reckoned that the two biggest aircraft using the airport *most* frequently were the B707/720 and the DC-8. The B707/720 was operated at Ezeiza at the time by Aerolineas Argentinas, Braniff, PanAm, Air France, the Chilean Linea Aerea Nacional, Lufthansa, Varig, TAP of Portugal, and AVIANCA of Colombia. DC-8-users were SAS, Varig, Braniff, PanAm, Alitalia, Iberia, KLM, and CPAL. (Other operators, like Swissair, used other types.) The two biggest types, and the frequency of their flights to and from Ezeiza, represented the 'critical aircraft' for this airport putting it in 'category X'. This international category required availability of

24,000 litres of water — but only 8,000 litres were available in July 1967; the strength of the fire brigade was well below the requirement; and only recently just a very limited foam-producing capacity was made available. The speed at which water could be discharged by the firefighting equipment could not be estimated because the only time the equipment had been needed in an emergency, during the above-quoted accident, it had not been in working order.

The hospital nearby would be quite insufficient to deal with a serious accident, and the first aid service was not equipped properly even with medicines. At one point in the long-drawn dispute Braniff had offered four of its own cars to the authorities for conversion into ambulances. The offer had been rejected.

The chief of the airport guaranteed to AOC in a telephone conversation that by the end of June 1967 the federal police would have forty-five firemen with three fire engines at the airport. By the end of July this was still a promise.

The latest developments have not been made available to the author but even if everything has now been put right, the twenty years' delay would still be deplorable enough.

Although an extreme case, Buenos Aires is not alone in underrating the fire hazard. One investigator, surveying the airfields used by his company, went to Cairo after a serious incident and found that the fire brigade had only 6,000 litres of water available — a quarter of the quantity recommended by ICAO for such international airports. When the crew of the airliner, aboard which the investigator was to leave Cairo, went to the tarmac, they found a considerable amount of fuel spilt on the ground and there was a sizeable puddle under the wing. They would not start the engine because that fuel might catch fire. The fire brigade would not deal with it and neither did the airport staff. Finally, a team of men had to be found by the crew to tow the aircraft away from the puddle so that the engines could be started safely.

Aircrash investigators sometimes uncover various short-comings even at the best-equipped airports. When a Viscount crashed at London Airport in fog only 700 yards from the Fire Station on January 7, 1960, a quick evacuation of the aircraft ensured that all the fifty-nine people on board got away without injury from the burning wreckage. The fuselage almost completely burned out because the fire brigade got lost in the dense fog. The first vehicle of their convoy to reach the scene was an ambulance which then guided two fire engines by ringing its bell. This was nine minutes after the crash. Another two vehicles arrived a few minutes later, and the Station Fire Officer was lost in the fog for thirty minutes. Other vehicles arrived even after that and the last fireman on the scene reached the wreckage seventy-seven minutes after the crash. Crash detectives found that there had been some confusion about the use of guidance from ASMI, the Airfield Surface Movements Guidance Indicator radar. The ASMI operator, seeing the lost vehicles on his screen, had the taxiway lightings turned on to guide the vehicles — but there had been no such prearrangements made and so the drivers did not know the lights were meant to guide them.

Petty quibbles between local authorities were probably the cause of the state of reduced readiness for fire at Miami International Airport, Florida, according to some investigators who dealt with an EAL Constellation emergency landing on January 17, 1959. Apparently, while the burning aircraft circled over the airfield, vehicles of the local fire brigade could not get through the traffic jam at the airport gates. Passengers escaped with minor injuries but the aircraft was badly damaged by fire and most of the invaluable evidence for investigators was destroyed. Firefighting was started by the airport's own firemen, but they soon ran out of foam, had no 'supplementary extinguishing agent, such as dry chemical or carbon dioxide', and 'no such important rescue equipment as power saws and escape stairs'. (The report said: 'Compared to NFPA — National Fire Protection Association — suggestions, which, in this field, are widely accepted in the absence of any regulatory matter, the amount of foam available at the scene was well below the amount suggested. The discharge rate capacity of the equipment was about one half that of the NFPA suggested rate.') Thus when the fire was 'nearly out', the foam supply was exhausted, and when 'two flashbacks of the fire then occurred', only water could be used until, at last, the local authorities' off-airport fire engines had struggled through the gate and reached the wreckage. It was this accident that forced the authorities to sort out who is responsible for what — the fire department, for instance, belonged to the airport which was owned by the state, but the state could only issue warnings instead of orders — and to bring about considerable improvements.

The various problems which are spotlighted by investigations seem to be particularly acute at smaller airports which are used mainly by the smaller companies. 'In Europe, the highest concentration of potential "killer airports" is in Spain, with Perpignan, in France, on its doorstep,' wrote Andrew Wilson, the *Observer's* Air Correspondent after the ninth crash in sixteen years in the Perpignan area.* But the expression 'smaller airports' does not necessarily mean insignificant volume of traffic especially in peak holiday periods when charter flights flood some of them. Based on personal comments by government and airline investigators, on an ICAO list published in 1966,† and on some other reports, this is only a *very incomplete* series of examples of airports which may have contributed to varying extent to accidents or incidents. (These comments, where not dated individually, refer to the situation up to mid-1967.)

* *Observer*, June 11, 1967.   † Air Navigation Plan.

At Manila, the airport authorities stubbornly refused to put up some cheap fences that would keep animals from straying on the runways. San Diego has for long been a notorious tyre-blower. Perpignan, surrounded by dangerous peaks and an area of heavy turbulence, has bad lighting and landing aids, and its lack of ground radar contributed to accidents ultimately attributed to 'pilot error'.

Poor judgment by the pilot was the verdict after the fatal crash of a Convair in 1958; he was trying to land on Nantucket Island, Massachusetts, which had completely antiquated runway lighting; this was known to the pilot but when the weather suddenly deteriorated and he made the wrong split-second decision to attempt a landing, better lighting would still have enhanced his chances to succeed.

At Southend, thousands of British holidaymakers had to land on and take off from a runway sandwiched between buildings and a railway line, their aircraft being guided by a 'poor man's radar', an incorrectly positioned beacon. Palma, frequently flooded during the summer, had no proper aids for landings at night when a great proportion of charter flights arrived. Like Palma, Ibiza can become fogbound unexpectedly but had no radar and no ILS.

ICAO listed eight Spanish international airports with lighting and runway deficiencies; and several French major airports with similar shortcomings at, for instance, Cherbourg and Lyons. The same problems were listed at Gibraltar, Bari, Milan, Naples and Venice.

On the night of June 30th, 1966, when a Trident crashed at Kuwait, no equipment seems to have worked at the airport. This was probably a supplementary cause of the accident because it imposed an additional burden on the crew in the cockpit. ICAO, the prototype of the 'toothless bulldog', passed a resolution at its Rome meeting in 1961 that Kuwait should introduce ILS facilities. By 1966 Kuwait still had not installed the equipment. Only a month before the Trident

278

crash, an airliner was asked to land there first with one, then with both sides of the runway lighting being inoperative. Finally, only the lights of a jeep on the runway guided the pilot.

Cairo has frequently been criticised in many respects — especially after serious accidents in similar circumstances. In 1965 members of the International Pilots' Association refused to make night landings after two bad crashes one of which, a 707 of Pakistan International Airways, killed 119 people. The airport had insufficient firefighting equipment and inadequate landing aids (it was rumoured that modern equipment had been bought but kept in storage for two years!) and a location which could create moments of grave danger even if the best possible equipment were installed to help the pilot. And on runway 34, even the special set of rules for each airfield and each runway, created by each airline individually, could not avert a series of accidents and incidents. For there the approach must be made over high ground where several aircraft crashed getting ready for a fast drop of almost a thousand feet of height to touch down at the runway threshold nearby. Even a successful 'drop' was not the end of the difficulties for the pilot had to bring his machine to a halt racing down on the barely two kilometres-long runway which is built on a rather steep slope. This was one of the cases when BOAC, for instance, overruled all commercial considerations and, after having heard about the accidents and incidents, instructed its pilots to use runway 34 only in emergencies until the runway was lengthened.

Even where the best *landing aids* exist, inferior maintenance to spot malfunctions or a shortage of standby equipment during maintenance may become a contributory factor in accidents and incidents. At Valencia in Spain, basic aids were missing, and although there was a navigational radio beam it never seemed to work, according to pilots quoted by Andrew Wilson. A BEA Vanguard pilot, with ninety passengers on board, was already preparing to land at Glasgow in reduced visibility, when suddenly he was told that the airport radar had been turned off for routine cleaning and so it would not be able to assist him.

When on November 30, 1962, an EAL DC–7B crashed killing twenty-five people at New York International Airport in rapidly deteriorating weather, the RVR, Runway Visual Range, a vital aid, was inoperative. It appears from the CAB recommendations and from the subsequent FAA corrective action that there was no alternative method to determine runway visibility in case of an RVR break-down, which — though not in this case — might play a major role in causing an accident.

Similarly, as a side issue of another investigation, it was discovered that when the BEA Vanguard crashed at London Airport in 1965,* the 'RVR lights had not been calibrated for a considerable time and as a result they were giving an erroneous figure. This erroneous figure was passed to the aircraft'. Thus the pilot 'was told that the Runway Visual Range was 350 metres when in fact it was 300 metres.' This was not named as a contributory cause of the 'pilot error' accident, but the report proved that the correct figures might have precluded the landing attempt itself! For that fifty metres difference was critical: although the report said that the 350 metres visual range minimum was not enough, the captain only obeyed his regulations when he tried to land having this official minimum visibility; but 300 metres was below his officially permissible minimum and so, had he been given the true figures representing the actual situation, presumably he would not have attempted to land at all. It was in this way that the mistake helped to create the situation in which the pilot could make the fatal error. The Public Inquiry criticised the Ministry of Aviation severely

* See Chapter Eight.

'for not instituting a regular check of the RVR system . . .'

This was a typical problem aircrash detectives must often deal with: a supplementary cause — but how seriously supplementary? Several investigators mentioned, for instance, the *runway lip* as a frequent contributor to incidents which may turn into accidents. The 'lip' is the elevation between ground and runway level. 'This lip is usually smoothed by dirt built up at an angle by airport authorities, but the turning jets soon blow it away,' said George van Epps, chief of the NTSB New York field office. 'Many airports in my area have a lip problem on two or more runways. We often recommend something is done about it, they review and rebuild it regularly, but the dirt is blown away in no time. They ought to taper off the end of the runway with cement but that, and its maintenance, would be an additional expense when, technically, the pilot is not *supposed* to touch down there anyway. They should land *on* and not before the runway, but in heavy rain or because of a gusta from 3 to 6 inches drop is not unusual — in fact, it's frequent and regarded as "slight" — and that may be enough to catch the landing gear and break it off. We have quite a few incidents like this.

'Apart from gusts, pilots themselves are anxious to use *all* the available runway length partly because it gives them an extra margin of safety and partly because if they miss the markings at the threshold, further up the runway there is no marking to tell them where they are. If we have a serious accident due to such landing gear failure, how much of the cause should be attributed to "pilot error" for touch-down before the runway, and how much to the lip that broke the gear?

'Take the situation at Boston. The runway is limited in length because there's no room. Because of the harbour nearby, the glide path had to be steep to clear even the highest mast of any ship. To achieve a more shallow glide path, the threshold marking had to be moved well up on the runway. The remaining runway is still enough for most certified operation's, but frequently, the pilots land well before the markings so that they could use the full length of the runway for extra safety. Can we really blame them for that?'

The *length of runways* has been a matter of dispute ever since the beginning of commercial aviation. Pilots always fight to get extra length for safety especially when using maximum take-off weight. In cases of 'marginal' length of runway they obviously have a strong point of argument. Investigators of accidents, however, cannot support their claims as the length of a runway has hardly ever caused an accident by being insufficient for the type of operation approved by the airline or, in American aviation, by the airline and by FAA. (The requirements of the latter two may differ considerably because the government may permit more landing weight for a particular length of runway than a conscientious company would accept.)

One of the few exceptions to the rule in Britain occurred at Portsmouth where in a single day, in 1967, two Hawker Siddeley 748 turbo-prop airliners skidded off the exceptionally water-logged grass runway. Nobody was injured but, as an immediate precaution, the Board of Trade imposed special temporary regulations increasing the landing distances at Portsmouth by ten per cent in dry, and thirty per cent in wet, weather. Channel Airways, the only company operating from Portsmouth, could cope with that only by cutting down the number of passengers carried in each aircraft because the existing length of runway was now sufficient only with reduced weight. After full investigation and tests, the Portsmouth restriction was replaced by an 'advice' to all operators of 748's, that their manuals should instruct their pilots to use 'special procedures' for grass airfields anywhere in the world.

It was by no means a coincidence that in America, too, perhaps the most disputed 'length of runway' case occurred on a rainy day. A Continental Air Lines 707, with sixty passengers and a crew of six, came in to land at Kansas City Municipal Airport, Missouri, on a runway that pilots regarded as very marginal in wet weather. As the investigation later discovered, the existing conditions (water on the runway) were not reported to the pilot who thus expected no difficulties. In fact, these conditions made the weight of his aircraft exceed his company regulations, which were, however, well under the FAA maximum gross landing weight (175,000 pounds) for 707's on this runway. 'When the crew's efforts to stop the aircraft were ineffective, and the captain was convinced that they were going off the end of the runway, he used differential power and rudder to cock the aircraft to the left. The aircraft slid off the end of the runway, went through the ILS localiser antenna building, struck a dirt blast mound, slid up over the mound, and came to rest with the nose section in the perimeter road between the blast mound and a river levee.' Luckily, there was no fire and only five people received minor injuries.

Even before the official investigation could begin it seemed fairly obvious that the braking had been ineffective because of *aquaplaning* — a film of water holds the tyres from contacting the runway surface — and the suspicion arose inevitably that the runway was too short for such aircraft in wet weather. Yet evidence to the contrary was printed on the runway: newsmen took pictures from a helicopter ten minutes after the crash and these showed what Ed Slattery, who arrived at the scene six hours later, described as 'scrub marks or brush marks which are different from the ordinary tyre marks and are caused by the tremendously heated water between the hot tyres and the runway surface'; these touch-down marks — as noted by William Lamb, head of the GO team, a former Navy pilot — were '1,050 *feet past the approach end of runway* 18'. This meant that on the remaining 5,950 feet of usable runway, in the given conditions, the heavy aircraft could not stop. Tests implied that had the crew been properly notified about the water on the runway, they could have landed with reduced speed using the full length of the runway which would have been sufficient for the aircraft to stop. (The extension of the runway has long been recommended, but the airport is on the bend of a river and there is no more available ground for a longer runway.)

Normally, it is up to the airline to judge a particular situation and, indeed, the big lines take such precautions. BOAC stopped using 707's at Manchester until the runway was lengthened. American Airlines moved all its 727 operations from LaGuardia to Kennedy from October 1964 to April 1965, as long as major construction work shortened the usable length of runways and heavy ground equipment was used on or parked near the runways.

Qantas is another of the major airlines that is quick to encourage remedial action by restricting or stopping the use of suspect airports. Captain Bert Ritchie, General Manager of the company once told this author: 'Safety, loyalty and profitability are a kind of passion in this company. It's amazing how well these go together. Even when our training seems excessive and even when some people suggest that we do over-maintenance — changing control cables, for instance, when repairs would do — we find that on the long run, these things keep down costs and keep up safety.' And Capt. Alan Wharton, Director of Flight Operations added: 'We stopped flying to Jakarta, for example, when there was a lot of ditch-digging along the runway, and heavy equipment parked there represented a hazard. We kept asking for those fence repairs to be done at Manila, kept an eye on Colombo where the facilities were just about acceptable, but suspended night landings and take-offs at New Caledonia because we were not satisfied with the facilities. Some of these decisions are hard to make because they may be inconvenient and expensive. But at the end, we reckon, a single incident, damage to our aircraft, not to mention anything more serious, would cost a great deal more.'

The *location* of an airport may also become a contributory cause of accidents or increase their severity. As airports must be close to towns there is an element of danger that a crashing aircraft may cause damage in populated areas. This hazard has never been better demonstrated than in December 1951 and January 1952, when three planes crashed into Elizabeth, New Jersey, near Newark Airport. Joseph O. Fluet, then New York regional CAB chief, remembers it as a horrible nightmare. In addition to the people on board the three aircraft, eleven peacefully sleeping citizens were killed in their homes. In the circumstances, it was not surprising that there was a near riot demanding the close-down of the airport, and when Fluet raced to take some photographs of burning wreckage, a fireman scoffed at him, 'What damn difference does it make now? This wouldn't have happened if you guys gave a hoot about the people on the ground.' Only Fluet's patience and unflappable manner got co-operation out of him: 'Look, bud, you don't feel any worse than I do. I'm doing a job same as you.' And, what the fireman was never to know was that it was due to a part of the investigation and to that 'photographer's' recommendation that it was not necessary to close the airport altogether: a change of runway direction was introduced which helped to avert the danger of aircraft falling on to the town when a crash occurs while landing or taking off.

Unfortunately, the Newark–Elizabeth situation is not unique — except that without crashes authorities are reluctant to take such expensive steps. Oddly enough, it is a completely different problem that occupies most of the headlines in any controversy over the proximity of airports to towns: *noise*. Due to increased traffic of jets, noise has become a cause of deep concern especially since the advent of supersonic transport.

Though it is a considerable source of annoyance — it is not a hazard in itself. If anything, it is the noise abatement procedure that may create some hazard because on take-off pilots must make a steep initial climb, then soon reduce power and sometimes even turn at low altitude in order to achieve the least noisy departure from populated areas. (Unfortunately, many of these populated areas near airports were built *after* those airports had been developed.)

Although take-off is a busy and somewhat tense moment for the pilot, and although no pilot likes to take the slightest risks with the controllability of the aircraft — like slowing down at low altitude — the procedure itself is a carefully examined, approved regulation which guarantees a reasonable minimum of safety. But the emphasis is on the word 'minimum'. Scores of investigators have stated in interviews that 'there has never been a single case with evidence to prove that noise abatement did cause an accident'. On the other hand, many agreed with the American crash detective who said that 'I cannot help but *feel* that on some occasions, this was the final trigger, an additional factor, that helped to cut the margin of safety just that little thinner. When the pilot needed maximum aircraft performance, he could not rely on peak engine performance at a crucial moment when noise abatement made it just that little bit more difficult to cope with all emergency actions that were needed.'

It was typical of the crash detectives' attitude that when they expressed such unsubstantiated opinions they wished to remain anonymous because their chief interest is in facts alone. The words of a German expert, however, summed up another of their opinions: 'There are no real, universally acceptable standards for noise abatement. In many parts of the world, under public pressure, local authorities have begun to disregard expert views and impose their own sets of rules. They, too, recognise the pilot's right to abandon noise abatement procedures whenever safety is threatened, but they want to hold him responsible for any "excess noise", the limit of which they may set arbitrarily on, say, the noise level of a passing lorry.' Undoubtedly, some international regulation is needed urgently, without waiting for any tragic factual evidence. But this is true about the entire airport situation.

Airline pilots, using these airfields regularly, are in an excellent position to carry out frequent surveys and compile reports. It would be much better to pay more attention to these than to wait for eventual accident reports even though pilots may make seemingly excessive demands, and international recommendations may advance faster than funds for improvement become available.

In 1963 ALPA surveyed more than half of the 600 American airports used by scheduled flights at that time.* They found that fifty-two per cent had runway lighting and marking deficiencies; about half had taxiway deficiencies; seventy-six per cent lacked sufficient obstruction marking; half had insufficient snow removal equipment, and so on. The International Federation Airline Pilots' Association has long encouraged central reporting of near misses and serious deficiencies encountered by pilots en route to or at airports. The Association has then initiated remedial action and usually the suggestions have been welcome. In 1968 they started publishing regional deficiency lists — compiled by the regional vice-presidents — in *Aeroplane*.†

A yearly review of the situation will most probably urge the authorites to take preventive action — especially in cases

---

* Quoted by R. Serling: *The Probable Cause.*
† The first, about Europe and the Mediterranean area, was published on January 17, 1968.

like Salisbury, Rhodesia, where there was reluctance to install ILS and full approach lighting on their precision approach runway because *usually* the weather they have is above the airlines' minimum requirements.

CHAPTER FOURTEEN

COLLISION COURSE

A THOUSAND feet of height separated an EAL 'Connie' (Constellation) and a TWA 707 as they approached one another over a New York suburb on December 4, 1965. Between them they carried 112 people. Looking up from 10,000 feet, it *appeared* to the EAL pilot that they were on a collision course. He knew there was no time to hesitate over taking evasive action: he pulled up the nose to increase altitude rapidly — only to hit the 707. With magnificent airmanship, both pilots staggered towards the ground with their crippled planes. Although a considerable portion of its left wing was missing, and bits of the Connie were embedded in its fuselage, the 707 came down 11,000 feet and landed safely at Kennedy. The Connie almost made it. It crash-landed and burst into flames killing the pilot and three of the passengers. A year later, the CAB report concluded that cloud conditions had probably created an optical illusion of a collision being imminent.

'To investigate the circumstances of a collision is, in my opinion, the most sickening of all assignments,' said an officer of the German Luftwaffe. 'A collision needs split-second coincidences. People leave their homes thousands of miles apart, take two different flights only to keep a deadly rendezvous with millimetre precision.'

Collision is one of the growing menaces of aviation. It is more a question of prevention than investigation, and therefore a matter of money and inventive human ingenuity rather than of detective skill. It is the natural outcome of the rapid growth of traffic density within the limits of available space. (Although jets opened up the upper layers of the air for aviation, the space for climb, descent, holding and landing cannot be increased — only better utilised.) The merest glance at the prospects will explain the general concern. As usual, what now happens in America can soon be expected to happen in Europe, too, and therefore the American situation is most revealing.

The United States airline fleet was about 2,000 strong in 1967. FAA expected that by 1977 the number of airliners will have increased to approximately 3,500. Similarly huge growth was also predicted for the 'general aviation' (all civilian business, private, etc., aircraft). In 1967 there were some 104,000 aircraft in this fleet. In 1977 the expected number will be 180,000, including at least 8,000 business jets.* In addition there are all the military aircraft, which numbered about 50,000 in 1967. Twenty years earlier there were fewer than 30,000 aircraft flying in America. Judging from the experience of statistical predictions in other spheres, for instance population explosion or the expected growth of motoring, it is not unreasonable to assume that the aviation predictions will soon appear to be an underestimation.

During the past decade, the Air Traffic Control (ATC), by far the best safeguard against collisions, has developed tremendously. Yet less than half the number of airports used by scheduled airline services have control tower services, and only less than a fifth have terminal radar service. Even so, the likelihood of one airliner colliding with another is

* As summarised by Stuart G. Tipton, president of the Air Transport Association of America, when testifying before Congress on the subject of 'keeping aircraft apart'.

infinitely smaller than that of an airliner hitting a light private aircraft which is often flying uncontrolled, without a filed flight plan, cutting across the air corridors, and with an inexperienced pilot in the cockpit. It can be regarded as a miracle that even in the 1960's there have been so few collisions — but the writing is on the wall: in 1966, in America's crowded air corridors, there were almost 500 *reported* near-misses, and so the true number of these very hazardous situations is almost anybody's guess. William McKee, Administrator of the FAA, told a Congressional committee investigating the collision problem in 1967 that it was impossible 'to guarantee hundred per cent safe air as long as we have people who make mistakes'.

In Britain, a serious rise in the number of near-misses was reported in 1974. In Category A, (significant risk of collision), there was a twenty per cent increase. In Category B (two aircraft close enough to cause anxiety) the number of near-misses was up by almost thirty per cent.

Collision as the cause of an accident is abundantly evident in most such cases: two crippled aircraft land or crash in the same area within a short space of time, quite frequently observed as two merging blips on and then disappearing from a controller's radar screen; one wreckage contains embedded fragments of another aircraft; paint from another aircraft is smeared on pieces of wreckage; reconstructed parts of wings and fuselage show corresponding, positive-negative, damage marks. After the elimination of all other possible causes, like instrument malfunction or some failure that may have rendered the aircraft uncontrollable, attention is focused on two areas where the cause of a collision can usually be found: one is the *navigation* of the aircraft, and the other is the *ground control* including all assistance necessary to the correct navigation of a flight. Mistakes made in these fields may bring one or both aircrafts to a spot at a time where and when they are not supposed to be.

Apart from human error and malfunctioning and mis-readable instruments, sometimes even elementary mistakes affect navigation — for instance the wrong markings of maps used in private aircraft. After Lord Malcolm Douglas-Hamilton had crashed with a Beechcraft plane into Mount Cameroon in West Africa, and the wreckage had been found two years later, it was suggested that an intense magnetic field set up by a part of the mountain might have distorted radio signals and led him off course. On French maps, the area was classified as dangerous, but this was not communicated to international agencies, and so British and American maps, used by the pilot, were not marked to that effect. A recent American mid-air collision between a light aircraft and an airliner is still being investigated but a crash detective suspects that a radio beacon, constantly referred to by ground control, was not marked on the type of map one of the pilots was using. The flights were not observed by ground control because there was no radar at the airport.

How unreliable navigation still is when the crew are left mainly to their own devices has been best demonstrated during an international dispute over the busy North Atlantic route. There has never been a collision there because aircraft are separated in three ways: vertically (the routes stretch at 2,000 feet intervals above one another because especially over 30,000 feet, where the planes fly in thinner air and thus save fuel, the altimeters are liable to give increasingly erroneous readings), laterally (each corridor is 120 nautical miles wide), and in time (they must maintain their planned speed so that they will not catch up with or be caught up by another flight using the same corridor). By 1966 it was intended to reduce the lateral separation to ninety nautical miles so that, especially in peak periods, more aircraft could use the same volume of space simultaneously. A long struggle fought with determination and led by the pilots achieved the shelving of the plan until more reliable instruments and better navigational aids could be installed. Supporting evidence in the pilots' campaign revealed that for transatlantic jet flights it was quite common to *stray forty or fifty miles* off the planned course — and even hundred-mile unintentional detours had occurred. (In all, about thirty-four out of every thousand aircraft strayed from forty to a hundred miles off course.)

Air traffic control can steer aircraft into collision with equal ease. Automation of ground control has not kept pace with the growth of traffic so that frantic pressure on controllers in congested areas is often inevitable. The VC10 has extra safety in its ability to land more slowly than other big jets — this also enables it to go in to airports with shorter runways — but the pilot is often asked by controllers to 'hurry up a bit' and thus not to upset the faster traffic pattern.

Just as in the air, the likelihood of human error on the ground increases with the mounting work-load. Accident and incident (near-miss) investigations — mainly through checking records of information the pilots were furnished with, flight plan clearance, taped radio communications between the flight and the various ground services, etc. — have yielded a list of probable errors of vast variety. These ranged from a kind of 'operational Murphy's Law' (using antiquated direction-finding equipment, a controller at Carlisle gave a pilot a reciprocal bearing and sent the aircraft flying in almost exactly the opposite direction); through cases when wrong information, no information or considerably delayed information was given to the pilot about weather, visibility or traffic conditions (the TWA Connie and the UAL DC–7, which collided over the Grand Canyon on June 30, 1956, killing 128 people in the most unlikely circumstances — it happened in clear weather, at high altitude, away from congested areas — had both filed flight plans which showed they would meet over a check point, but nobody warned the pilots because nobody paid attention to the 'planned coincidence'); to cases in which overworked controllers had to work with stacks of high-speed jets but still used equipment designed for much lighter traffic and with systems which become a mesh of loopholes for errors when so stretched to the limit and beyond.

In the collision of a UAL DC–8 and a TWA Connie over Staten Island, New York, on December 16, 1960, again 128 people were aboard the two aircraft. There were no survivors. The DC–8, crashing into Sterling Place in Brooklyn, fatally injured six people on the ground, considerably damaged a dozen buildings, and narrowly avoided a school packed with children. The CAB report established that the UAL pilot had failed to notify the controller that some of his navigation instruments were faulty and he had strayed into an area 'beyond its clearance limit and the confines of the airspace allocated to the flight'. But it was not all that simple.

Critics of CAB had a better reason than ever before to suspect that the Board tried to shield FAA and its controllers. For the report included details like the radioed script of disaster on tape, which clearly showed that at least a share of responsibility for creating the hazardous situation had to be shouldered by the ground control service although the 'probable cause' laid all the blame at the UAL pilot's door.

It was the New York Air Route Traffic Control Center that conducted and cleared the descent of the UAL Flight 826. The controller was using an experimental short-cut in the air to speed up the operation. At 10.30 he cleared the flight to 'descend to and maintain 5,000 feet' and then asked 'Look like you'll be able to make Preston at 5,000?' According to *Time* magazine (January 2, 1961), the flight replied 'Will head it right on down; we'll dump it.' In the meantime, the TWA flight was controlled by LaGuardia tower during its slowed-down descent towards the airport.

The CAB report said that approximately one second past 10.33 the flight reported passing the 6,000 feet altitude. Seven seconds later the Center called '826, I'm sorry I broke you up, was that you reporting leaving 6,000 for 5,000?' Just as the pilot replied 'Affirmative', the TWA flight told LaGuardia that its altitude was now 5,500 feet. Not more than thirty seconds from disaster, the two flights and the two controllers still knew nothing about the proximity of the two aircraft.

Twelve seconds later, the New York Center gave its final instruction to Flight 826 and said *'Radar service is terminated'*. This was acknowledged with a 'Good day' by the UAL pilot who thought he was still *approaching* Preston, because at the very high speed he was still maintaining, and with one of his instruments inoperative (he had reported it to his company so that maintenance men could be alerted), he had no time to determine his real position. Twenty-eight seconds past 10.33 — eight seconds after radar service had allegedly been terminated — he called Idlewild (now Kennedy) Approach Control and said 'Approaching Preston at 5,000'. Meanwhile, unknown to him, LaGuardia gave warnings to the TWA pilot about some unidentified 'jet traffic off your right'. The LaGuardia controller saw the intruding blip on his radar screen.

At 10.33 and 33 seconds, the man at LaGuardia heard 'a noise similar to that caused by an open microphone' which lasted for some six seconds. Contact was lost with the TWA aircraft. Also at 10.33 and 33 seconds, Idlewild began to give the UAL aircraft twenty-one seconds of landing instructions. But these were never acknowledged.

The Preston marker, en route for New York, and the route to LaGuardia are separated by a 'no-man's-land' which is like the grass barrier between motorways running in the opposite directions. It was this zone that had been crossed by the UAL flight to the point of the collision. On its actual route this was some eleven miles beyond Preston. If, for argument's sake, the UAL flight was *only* one mile from Preston when calling Idlewild, it would have had to fly twelve miles to the collision site in less than ten seconds — which is an impossible, hypersonic speed of at least 4,300 miles per hour! Such considerations make it obvious that during both contacts — the last with New York and the first and last with Idlewild — the UAL aircraft *was already well beyond Preston*. Had the New York controller really been watching it on radar, until termination of service, the navigational error would undoubtedly have been spotted. At that time, the controller was not bound by regulation to make a radar hand-over to his colleague at Idlewild — not to terminate service until Idlewild had identified the flight on its own radar — but investigators, who disagreed with the CAB finding, claimed that he had a moral obligation to use his discretion and not to let the aircraft out of sight especially on this occasion when an experimental short-cut was used.

At a staggering cost, a long series of recommended improvements in ground control followed the collision. Speed limits near airports, new equipment, and rules to achieve more precise control were among them. The investigations, research and statistical evaluation defined the most collision-prone situations. As expected, this occurred mainly in congested areas (near airports at low speeds) and to aircraft which had filed no flight plans, flew under Visual Flight Rules, in good weather, without utilising ground control assistance even if it was available. But the constantly recurring questions remained unanswered at least initially: couldn't the pilots see one another? Couldn't they make use of the original basic 'see-and-avoid' principle, the do-it-yourself system of averting collisions?

The mounting work-load for pilots near airports explained that they had less and less time to look out for other aircraft. But perhaps the greatest discovery made by research connected with collision investigations was the realisation of the fact that even the pilots' exceptionally good eyesight could not be relied on as a safeguard against high-speed collisions, because the capabilities of the machines have surpassed the limited adaptability of human physiology and the speed of the brain working as a computer.

A few points will demonstrate the magnitude of the problem. Table 1 was presented at a University of Southern California Institute of Aerospace Safety course. The part dealing with reaction times comes from the U.S. Naval Aviation Safety Bulletin. On the left it shows examples of the 'closure speed' of two aircraft (the sum of speeds at which they fly) and the number of seconds needed to travel various distances (marked in the first column). The box on the right gives the time needed for perception, decision and response. If two aircraft approach one another at 200 and 160 mph, closure speed is 360 mph. At that speed, supposing that the pilot of an airliner can spot the 'speck of dirt in the sky' — what a fighter aircraft appears to be ten miles away (the images in the middle) — and accepting that he can recognise that they are on a collision course, he will have a *hundred seconds to take evasive action.*

The 'recognition and reaction times' appear to be somewhat optimistic. To 'see object' or 'the time it takes to transmit the image from the retina to his brain'* takes a tenth of a second but only if the pilot is *already* looking in exactly that direction and focusing on that distance. If he notices 'something' only from the corner of his eye, it will take him almost half a second to look, focus and 'see object'. These

* Why Mid-Air Collisions? The Role of Vision. Lecture at the above course by Earl J. Ends, Ph.D. Head, Human Factors Engineering. Lockheed-California Company.

TABLE 1

CLOSURE SPEED			
DISTANCE BETWEEN TWO AIRCRAFT	960 mph	600 mph	360 mph
	COLLISION IN SECONDS		
10 m	37.5	60	100
6 m	22.5	36	60
5 m	18.75	30	50
4 m	15	24	40
3 m	11.25	18	30
2 m	7.5	12	20
1 m	3.75	6	10
½ m	1.8	3	5

RECOGNITION AND REACTION TIMES
IN SECONDS

SEE OBJECT	0.1
RECOGNISE AIRCRAFT	1.0
BECOME AWARE OF COLLISION COURSE	5.0
DECISION TO TURN LEFT OR RIGHT	4.0
MUSCULAR REACTION	0.4
AIRCRAFT LAGTIME	2.0
TOTAL	12.5

tenths of seconds increase the hazard considerably because if the closure speed is 1,200 mph, during the 0·1 second of 'see object' the distance between them will decrease by 176 feet, and as it takes at least a second to 'recognise aircraft', during the perception process 1,840 feet of the separating distance will be lost.

A further limitation of the human eye (already referred to in Chapter Eleven) is the 'empty field myopia' — the normal tendency of the eye is to focus for near vision when looking at the empty sky. Even in most favourable conditions, to notice something 'right in front' of the pilot but at a great distance may thus take a considerable time and encroach on the safety margin. Another additional problem is easily demonstrated by looking at books on a shelf only a few feet away. Without *any* eye movement, one can read the title of only one or — depending on the distance — two books. This is because full clarity of sight exists only along the central vision axis. Off this axis on either side, vision deteriorates rapidly. The aircraft that can be noticed ten miles away if it appears along the centre line of the pilot's eyes fixed 'dead ahead' will be noticed only when it is one mile away if it approaches ten degrees off the axis and less than half a mile away if it comes at thirty degrees to either side. Scanning the sky regularly is some protection against these vision limitations — if the pilots have the time and if there is a brightly contrasting background in perfect visibility.

Thus to entrust human eyes with guarding the lives of millions of passengers would be absolutely criminal. Nobody in the world has such ideas, particularly in these days when the closure speed of two Concordes will be almost 3,000 mph (The American supersonics will be even faster.) Automation of air traffic control is on its way, and some equipment, which almost seem to be the figments of a science fiction writer's imagination, is available or being developed. Like the automatic landing device, these could relieve the pilot of the duty of looking through his windscreen at all.

Since 1956 and the disaster over the Grand Canyon, giant steps have been taken to reduce the collision hazard. The cost of this progress must be approaching the one billion dollar mark in America alone. There is still room for better prevention methods through further reorganisation of air traffic, restriction and better control of military flights and light aircraft movement, but now, with the airspace crowded and an 'air traffic explosion' imminent, vast sources of funds — to be calculated in billions — are needed to install all the technically already-viable safeguards like the search radar system. Will voters and their governments be willing to foot the enormous bills?

In this respect, not all the omens are good. While a considerable research effort goes into finding out what will happen when a supersonic airliner collides with millions of raindrops — at a special 'firing range' at Farnborough, Andrew Fyall, a principal scientific officer, shoots supersonic bullets at single raindrops — another type of mid-air collision is still being combated sometimes with the most primitive methods. This type of collision takes place between aircraft and birds.

As the investigation of several accidents and numerous incidents shows, *birdstrike* is not a hazard to be ignored. First windscreens were reinforced against the shattering impact of birdstrikes. Then it was found that jet engines would ingest gulls and other birds at low level. When that happens in a critical moment, the momentary loss of power can have disastrous consequences. A Lockheed Electra of EAL hit a flock of starlings during take-off at Boston in 1960. The engines swallowed some birds and the plane crashed. Sixty-one people of the seventy-two aboard were killed. Crash detectives found the cause when dismantling the engines. In 1966 a military aircraft over Germany was endangered by a mouse: coming down through 1,000 feet, the plane was on collision course with an eagle that carried the mouse in its beak. The eagle released the mouse directly into the No. 2 engine. The pilot managed to land safely.

In America alone, the yearly number of birdstrikes approaches the 2,000 mark and some of them cause injuries or even fatal crashes. The U.S. Air Force estimates that birdstrike damage repairs — engines and surfaces — cost about ten million dollars a year. In Canada, at least five military jets have been destroyed by birds in two years. In France, a military aircraft hit a flock of geese at 700 mph. The multi-impacts tore off parts of the wings, dented the fuselage, shattered the windscreen and knocked out the pilot who luckily regained consciousness in time to execute a crash landing. In the same year, 1966, a vulture hit a Pakistani Airlines helicopter which crashed near Faridpur, East Pakistan, killing twenty-three of the twenty-seven people on board. But perhaps the least expected type of crash occurred on November 23, 1962, 6,500 feet up; a UAL Viscount hit a sixteen pound whistling swan and the pilot never had a chance to save his passengers. Said Ed Slattery of the NTSB: 'We found the tail separated from the rest of the wreckage. The carcass, embedded in it, had found its way to the most vulnerable point of the aircraft. It broke and jammed the elevator controls so that an uncontrollable dive began. It happened in a spring migratory area frequented by birds in other seasons, too. The pilot had received a bird-warning just prior to impact but the swan must have come too fast for him to do anything about it.'

Now, at last, the crash detectives' reports are being taken more seriously and some funds are available for research. Designers give aircraft extra strength to withstand the terrific blows. Radar can spot large flocks but a single large bird, if it flies at altitudes where jets go at high speed, can cause very grave damage. In Canada, ornithological forecasts — based on radar observations and assisted by meteorologists because birds fly with tail winds and follow the pressure patterns — have achieved an accuracy of seventy per cent in the autumn and eighty-three per cent during spring. And now the British RAF, which has to fork out a million pounds a year to pay for bird damage to aircraft, is also urged to have daily forecasts of bird movements.

Although only exceptional cases, like the Viscount crash in America, can combat the general belief that civilian aircraft fly high enough to be safe from birds, it could be argued that airliners are as much exposed to birdstrike during take-off and landing as are fighters. And yet the methods of protection are primitive. Boston, for instance, is still an airport where pilots are constantly warned about the hazard of birdstrike; on Midway Island, the U.S. Navy, in despair, still have to shell albatross flocks with mortar fire — in vain because the birds keep returning to nest along the runways; some airfields still record birds' alarm calls which they relay through loudspeakers and hope the birds will escape; and at Lossiemouth, in Morayshire, 'Ailsa' the falcon, sole survivor of a squadron of six, is still the most effective guard of the Fleet Air Arm base against seagulls. Crash detectives wonder if we really must wait for another 'spectacular' disaster before more is done to prevent birdstrike.

CHAPTER FIFTEEN

MEDICAL CRASH DETECTIVES

Two pilots and a mechanic were killed, trapped in their seats, as the Alpha crashed and sank into Bowery Bay while trying to return to New York on a training flight. The death of the men was bad enough news to their families but, in the event, it was made even worse by the implication that they had died in the stupor of their drunkenness. The Queens County Medical Examiner's autopsy report stated beyond any doubt that the men's brain tissues and various organs contained a very high percentage of alcohol. Friends', colleagues' and relatives' testimony defending the men's reputation of sobriety was brushed aside by the shocked and furious District Attorney who was, quite understandably, convinced by the autopsy that the men must have been completely under the influence of drink during the flight. He demanded at the public hearing that all crews should be checked thoroughly before take-off.

Robert Chrisp, the investigator in charge (now retired), had only opinions to support his hunch that something must have been wrong with the post mortem which was then, in 1947, a novelty in crash investigation. Ed Slattery, who was working with him on the case, recalled: 'He talked to dozens of people who had met the pilots in the twenty-four hours before the crash. Wives, relatives and friends accounted for all their activities and denied any drinking. We traced their movements at the airport: dispatch and weather briefing officers, a ground inspector and some two dozen airport employees claimed that they had talked to the crew before the flight, and there had been no chance for any sign of even slight tipsiness to go undetected. An instructor had briefed the pilots about the purpose of the training flight — the use of some complicated novel blind flying instruments. He said the crew had gone through a very complex check-list with him which they could not have done if their mental alertness had been impaired in any way. All these people also testified that it would have been impossible for the crew to take any liquor aboard undetected. Their testimony drove Chrisp on and on looking for a clue.'

The search led him on dangerous ground. For even though it was accepted that the men could not have carried drink on board, there were ten to twenty-gallon tanks behind their seats containing alcoholic fluid for windshield de-icing. This used to be ordinary grain alcohol but due to a regulation issued much earlier it had to be replaced by iso-propyl, a more effective chemical. And isopropyl was un-drinkable. Divers went down to search for the tanks under the water, but what they found was very disappointing: all tanks had been ruptured forward and the contents had drained away. This suggested that the men, sitting right in front of the tanks, had been drowned in the fluid and that — not drinking — could account for the saturation of their lung and brain tissues. Some specialists whom CAB consulted accepted this theory — others refuted it. All Chrisp needed now was proof that the tanks had contained isopropyl and not grain alcohol. But a painstaking review of all the aircraft's maintenance records led to yet another bitter disillusionment: the order that had required the intro-duction of isopropyl permitted the use of grain alcohol as long as the airlines' existing stocks lasted. Several aircraft, like this one, hardly ever needed to use de-icer fluid — and now it was found that these tanks had last been refilled with grain alcohol.

The CAB now hired a medical specialist who conducted a

series of laboratory tests. Tanks were filled with seawater and alcohol was released into them. Mice were thrown in and drowned while being exposed to the stream of escaping alcohol. Like the men in Bowery Bay, the mice were left lying in the tanks for several hours. The result showed that the lung and brain tissues of the mice had absorbed a great quantity of alcohol faster than the sea would be able to dilute it. This evidence finally convinced the District Attorney and the crew were exonerated.

Today it is most unlikely that such a false charge could be levelled. This is partly because modern methods of detection (gas chromatography) are widely available — and partly because aviation pathology, the work of the 'medical crash detective' who can correlate aviation with medicine as well as the circumstances of accidents with injuries and pre-crash human conditions, has grown into a specialist job in its own right. In America it was, in fact, the Bowery Bay crash that greatly urged the development of the CAB human factors group and the regular participation of pathologists in the team-work of investigators.

The search for traces of alcohol in the tissues and blood of aircrews is now a standard feature of *airline* accident investigation although no major carrier has ever had a crash in which crew drunkenness could be suspected even as a contributory cause. (All respectable airlines insist on their pilots' complete abstention for at least eight hours before flying — some airlines require from ten to twelve hours — so that alcohol should be eliminated from their systems.) In several countries, however, there is still a great deal of objection to autopsy on religious grounds.

The role of alcohol in *general aviation* crashes throughout the world has been mentioned in many cases. How much inconsiderate carelessness is involved has been demonstrated by the frequency of such occurrences and by the high level of alcohol found in the blood. Autopsies were performed on 900 of the pilots killed in American light aircraft crashes — and a third of them had alcohol in the blood representing from two to ten or more drinks! If one considers that the number of mid-air collisions in general aviation operations was twenty-six in 1965 — compared with twelve in 1964 — stringent regulations appear to be overdue to protect the air carriers, too, from drunken pleasure flyers.

In Britain, when a Cessna aircraft crashed near Biggleswade, Bedfordshire, in June 1966, killing the pilot and injuring three passengers as well as striking three motor cars in which two spectators were killed and four injured, the pilot's blood contained twice as much alcohol as the legal level above which car drivers are convicted automatically. Witnesses testified that although he had been drinking brandy and beer during the day and at a refreshment tent immediately before the flight when he said 'We will now go and give the Cessna a thrashing', nothing in his speech or manner indicated that he was under the influence of alcohol. But the autopsy told the investigators that his skill 'was significantly impaired by the effects of alcohol' at a moment when control was lost and appropriate corrective action needed to be taken at once to avoid the crash.

The medical crash detective, like the rest of the investigators, will usually try to raise and answer the question 'why'. Although many specialists would probably disagree with the conclusions drawn by Dr. Stanley R. Mohler of FAA, it is interesting to note how the pathologists', statisticians' and, for instance, weather experts' findings pose problems which require further inquiries by the psychologist — still within the framework of crash investigation.

Dr. Mohler claimed, according to the *Washington Post* in October, 1967, that 'Accident is defined as "unplanned occurrence". We think most of these crashes (of small planes) are deliberate at the unconscious level.' He referred to investigations which had shown that psychological factors were

305

involved in about ninety per cent of these accidents. Almost a third of such crashes occurred in 'unwarranted low-level manoeuvres' or 'buzz jobs' which were aggressive acts to harass somebody; and almost another third were due to pilots taking off in face of 'extremely adverse' weather forecasts, a defiance which could be regarded as a sign of subconscious suicidal tendencies. He claimed that some men learn flying to counterbalance feelings of sexual inadequacy, regard their planes as 'mistress symbols' and for them 'not to fly may be tantamount to rejection by one's mistress'. An emotionally insecure pilot is more likely to become unduly frightened in the air, and he will probably use alcohol to suppress his fears without realising that it will cost him the sharpness of his skill and reflexes — to a greater extent in the air than behind the wheel of his car because of the specially increased effect of alcohol at high altitudes.

Alcohol is, of course, only one — and, in the case of accidents to airliners, only a minor — hazard among many medical crash detectives must keep in mind. Strangely enough, the importance of their work has really been largely understood only since the mid-1950's. Because of their unique source of experience — for instance supersonic military aircraft fly well before such civilian transport, and the military accident rate is higher than the civilian — military institutes of aviation pathology, which tend to take the initiative in research, are also entrusted with handling the majority of civilian accident investigations.

Unfortunately, many authorities still fail to alert pathologists in time to be among the first at the scene of accidents. This often leads to destruction of medical clues and makes the identification of bodies — done with the aid of dentists and radiologists — immensely difficult. Even in ICAO countries, where local officials have learned how to handle and preserve wreckage, bodies are still not recognised as evidence. Burial may be urged and hastened for

306

sociological reasons and the sake of public health (heat, humidity, etc.), bodies are removed from the scene without their positions being mapped, then stripped of identifying personal effects without any record, and, in an African case, for instance, even relatives searching for a local passenger were permitted to handle the bodies.

Apart from comparatively minor problems like giving information to solicitors and helping them to establish, for reasons of legal claims, who of the same family died first in the same accident — the husband might have been killed on impact whereas the wife might have been incapacitated but alive for another thirty seconds — the medical investigator has two main areas of concern: (1) to help the rest of the team in finding the probable *cause of the accident* after the elimination of possible causes; and (2) to establish the immediate cause of injury to or death of each person aboard — for example metal frame of back of seat gashed face of passenger who had been thrown forward — so that the *survivability of accidents* could be studied and increased. In both these areas medical investigators accumulate a great deal of data which on the basis of a single case may seem insignificant but through long-term research may open up new avenues of accident and injury prevention.

The aviation pathologists' work is based on four major steps: identification (using all possible aids like scars of an earlier operation, clothing, jewellery, etc.), a full external and internal examination (in order to establish the nature of injuries, cause and if possible timing of death, and, especially in the case of crew, to trace the presence of any pre-crash injury or natural disease), the removal of specimens from all major organs for laboratory examination (still searching for signs of disease), and specimens for toxicological analysis (level of carbon-monoxide, drugs which may reveal illnesses that help identification or, in the case of pilots, may give clues, like the presence of barbiturates or alcohol, to the cause of the accident). Throughout this process the closest possible co-operation must be maintained with all other members of the team because even the least significant fragment of technical information or detail of the flight history may provide a clue, say, to a particular injury and vice versa. This co-operation is what turns the aviation pathologist, a man with combined medical and aeronautical knowledge, into a medical investigator of accidents who will hardly ever provide the complete solution of a case but will often make a most remarkable contribution by eliminating causes or providing vital supporting evidence.

It would be impossible here to give a full survey of this work but a few examples, described briefly or in some detail, will demonstrate how the medical crash detective helps to determine the cause of an accident.

One of the most obvious examples is the case of suspected sabotage (mentioned in Chapter Four), but the medical evidence often helps only to eliminate this explanation by, say, showing that the madman who was allegedly on board did *not* shoot the pilot. When in 1961, a DC–6B crashed at Ndola, Rhodesia, sabotage was immediately suspected for Dag Hammarskjold and his party of fifteen were the victims. An RAF scientist who assisted the local pathologists to investigate the case,* recorded that all bodies were X-rayed, and metallic objects were found in six of them. In two bodies there were bullets. This needed closer attention, but it was found that the bullets lay superficially in tissues near the skin, the wounds were not associated with any discernible bleeding, there was no sign of shots being fired, 'and, perhaps most important of all, [the bullets] were accompanied by percussion caps and debris of disintegrated cartridge cases'. This proved that the bullets had not been fired by any firearm. Both men were soldiers who carried

* Lecture at British Association of Forensic Medicine, July, 1967.

308

magazines of ammunition which exploded in the post-crash fire so that bullets *and* cartridge cases penetrated the bodies.

Medical investigation can give a great deal of evidence of fire in the air in the same way as it proves (as seen in Chapter six with considerable certainty whether a person on board was already dead or not when affected by post-crash fire. But carbon-monoxide poisoning, if post-crash contamination in fire can be eliminated, may even indicate a technical cause of the accident: an engine defect that may affect the pilot adversely in some older or military aircraft. Over fifty per cent of carbon-monoxide in the blood would render him unconscious. In June, 1967, a twenty-five-year-old DC–4 of Air Ferry crashed into a mountain near Perpignan, France, killing 88 people. It had deviated from its usual coastal route for charter flights. The navigation error was obvious ... but was it due to pilot error or lack of ground aids? The French Ministry of Transport investogators found another explanation: a high level of carbon-monoxide in the blood of the crew was due to old cracks in a heater from which fumes had entered the cockpit impairing the judgment of the pilots, who thus failed to notice the navigation error.

Medical evidence may be vital concerning events on board before a crash. When an airliner hit the side of a mountain after the pilot had radioed to the ground that his intention was to stay at a safe altitude waiting for expected weather improvement and not to descend through clouds, the possible explanation of the crash was that the descent had been due to a sudden loss of control. The medical investigator reasoned that if there had been sudden loss of control, it must have thrown at least some of the eighty-two passengers about inside the cabin. This would have caused non-lethal bony injuries, with fat and bone marrow being carried by the bloodstream into the lungs (pulmonary embolism). Lung specimens were taken from a representative thirty per cent of the people aboard but full histological examination showed no sign of any embolic phenomena in anybody before the impact caused *immediate* lethal injuries to all. A medical investigator reported in the above-quoted lecture that 'while by no means conclusive, this provided evidence to offer to the Commission of Inquiry suggesting that the aircraft's descent had not been due to loss of control with consequent violent change in attitude, and supplemented non-medical evidence suggesting a deliberate descent'.

Clothing, too, must always be examined in the light of the medical investigator's experience. This may give an indication of events on board before the crash. For example, 'the condition of the shoes may give evidence of pilot control at the time of an impact accident, the heels of the shoes or boots being commonly wrenched backwards if the feet are on the rudder controls'.*

Sudden incapacitation of the pilot is always uppermost in the medical crash detective's mind and the search for any sign of pre-existing disease is a major part of the routine, but the discovery of some illness in the deceased is no more significant than the discovery of some metal fatigue is to the technical investigator: both may or may not be pointers to the cause of the accident. It is the particular set of circumstances that determines the importance of such findings.

The crew of the Lockheed Electra (American Flyers Airline Corporation) reported for duty at Ardmore, Oklahoma, at 4.30 on the morning of April 22, 1966. With two captains, a first officer, an engineer and two stewardesses on board, the aircraft flew to Lawton, Oklahoma, to pick up some soldiers and take them on a military charter flight to McChord, Washington. Then it made another ferry flight to Monterey, California, from where it was to make a second

* Aviation Accident Pathology. See Bibliography.

military charter flight, to Columbus, Georgia, with a crew change and refuelling stop back at Ardmore. At Monterey, all the ninety-two passenger seats were occupied by soldiers, and so when a new flight engineer joined the crew, the original flight engineer had to take the only remaining jump seat — and one of the two captains had to return to Ardmore by another flight. It was perhaps a slight inconvenience to him, but it saved his life.

Captain Reed W. Pigman, the man remaining in charge, was also the founder and president of the airline. He had logged 16,247 flying hours. The flight was rather uneventful until the descent to Ardmore. Approaching the airport in poor weather, the pilot made a sudden last-minute change in his choice of runway for landing. This was at 20.29. One minute later, the Electra crashed into high ground. All crew members, the man in the jump seat, and seventy-four passengers were killed outright and three of the eighteen initial survivors died subsequently of injuries. The aircraft was destroyed by impact and fire.

Thomas Saunders and his CAB GO team were on their way without delay but the weather was deteriorating and their aircraft had to divert to an Air Force base ninety-five miles away in Texas from where they returned by bus. They reached the scene of the accident only at dawn the following morning — with practically minutes to spare before a local mortician completed the embalming of the pilot's body. 'We had to invoke a then new federal law which authorised us to order autopsies,' said Saunders. 'In the strange circumstances of the accident — survivors could not recall experiencing any negative or positive "g" force just as if nobody had tried to avert disaster — I would have wanted post mortems anyway. But now that somebody had ordered the removal of the body and the embalming without authority, I wanted a post mortem even more.

'As I saw the hands of the pilots, another oddity struck

me. The co-pilot's thumbs were broken in a way that could be the probable result of holding something when the impact came. I knew that the Armed Forces Institute of Pathology had studied some two thousand such cases and I was anxious to get them to look at these bodies particularly as the captain's hands showed no such sign of holding the controls. Although I knew that some pilots would grab something when crashing while others' natural reaction would be to raise the arms in defence of the face, it looked possible that the co-pilot was flying the aircraft. Why would the captain let the less experienced man do the landing in bad weather? In addition to that, from witness accounts and survivors' scarce recollections it occurred to me that *nobody* was perhaps in active control of the plane. Why?

'Together with my team, I was determined to get Dr. Stembridge, one of our most outstanding pathologists, to Ardmore, but because of some communications breakdown he was delayed. While Dr. Rose from Parkland Hospital, Dallas, began the autopsies — the same man who prepared the post mortem on President Kennedy until it was decided to transfer the body to Bethesda Naval Hospital, Maryland, and who later did the autopsies on Oswald and Ruby — we proceeded with the rest of the investigation which yielded further unusual clues. In the wreckage of the lower forward baggage compartment we found a pills container, paper tape and an empty medicine bottle labelled with the captain's name.'

The technical investigation showed a few insignificant deficiencies — it was a bitter disappointment that the flight recorder was found to have been inoperative during the flight and the accident — which could not suggest any explanation of the crash. But the medical investigation disclosed some startling facts. Although fifty-nine-year-old Captain Pigman's last first-class medical certificate, dated exactly two months before the crash, only specified that he must

312

wear glasses while flying, the autopsy showed a very serious heart condition (coronary heart disease and 'severe and very vast coronary arteriosclerosis') of long duration. At the public hearing, pathologists found it impossible to state with absolute certainty whether it was the heart disease or the crash injuries that had actually killed the pilot. But they could testify without doubt that in the absence of injuries death would certainly be attributed to coronary insufficiency, and that at such advanced state of the disease sudden incapacitation, collapse and death within seven to twelve seconds would be highly probable particularly under conditions of physical or mental stress which occur during take-off and landing (higher blood pressure, increased pulse rate and respiration, etc.).

And that was not all. Toxicological examination, analysis of some residue in the prescription bottle, the identification of the paper tape as a container of tablets for testing the sugar level in urine, and, above all, Captain Pigman's medical record — obtained by court order from his personal physician — proved a long history of heart disease and diabetes. At his semi-annual checkups, part of the airline pilot licence requirements, the captain always denied that he had ever had either disease and that he had consulted a physician or was under medication. The heart disease had been concealed for nineteen years (it had become increasingly severe in the last three years with symptoms culminating towards the time of his last visit to his private doctor eleven days prior to the crash) and, regarding his diabetes, his medical record had been falsified by negative answers to the FAA doctor for three and a half years. The diabetes was apparently controlled by some prescriptions, but the heart condition required an increasing dosage of nitroglycerin and similar drugs.

The grave heart condition which could cause sudden incapacitation (the captain might have suffered severe pain in the chest, slumped over the wheel rolling the aircraft slowly into an excessive rate of bank or fallen back in the seat allowing the same roll to take place) put renewed emphasis on the hand and arms injuries suffered by the co-pilot but not by the captain. Some medical investigators find such evidence inadmissible in certain circumstances, but nobody disputed the opinion formed by a pathologist of great experience — according to the CAB report, he had performed autopsies on over 2,000 aircrash victims — that 'the fractured condition of the first officer's hands and arms was of such a nature that it indicated he had control of the aircraft and had his hands on the controls at the time of the impact'.

However definite, all this medical evidence was not acceptable as the cause of the accident until the rest of the investigation could confirm all the details and rule out any other possible explanation, such as turbulence or altimeter error. On the basis of actual and corroborated evidence, the final moments could be reconstructed only in one way: 'It is probable that the captain entered a standard rate turn to the right in preparation for making a downwind leg for landing on runway 30. While turning through a heading of 142 degrees, the captain may have collapsed permitting the aircraft to enter a sink rate of 1,950 feet per minute.

'The first officer, who was probably looking out of the right window and keeping the field in sight, may have been warned of the event by the flight engineer, or noticed the change in attitude. His immediate reaction would have been to grab the control wheel and order more power. (It has been established that power was applied and the aircraft was rotated nose up immediately prior to impact.) It would take approximately three to five seconds for the first officer to respond effectively and grasp the controls. An additional one and a half seconds would be required for the aircraft to respond and rotate through an attitude of twelve degrees.

314

Since it would take approximately six seconds to descend' at the above-mentioned sink rate from the flight path of the aircraft to the altitude of high ground below, the recovery time was not enough to avoid the impact.

Undoubtedly, it was a most disturbing case. Not only because it did happen, but also because in everybody's mind it raised the question: *could it happen again?* Invariably, whenever the author repeated this question to licensing authorities, doctors and airline officials in numerous countries, the somewhat reluctantly given answer was 'yes'. Heart disease is often 'silent': normal electrocardiograph tracing may be recorded and there may be a complete lack of symptoms so that the pilot has nothing to report even though the condition may already be potentially incapacitating. (Such was the case when a BOAC pilot died at the controls, but — luckily for the public — it happened during a training flight.) The letter written by William McKee, Administrator of FAA, to the Chairman of CAB is most revealing.*

'. . . The problem of early detection of coronary disease is, of course, one that confronts the medical profession in general. Unfortunately the state of the art of diagnosing this condition leaves a great deal to be desired . . .' What Captain Pigman and his physician knew about the symptoms 'would have declared him ineligible to hold an airman certificate. Failure of the pilot to disclose this information, by falsification of his applications for medical certificates, denied us the most important tool for the diagnosis of these conditions, namely, an accurate medical history . . . Treating physicians are now under an obligation to their patients not to reveal to others information they obtain in the course of the physician–patient relationship. We are exploring the possibility of seeing the removal of any legal restraints which now prevent physicians from reporting, in the public

* May 23, 1966; attachment 3 in Ardmore accident report.

interest, information of vital importance to the maintenance of aviation safety . . .'

This latter point is, of course, a very long shot, but it would certainly deserve more attention because the debate, even after it started in earnest, would be vehement and possibly endless. Medical investigators, on the other hand, stated most emphatically — both in literature and interviews — that the problem must be kept in perspective and *heart diseases as an aviation hazard must not be overstressed* mainly for two reasons.

One is that the majority of people, especially over forty, have some unnoticed or unrecognised heart disease, about a quarter of these may even need treatment when the condition becomes known, but most will live with it and experience none of its effects. (In America, where coronary disease is the most common cause of death among males, about sixty per cent of male bodies show some evidence of it on autopsy, and it is fairly widespread even among younger men, said the FAA letter. About half of those who have heart attacks have no prior history of symptoms, but — and this is where pilots bear a tremendous responsibility — sudden death is ten times more likely to come to those with earlier symptoms than to those who had no previous evidence of coronary disease.) It happens therefore very frequently that some evidence of coronary disease which is found at autopsy is proved to be — after the elimination of other causes and examination of all circumstances — even a contributory factor in an aviation accident, although such a heart condition is often discovered when death and the accident are due to other causes.

The other reason why the hazard should not be overemphasised is that pilots belong to one of the healthiest categories of the population and are under regular, strict supervision.

Admittedly, in both these ways of reasoning there are

316

loopholes: it is possible that under stress a young man of apparently excellent health with no previous symptoms will suddenly drop dead at the controls of an aircraft from some patchy inflammation of the heart, a condition with which another man might live to be a hundred. So crash detectives are greatly concerned with the degree of likelihood of such an unlikely death becoming the cause of an accident. In short, the chances are infinitely small in passenger-carrying air transport.

The above FAA letter mentioned that on the basis of statistical estimation 'approximately three U.S. pilots will die in flight in air carrier operations each year', but airlines which have medical departments (the biggest carriers) are more likely to be forewarned of the disease in a pilot than are smaller companies, and records clearly indicate that even if a pilot on duty is killed by coronary disease, death will have to come within a very few critical seconds — as at Ardmore — to cause a crash. (Until this case, there had been only one U.S. airline accident, the Constellation, Flying Tiger Line, Burbank, California, December 14, 1962, attributed to heart disease, but it had been a suspected factor in another three cases.)

If the pilot became incapacitated at any other time apart from those few critical seconds, disaster could most probably be averted. When on February 25, 1966, a Braniff BAC One-eleven with fifty-four passengers had just touched down under the captain's control at O'Hare, Chicago, 'CAPTAIN YELLED TO F/O (First Officer) "YOU GOT IT" THEN BECAME INCAPACITATED. F/O REQUESTED AMBULANCE TO MEET AIRCRAFT AND TAXIED TO GATE. CAPTAIN TAKEN TO RESURRECTION HOSPITAL 7435 WEST TALCOTT CHICAGO WHERE HE WAS PRONOUNCED DEAD ON ARRIVAL' (From Telex to CAB).

Perhaps one of the most dramatic situations of this nature occurred aboard a KLM DC–8 only 150 feet and 30 seconds from touchdown at Haneda International Airport, Tokyo, on the night of August 7, 1966. The co-pilot, Cornelius de Jager, was reading out the approach bearings when Captain de Groot failed to acknowledge. He glanced at the captain, saw him slump forward and — most probably like the co-pilot at Ardmore — acted instinctively in taking over the controls, applying full power and lifting the nose of the aircraft. The difference was that de Jager had a few more seconds to spare. The airliner climbed away safely. At 3,000 feet up, while the DC–8 was on auto-pilot, the crew lifted the captain from his seat and gave oxygen. It was too late — the forty-eight-year-old captain had died of heart attack. He had passed his last six-monthly medical check only five weeks earlier. The fifty-six passengers knew nothing of the emergency when they landed seventeen minutes behind schedule.

One of the numerous controversial issues raised by the BEA Trident (call-sign Papa India) accident at Staines, 1972, was the dead captain's seriously abnormal heart condition. It was revealed by the autopsy. Several leading cardiologists participated in the investigation and they all agreed that under physical or emotional stress (plenty of which must have affected the captain on that fatal day before and during the flight), his weakened blood vessels had ruptured and the resulting haemorrhage had probably caused some 'disturbance of thought processes'. (The effect might have ranged from slight indigestion type pain to collapse, unconsciousness, blood and oxygen starvation of the brain and death at the controls.) The investigators concluded that one of the underlying causes of the accident was the captain's abnormal heart condition 'leading to lack of concentration and impaired judgment sufficient to account for his toleration of the speed error and (possibly) his retraction of or order to retract the droops in mistake for the flaps.'

What the specialists could not fully agree on were the

318

answers to the two essential questions: could this heart condition be recognised in time, and what could be done to prevent a recurrence?

An American cardiologist claimed that the captain's medical record (electrocardiograms) would have told him about the abnormality. His eminent British colleagues dismissed this: those ECG readings would have alerted no medical authority. Some specialists believed that the ordinary 'resting' cardiogram was insufficient to reveal such heart conditions (perfectly true in this case), and advocated the 'stress test' (readings taken after some rather strenuous exercise) which was, in turn, held in contempt by their opponents as unreliable and of little value. (No country insists upon stress testing for pilots although a couple of American airlines had already introduced it as part of the standard medical examination.)

The final report could only recommend that the development of the stress testing technique should be kept under constant review so that eventually, when it became more reliable, it should be utilised. Until then, however, only better training, alertness and the specific preparedness of the rest of the crew for pilot incapacitation can protect passengers in those few seconds between a captain's heart attack and disaster.

Beside heart disease there are some other illnesses which may attack without any previous warning and which may cause a sudden collapse or even incapacitation — for instance the rupture of an artery in the skull has struck down young men; the infiltration of air in the chest cavity may cause pain in the chest, lead to the collapse of the lungs and may even be incapacitating — but these occur very infrequently and there has been no record of any of them causing an air accident. That is why medical investigators seem to become much more worried about illness causing *partial incapacitation.*

Whenever the skill of an airline pilot is doubted, and even when it is only suspected that a pilot has not been in 'top form' to deal, say, with an emergency, medical crash detectives and human factors specialists are increasingly convinced that the key to the case may be buried far away from the accident scene, somewhere in the background of the pilot, in his private life, in the school report of his child or in the bad mood of his wife, or other trivial causes. The suicide rate among airline pilots is extremely low and so it is most unlikely that any of them would want to conceal heart disease. But, however responsible to their passengers and colleagues they feel, they cannot avoid having problems and worries like everybody else, and due to a family row, for instance, they are no more likely to refuse to fly than a bank manager is to refuse to keep the bank open. The difference is obvious: a distracted, moody bank manager may only be less sympathetic towards overdrafts — a distracted or moody pilot may kill a planeload of people.

'We learn as we go, but we move in the dark,' a German medical investigator admitted. 'It is most urgent that we should learn how "pilot error" accidents are related to physiological and psychological factors. If the current studies were successful, we might have to review the findings in a good many cases. But this is unlikely to happen in the near future.'

CHAPTER SIXTEEN

ARE CHARTER FLIGHTS MORE DANGEROUS

BOTH privately and officially, crash detectives are frequently expected to answer this question. Each time, they are quick to point out that concerning safety 'there's no such bird as a charter flight'. When a big international company's plane is chartered for a tour, it will be flown by the same crew and operated with the same high standards of safety as it would be on a scheduled run. For example, Condor is the Lufthansa subsidiary for charter, Skanair serves the same purpose to SAS — both work according to the strict regulations of the parent company. Recently, at London's Heathrow Airport, there was a brief but sharp clash between the head of a small package tour business and a KLM pilot whom he had chartered with his aircraft. The businessman insisted that the pilot should take an extra few passengers instead of extra reserve fuel *above* the minimum. 'I don't like the weather reports,' the pilot said firmly, 'and I want to have that extra safety margin of fuel in case we have to hold, divert and hold again. It's none of my business if you save on food and things like that. I don't care how old the sandwiches you serve are. But otherwise the flight is a KLM operation and in this respect the decision is mine.'

No reputable airline would ever argue with its pilots over such matters of safety. And the same is true for the overwhelming majority of the so-called charter or independent companies, irrespective of size. If there is a safety problem with 'charter flights' it is because a few, usually small, operators employ some shrewd corner-cutting in the name of 'efficiency'. If they are clever, they will do this well within the legal limits and then, although the profit margin will increase at the expense of the safety margin, their conduct will appear irreproachable.

Public ignorance alone cannot be blamed for the habit of lumping *all* charter operations together. The real explanation is that no authority has ever devised even an approximate method by which one could differentiate between good, reasonable and barely legal operations. In 1968 the British Board of Trade published a Special Review Committee report which is a frank and critical examination of

'The Safety Performance of United Kingdom Airline Operators'.* Its conclusions refer to the record of the forty-one current operators of public transport aircraft 'varying in size from the two Corporations (BOAC and BEA) and the larger Independents to small companies operating local pleasure flights'. But even this report makes the error grouping 'Corporations' against 'Independents' which may well serve administrative purposes but certainly not as a basis for safety comparisons. After all, British United Airways, for instance, with its extensive scheduled and charter services, with its staff of 5,000 and fleet of forty-five aircraft including two VC10s and ten BAC One-elevens†, with sizeable financial resources and considerable training, operational and technical facilities, and with a safety record of no fatal accident in the eight years since its foundation, must surely be compared with another big airline or be grouped together with the Corporations rather than with a small, however safe, operator of a couple of old flying machines.

Not that the mere size of an airline determines its safety, but nor will its being independent or government-sponsored serve as a dividing criterion of safety. This administrative grouping is exactly what generally lends a bad name to 'charter flights' — or, as in this case, to 'independents' which have been shown up by this report, and similar reports in other countries, as having a considerably worse safety record than the national airlines. The report accepts that the size of an airline is not a satisfactory indicator of its safety, and goes on to state that 'U.K. operators operate to an entirely satisfactory standard. It is evident, however, that there are some who meet the minimum standards evolved for the AOC (Air Operators' Certificate) only by virtue of close supervision and constant prodding to which they are rightly

* H.M. Stationery Office, London, 1968.
† After unification with its sister companions in May 1968. Since 1970 it has been part of the large British Caledonian Airways Ltd.

subjected. There is a tendency for the smaller operators to fall into this category.'

This, once again, is a wholly unfair statement. No authority, entitled to introduce or change regulations for public safety, has the right to complain about the need for 'prodding'. *Some* prodding is applied to builders of big development schemes, to drivers who may have another drink, and even to big airlines especially after accidents. If the need for prodding becomes *constant*, the regulations must be changed because no controlling authority has the staff continuously to look over the shoulder of each employee of such companies. But how strictly can regulations be made?

In a very few, guarded public statements, yet in many 'off the record' interviews conducted by the author, American and European aviation authorities have submitted that they must 'tread with caution on the tightrope of anti-monopoly principles'. They explained that they had to be careful not to put people out of business as long as these were willing to maintain an acceptable minimum safety standard'. But the 'live and let live' principle fails when some companies which are licensed to live cease to let their passengers live in as much safety as others do. If this is accompanied by sharp practices, corner-cutting or blatant flouting of the law, the controlling authorities are usually quick to spot the hazard sometimes before, but at least soon after, a fatal accident with the tell-tale signs. (In Britain, for instance, in a seven-year period fifty-two per cent of the AOC holders have ceased to operate, some through mergers, more than ten per cent through liquidation, and *twenty-two per cent through their certificates being revoked because they had failed to maintain a required minimum level of safety*.) Hence it appears that it is the *marginal case* which represents the most persistent source of hazard to the public.

This is the consideration which, with due respect to the

excellent exceptions, must take the size of the company into account — size meaning the extent and type of operations, financial, technical resources, quality and quantity of fleet, numerical and training adequacy of staff, skill of management, firmness of control, etc. For it is at these points that within the acceptable limits of safe operations, at least *double standards of safety* are created, and these standards — with or without prodding — may be set worlds apart.

From various European interviews it emerged that meticulous maintenance, precision of operations, fast accumulation of experience and healthy growth (which involves additional problems with the introduction of more sophisticated aircraft) could be achieved more easily with what the above-quoted British report called 'fewer and stronger operator units'. Appendix K of the report concluded: 'If civil aviation in the United Kingdom is to achieve its proper development and rate of growth, commensurate with air safety, the operating units must be of optimum size. There is good reason to think that the optimum size is appreciably larger than that of many present day operators.'

It is a pity that such conclusions must be reached by each country individually instead of each taking advantage of the others' experience. At the time of the above interviews and of the preliminary moves by the Special Review Committee, Ed Slattery of NTSB had this to say in Washington:

'I guess what's happening now in Europe is the same as what we went through some ten or fifteen years ago. In the years after the war, phased-out military transport aircraft were cheap and there was a growing demand for air transport especially if it was cheap. The companies mushroomed all over the place and at one time we had some 400 non-scheduled operators who operated at a lower though still acceptable safety standard. Today, we have only thirteen supplemental or charter carriers. They use the same type of modern equipment and crews as fine as in the scheduled services. The dual safety levels were replaced with one rigid set of safety standards. I expect that a very similar development will be inevitable in Europe, too.'

The existence of such duplicity of safety standards has often been denied. In Britain, after two charter crashes had killed 160 people in twenty-four hours in June 1967, there was widespread public anxiety. At the public inquiry into one of these disasters (Argonaut), Sir Elwyn Jones, the Attorney General, said: 'There appeared to be a suspicion that because charter flights are so much cheaper than scheduled flights the saving was effected by some lowering of the safety standards. In fact, the same safety standards applied to aircraft operating under charter as to aircraft operating scheduled services. The main reason for the reduced fare for charter flights was the guarantee of payment for a full load of passengers or cargo.' But, apparently, the Attorney General was not made fully aware of the facts because the Special Review committee, which was still examining the airlines' safety performance at the time, found that 'the record of the Independent operators' (mainly of the smaller ones, presumably) 'was inferior to that of the Air Corporations so far causal factors involving *shortcomings of the flight crew, the airline and airworthiness* were concerned.' (The author's italics.)

If one adds three comments, the multi-level safety standards become very obvious: a French investigator stated that 'charter flights are no more dangerous than others, but some companies are, and I certainly wouldn't fly with any Tom, Dick or Harry who sets himself up as an airline'; a British inspector said that 'I'd always choose very carefully among the airlines before I'd trust my family's lives with one because my experience with accidents is that the government's supervisory staff shortage permits some operators to get away with hardly more than the bare minimum of safety'; and a German crash detective admitted that 'in charter accidents of certain operators, I would — without trying to prejudge the case — look for certain points where shortcomings are specially likely to occur ... and I guess that my approach is not unique among the international accident investigating community.'

The factors which may give rise to suspicion are usually marginal differences in safety well within the law. These are only some examples collected from crash detectives.

Older Aircraft: in ordinary circumstances age does not matter at all. It has often been stated that an old aircraft may be in the prime of its operational life, that like a well-maintained old car it may be 'easier to drive', and that manufacturers and users had plenty of time and experience to iron out all the early design deficiencies, dangerous flying tendencies and structural weaknesses of the type. One of the difficulties that must be faced when the safety records of an old and a new type are compared is that new types have a sometimes very extensive 'learning' or 'proving' period which means that there may be three times as many accidents in the first million flying hours accumulated by all aircraft of the new type in service as in the third or fourth million hours when the accident rate settles to a minimal level for many years. (Elaborate test rigs, like the one used for the VC10, help to cut out these teething troubles.) An advantage of older types is that their slower descent requires shorter runways, and also that they are more 'forgiving' in difficult moments brought about by errors or turbulence.

On the other, often forgotten, side of the balance sheet are their marginal disadvantages. It would be a complete denial of the tremendous advance of aeronautical knowledge not to recognise that as a result of research, flying experience and warnings from accidents, modern aircraft use more suitable materials, have the benefit of extensive applications of the fail-safe principle, and the intrinsically safer overall design. Although all planes must be maintained in an almost 'as new' condition, and parts are changed so regularly during predetermined cycles of checks and overhauls that, after a few years, hardly anything is left of the original aircraft, the basic earlier and so somewhat inferior design remains unchanged. Even if some safety improvements could be achieved in certain respects at a price, the controlling authorities cannot enforce them because the cost would be too high in relation to the safety benefits.

Some older types are more likely to suffer corrosion (for instance, the wings of Electras) which can be detected by advanced inspection methods using X-ray and ultrasonic equipment — if these are available; others with age show a slightly increasing tendency of fatigue failures especially in landing gears. These are not immediate threats to safety, but in marginal cases, in the hands of the less careful operator, they may make the slight difference between a mishap and a crash.

Many of the older types are converted and put to a different use from the original in the hands of the new owners. The DC–4, for instance, was designed to carry fifty-five passengers over the longer routes. Charter companies usually convert them to carry ninety people on short-haul flights. The conversion is a closely scrutinised operation — the users save the extra passenger weight on lighter equipment like food galleys and on smaller fuel loads for the shorter journeys — so that it is perfectly legal and well within the certified limits. But when the pilot wants to make an emergency belly-landing with undercarriage trouble, there is a marginal disadvantage: he will burn up or jettison all his fuel mainly because of fire risk when the sparks start flying as the fuselage skids along the runway, and also because of the resultant reduced landing weight. When the aircraft has no more fuel left, the extra thirty-five passengers represent extra weight he must contend with and make allowances for when the airspeed drops and the plane begins to sink faster because of the additional load. A crash detective commented: 'This, in itself, is not a real hazard. Authorities, which control airworthiness, know that charter planes are usually filled to the brim, that extra passengers cannot be jettisoned like fuel, and that they must make allowances for these loads when issuing a certificate. But it's an additional factor. If we had a points system for hazards, the conversion would add an extra few points especially in certain situations of additional complications like bad weather, crew fatigue, the pilot's daughter dating the "wrong kind" of fellow, half the airport landing aids being out of order and a couple of drunken holiday-makers trying to enter the flightdeck to thank the crew for the wonderful trip.'

Engines may also make a marginal difference to safety. Jets have more reserve power than the piston or turbo-prop engines used on older types of aircraft. Those who certify airworthiness see to it that there is enough power left to make a safe landing even if two of four engines fail. When three engines are 'out', a jet pilot still has more control over his aircraft than his colleague in the fully loaded and correctly functioning older type. The difference becomes even more prominent if the failure occurs during the more critical periods of flight such as initial climbing. The greater reserve power and marginal advantage of the jets is best demonstrated by the fact that engine failures over the ocean have led to many emergency ditchings even with turbo-props, but it has never become necessary to ditch a jet en route.

Crashworthiness: here, too, the older aircraft have certain disadvantages, because in some, mainly low-speed, accidents the stronger structure and anti-injury design of the modern aircraft may give additional protection to the passengers. In Germany, for instance, more than half of the 1,000 aircraft now in use were built between 1938 and 1948. The older types do not incorporate the latest designs which increase crashworthiness — and these are the types which are used by the smaller charter operators. The lower level of crashworthiness increases slightly the likelihood of a serious accident becoming a fatal one.

The result of the medical investigation into the Stockport Argonaut accident was remarkable in this respect. The aircraft was eighteen years old and nobody had ever suspected that its seats were potential killers. Group Captain Mason, the RAF pathologist, found that thirty-five of the seventy-two fatalities had died from burning. He drew attention to the large number of leg injuries caused by the seat structure in front. There was a thin outer strengthening bar in each seat about nine inches off the floor and in the majority of the seats recovered these bars were bent or broken. They were identified by the pathologist, the Attorney General said, as 'the major factor resulting in the failure of passengers to escape from the crash; a major factor in the causation of multiple deaths from burning . . .' in a potentially survivable accident.

It is, of course, highly significant to consider *who operates a particular aircraft and in what circumstances:*

Financial resources: it is only logical that an aircraft, in its middle age, loses a great deal of its value and passes into the hands of smaller and smaller companies which have less money to maintain it to much higher than legal minimum standards. In the name of efficiency they have to cut costs wherever they can and even minor items of expenditure — like a set of new tyres — may be delayed until they become absolutely inevitable. This profit-hungry attitude of some companies affects every phase of their operations. While all authorities which license new air carriers have certain rights to ascertain that the applicant has sufficient financial resources to maintain acceptable standards of operations and safety, only the Americans have really far-reaching powers to obtain any such information any time before or after the start of operations.

The *choice of airports* is one of the easiest ways of saving money, because those with inferior runways, aids and facilities charge smaller landing fees. The big companies judge every single airport and even runway on merit, and issue tailor-made regulations for their use. (BEA, for instance, did not let its pilots land at Corfu at night as long as the landing light system there remained inadequate.) Much smaller companies are not so 'fussy'. They cannot afford to be. If even major airports have various problems and shortcomings, as seen before, the airports in the wilderness — tucked away among mountains, with short runways in bad condition, without decent landing aids and with frequently inoperative bare necessities — can hardly be regarded as more than glorified military landing strips in wartime. Yet sharp European charter companies use them happily.

Using the *minimum of staff* is another way to increase efficiency — and profits. It is perfectly true that many of the big airlines are often overstaffed with pen-pushers. Their more sophisticated aircraft need more hands in flight as well as on the ground, they need a huge sales and administration force, staff en route, and so on. The size of the staff in itself does not mean safety or the lack of it. But it does mean that the bigger companies do much of their own maintenance and have therefore better control over it than the smaller ones which contract out the work on an *ad hoc* basis to various engineering firms, licensed and government controlled (mainly *after* mistakes), but which, nevertheless, vary a great deal in adequacy especially during their overworked peak summer season.

A big company with an abundance of funds — not to mention those which are government-backed and can rely on the Treasury to foot the bill in case of losses — can always make safety-conscious gestures. BOAC, for instance, made one in 1967: because maintenance staff shortage had delayed the overhaul of its fleet the previous winter, the airline simply cancelled ninety-six of its extra summer flights. A miniature airline which cannot get its work done by a good engineering firm must go to the second best or even further down the scale, because the cancellation of even a few flights would ruin the business.

The size of the staff also reveals some of the big companies' other advantages such as having their own medical department, own safety and accident investigation specialists, and, in all respects, specialists doing specialist jobs instead of a jack-of-all-trades changing his caps according to need. So even if crash detectives cannot name 'skeleton staff' as an obvious causal factor of accidents (although regarding maintenance work this has been named several times), it must have some effect that differences like this exist: Lufthansa, certainly not the least efficient big company had ninety-one aircraft and 16,483 employees, 191 people per aircraft, in April 1967, when another German air carrier had twenty-eight and a third company had four employees per aircraft. Similar disparities can be found everywhere else, too.

Needless to say, the smallest companies have the most problems with the quality of staff they can get, and with the training they can provide to achieve a high degree of constant reliability. These difficulties are most acute concerning air crews.

Pilots: due to the unprecedented growth of the industry, there is a shortage of well-trained pilots, even though in some countries the new fewer but bigger aircraft may periodically reduce the demand.

In these circumstances, it is not surprising that pilots can practically pick and choose their jobs, where through industrial agreements the pay, prospects, training and working conditions are best. These are usually with the most reputable companies which can provide the additional benefits of flying the best air routes with latest aircraft and equipment like automatic landing instruments, using the major airports and enjoying top class accommodation en route, etc. Thus the smallest companies often tend to get pilots who are older, less willing to train for new types of planes, anxious to get promotion to captain without queueing in the long waiting list of bigger lines where promotion is tied strictly to training and experience, and even those who have been dismissed by bigger companies as a disciplinary measure short of licence withdrawal.

A direct result of penny-pinching 'efficiency' is some pilots' insufficient route training. There have been numerous accidents to European charter flights which, on investigation, have led crash detectives to believe that lack of knowledge of a route or airport was a contributory factor of some degree. Occasionally, this may happen even to big companies. 'Considerable weight is attached in France to reports that the pilot of the Air France Boeing that hit a mountain in Guadeloupe while trying to land had protested before taking off that he did not know the airfield well enough to attempt a night landing.'* Many pilots of small charter companies are so used to such 'minor deficiencies', that they would not even bother to protest. The big lines have their own training and refresher courses, and when they regard a pilot as being familiar with the route or an airport, it means exactly that. A small company may often satisfy itself in this respect by letting a captain fly the route — or even a part of it — as co-pilot before taking his own aircraft. That he landed at an airport once in good weather and daytime with landing aids working, and that he might have to land at night in a storm struggling with faulty

* *The Economist,* July 14, 1962.

landing aids, may make no difference to some companies which would still not be treated as law-breakers.

But the biggest scope for 'interpretation' of the law is in the pilots' working hours.

Fatigue: this problem is far from being restricted to the small charter companies, but it is most apparently acute in their case partly because this is the field where corner-cutting is easiest with or without breaking the law, and partly because the vast seasonal upsurge in their operations is incompatible with the chronic pilot shortage and forces them to utilise their manpower to the limit.

Many crash detectives are convinced that, as a French investigator summed it up, 'our lack of knowledge about fatigue may well prove to be the chief explanation of those accidents which are now put down to "pilot error" or "the human factor" simply because we don't quite understand what makes well-qualified conscientious specialists, like pilots, commit almost unbelievably stupid mistakes'. Misreading an instrument, failure to recognise the nature of sudden difficulties or an emergency and the delay in reacting to it, poor judgment, over-confidence, stubborn attempts at landing instead of diverting, slips in the competent handling of aircraft in merely difficult circumstances, over-sensitivity to hardly more than ordinary stress, and plain mistakes are much more likely to occur at the end of a long, tiring journey than otherwise. Although one such mistake is usually insufficient to cause a disaster, it certainly has the potential of increasing the gravity of a given situation.

In most cases it is almost impossible for the investigator to prove conclusively the culpability of fatigue. The most acceptable piece of evidence is the length of time the crew has spent on duty. 'But even then, how do you assess the extent of influence by fatigue?' asked Ed Slattery. 'We named fatigue as a contributory cause of an Alitalia accident, for instance, because we knew that the crew had been on duty for almost twenty hours flying their DC–6B from Rome, via Milan and Lisbon, to New York, and encountering delays, due to bad weather everywhere, and because the circumstances of the accident supported the fatigue theory.' Or a vague indication that the co-pilot 'was probably not at his freshest' was found in the BEA Vanguard accident (see Chapter Eight) when, at 'the end of a long and tiring day', during the third landing attempt, 'his flying was not as polished as it might or should have been', although his hours of duty were far below the legal limit and he had sufficient rest before the flight.

The length of time spent in the air is, of course, the most obvious cause of fatigue and, although it is a gross oversimplification of this complex problem, time can be measured and regulated. As we have seen before, when the rules are broken directly by a pilot spending excessively long hours in the cockpit, it is comparatively easy to pinpoint fatigue as a contributory factor in an accident. Some may argue about the exact measure of its contribution, and when it comes to a really tangled affair like the Globe Air crash at Nicosia, on April 20, 1967, the investigation may never settle the dispute beyond any doubt.

In several respects, the case was not untypical. The Basle-based company had operated charter flights from 1959 without any accident. Yet not all was well with its affairs. According to press reports, the Swiss Federal Air Office threatened the company with the withdrawal of its licence if certain requirements affecting better control, compliance with regulations and changes in key personnel were not satisfied. Globe Air complied with this order, but in September 1966 a Basle court started an investigation into alleged falsification of company documents. These concerned mainly the records of pilots' flying hours. (Among the effective duty time fiddles, an old international technique is, for instance, to note in the log book a different pilot's name aboard as the captain of the aircraft for each sector.) According to a *Sunday Telegraph* report (28/4/1967), some allegations came from former employees of the company and the material supplied to the examining magistrate 'included a cinéfilm in which a woman guest occupied the co-pilot's seat of a plane then in flight'. The head of the company gave an interview to the paper and claimed that the inquiry was about two officers who made mistakes with statistics and so had nothing to do with the company, and that others who made accusations were suffering from 'psychological tension' or tried to put Globe Air, a competitor, out of business.

In April 1967, a Britannia turbo-prop airliner of the company, with 128 people on board — mainly Swiss and German tourists chartered by travel agencies in Zurich and Frankfurt — was on a cheap return all inclusive tour flight and was diverted from Cairo to Nicosia because of bad weather. Why Nicosia was chosen as an alternative when Cyprus had about as bad weather, with heavy rain and bad visibility, as Cairo is still not clarified. Tel Aviv, with good weather, would have been a much more obvious choice. The pilot made two unsuccessful landing attempts. Most probably, by then, he had not enough fuel left to make yet another diversion — he had to get in. During the third attempt the aircraft crashed. There were only four survivors.

'I was there as an observer,' said Dr. Widmer, 'and the Cyprus investigator was an administrator — so we were lucky to get assistance from Britain. These people from the manufacturers and BOAC really knew how to look for the causes, had all the experience to do the job without walking about with the ICAO manual all the time.'

Several irregularities were discovered almost immediately. Captain Michael Miller, a Briton, had insufficient rest before the long flight during which he allegedly exceeded the maximum permitted Swiss duty time by some fifteen hours (although the Swiss official limit is rather excessive in itself); and another Englishman, the co-pilot Michael Day, holder of a valid English pilot's licence, failed to pass a Swiss flight test twenty-four hours before the flight and was thus claimed to be unqualified for the job according to Swiss law.

Within twenty-four hours of the crash, Globe Air shares dropped heavily, and the Basle Stock Exchange, as a precautionary measure, suspended trading in these stocks. At that time, Globe Air was still planning expansion and negotiating the purchase of further second-hand airliners. The crash in itself was a financial blow, but not fatal to the company because the hull of the aircraft was insured for almost £300,000. A much bigger blow came from Germany, the only country that acted swiftly: Globe Air was banned from all German airports indefinitely. In October the company made a winding up petition against itself. A day later, the Swiss authorities grounded all its aircraft pending investigation. The head of the company was taken into custody. In April 1968, the assets of the company were auctioned.

One must repeat that the Swiss law itself was also blameworthy for being too permissive. No lorry or engine driver is permitted to work for twenty hours or be on duty for up to forty hours even if he is sharing it with a complete relief crew on board. And the same goes for statutory rest periods, too. A British charter pilot, for instance, was fined for cutting his rest periods somewhat short. It was a breach of regulations even though it was not a serious case, led to no accident and one could sympathise with his defence that after he had arrived at Bangkok after midnight with a 'dangerous cargo' of seventy-five Chinese seamen bound for Hongkong, he was warned that his passengers were unwelcome in such a centre of smuggling, and also that the longer he let them stay there the greater would be the likelihood of their getting illicit supplies — valid grounds for cutting the rest short and pressing on.

To assess fatigue as a contributory factor in an accident becomes inestimably more difficult when the existing regulation is not actually broken, and when — as is the case today — nobody really knows what the safely acceptable maximum should be.

Length and conditions of rest are probably as important as the length of flying and stand-by duty (it is sometimes more tiring and unnerving to hang about waiting than to be working). Cockpit conditions, heat and humidity may be other factors. The number of pilots on board makes a great difference, and so does the presence of engineers. The number of landings and take-offs may increase the workload, and the effects of bad weather or the lack of certain navigation aids are also significant. Although governments and companies try to prevent cumulative fatigue (for example, by monthly and yearly maximum duty time) little is known about its function. Time zone changes when flying east or west upset the body's 'circadian rhythm' (*circa diem* — round the day) and may deprive jet travellers of essential sleep. Businessmen and politicians are often warned not to make important decisions soon after having crossed time zones because in a state of resultant fatigue they are ill-equipped to judge their own abilities and alertness, and may thus take risks they would normally avoid. Interference with the body's metabolic clock is, of course, an even graver offence in the pilot's case.

Because the available scientific knowledge of fatigue is insufficient to form the basis of strict legislation, governments tend ' to leave it all' to the operators who are expected to make their own duty time adjustments according to their particular operations. But if the governments are uncertain about what is best to do, how can they expect a miniature charter company to make the right decisions?

One of the most taxing factors is that which affects the majority of charter flights: night duty. Some pilots call it the 'graveyard shift', which is exaggerated but not entirely divorced from the truth. The American Flight Safety Foundation studied statistics to discover if any particular hour of the day had featured prominently as the time of accidents. They found that the most ominous four hours were between 2 and 6 a.m. at dawn when almost ten times as many crashes had happened as the hourly average in the rest of the day. Having discounted hazards like weather or sabotage which could not be related to the time of the day, the indication was that there was a direct relationship between 'pilot error' and the time factor. This is also confirmed by medical researchers who have found that alertness and the speed of mental and physical reactions drop appreciably in those hours, and that the disruption of the natural body rhythm has the worst effects when there are frequent changes — say, different shifts every two days — so that the 'metabolic clock' has no chance to adjust itself.

Such changes in routine may give some clues to crash detectives who find them, nevertheless, hard to evaluate. Several of them recalled their own experiences although they were aware of the dangers of generalisations. 'When I was an airline pilot,' one of them said, 'I found the first night duty after a few days off the most difficult. I always tried to sleep in the afternoon before the flight, but never could. The second night was easier because I could sleep in the morning after duty. But then I would return to normal hours while at home, and it would start all over again. The most terrifying aspect is when you suddenly realise that although you feel perfectly fit, your mind is not working as it should. I once flew with a co-pilot for a month regularly — he was an old friend, too — and one morning after a long night-flight, when checking in at a hotel, I couldn't fill in the register because I just couldn't remember the chap's name.'

A German investigator referred to 'a DC–6 case in the early 1950's' as 'the textbook example of fatigue that lulled the crew into a false sense of security'. The flight was delayed several times en route and, since the regulations then left much to the captain's own judgment, the pilot decided that they should 'press on for the sake of their passengers'. This meant that by the time they approached Frankfurt, the crew had been on duty for almost thirty hours. The aircraft had to overshoot and the tower told the pilot to make a left turn. The instruction was acknowledged, and 'left turn' was repeated by the pilots while they were making a right turn. 'They were obviously in a state of stupor brought about by fatigue which could be likened to the light-heartedness of a drunkard who will try to walk with perfect self-assurance between the two headlights of a car which to him seem to represent two motorcycles,' commented the investigator.

Oddly enough, until recently, hardly any attention had been paid to the rest and duty time allocated to one part of the crew — cabin staff. It is known that some small companies regard stewardesses as 'waitresses who are over-paid and over-glamourised for being sometimes over-worked', employ hundreds of them on a seasonal basis like holiday resorts do with staff, and seem to take the view that it is a waste of time to give these girls proper training in emergency drill. Such companies, and unfortunately the controlling authorities with them, have apparently forgotten that the law does not require the presence of cabin staff to serve drinks and food, and smile reassuringly at passengers, but to help people escape in an emergency by operating exits and life-saving equipment. Yet in Britain, for instance, it was only in 1968 that legislation requiring the restriction of duty hours and establishing minimum rest periods for cabin staff came into effect.

Crash detectives seem to take a reserved view of the

effectiveness of legislation for several reasons: many girls are so anxious to get the job that they are willing to co-operate in a little corner-cutting; cabin duty, too, can be affected by many factors, such as the number of passengers they have to serve en route, for which it is impossible to legislate; their health is not as closely checked as that of pilots; authorities are understaffed in most countries and struggle to exercise control even over operational standards so that checking the training of cabin staff is often 'the least of their headaches'; and the 'minimum rest period' is a meaningless formula both for cabin staff and flight-deck crew.

Without actual police methods the inspectors cannot check how a pilot or stewardess has spent the legally accept-able rest period, and police methods cannot be applied if only because the results would not justify them so long as scientists cannot tell investigators how to evaluate exactly the role of six hours' pre-flight gardening as a factor in a fatigue-induced accident. (Crash detectives can recall sev-eral cases of suspicion — for instance, a stewardess whose reflexes might have been slowed down by cumulative fatigue due to her day-and-night 'off-duty' studies for a university degree — but had they mentioned these in their reports they would have been accused of guessing. They also emphasise that shorter flying hours and longer rest periods create ad-ditional spare time without any guarantee that it will be spent in recreation rather than on some profitable second profession like farming.)

Much of this chapter has dealt with 'unsubstantiated ex-perience' gathered from accident investigators. If science cannot give them the proof and bold legislation cannot give them the support when they check performance in retro-spect, they will have to wait for statistical evidence which has a sombre disadvantage: each figure that builds up sta-tistical data represents calamity, but many figures like these must go on record before statistics have any meaning and start to reveal hazardous trends and the weak spots in aviation.

CHAPTER SEVENTEEN

SAFETY IN PUBLIC *v.* PUBLIC SAFETY?

THROUGHOUT the investigation of an accident, crash detectives must keep in mind that some day they will have to answer questions, even unimportant and irrelevant ones, and then it will not be good enough to say 'No, sir, that particular bolt had nothing to do with the accident so I did not examine it'. In countries where these inquiries may have to be done in public, the investigators must appear in open courts. Although these public hearings in America or public inquiries in Britain are often tragic and harrowing, they hardly ever produce breathtaking twists and brilliant surprises in the style of criminal proceedings and television drama. If they do, the value of the drama can usually be calculated in the amount of money, time, effort and newsprint wasted on them. Whether the findings are published or are merely accessible in some archives, the prevailing principle in air accident cases, too, is that 'justice should not only be done, but manifestly and undoubtedly be seen to be done'.* But by whom should it be seen? By the public? The government? The lawyers? The experts? Those who may be blamed? Who may claim or pay compensations?

On October 23, 1957, a BEA Viscount was chartered to bring the Northern Ireland Minister of Supply and members of his staff from Belfast to London. To pick up the

---

* Lord Hewart, Rex *v.* Sussex Justices, November 9, 1923.

party, the aircraft — G-AOJA — took off from London Airport at 15.16. It was manned by a crew of five, and had two passengers, a BEA employee and his wife, on board. Robert Malcolm Stewart, the thirty-five-year-old captain, was married, with one child. An experienced, ex-RAF pilot, he was known as a reliable man with highly praised human and professional qualities. First Officer William Gordon Tomkins, thirty-five, father of two, also had an outstanding career covering sixteen years.

At London Airport, forecasters told the Captain that low clouds and some deterioration in the weather could be expected because a cold front was approaching Belfast, but that there would be an improvement when it passed between 16.00 and 18.00 hours. The flight was uneventful. At 16.17, the Zone Co-ordinator and Supervisor at Nutts Corner, Belfast, began to talk with the aircraft. Ninety seconds later, the Captain was considering a diversion but was told that down at 500–600 feet the clouds seemed to be very thin. 'I don't know if you've got enough fuel, it might be worth your while coming down to your critical height to see whether you could make an approach.' 'We'll do that, we've got a bit extra,' was the answer.

Routine conversation followed and there was a suggestion of diverting, but at 16.38 there was a reasonable hope that the weather would soon improve at Nutts Corner, too. 'I think we'd rather hang around for a little while and see if we can get into Nutts Corner; we'll make an approach here anyway.' And a few seconds later this opinion seemed to have been confirmed when the Captain radioed: 'The cloud seems very thin, I can see the ground where I am at 4,000 feet.'

16.39: ground control said 'I think you've got a sporting chance on a 28 approach, it doesn't look too bad'. It meant a sporting chance of becoming visual above the aircraft's critical height. 16.41: down at 3,000 feet, the Captain was told that it would be a precision approach. A van for Ground Controlled Approach (GCA, also known as PAR, Precision Approach Radar, but the ILS technique is now preferred to this) was parked towards the western end of runway 28, about 350 feet off its centre line. 16.45½: the altitude of the aircraft was 2,200 feet and a 'completely normal' talk-down began.

16.49: the final phase of the talk-down began. At $\frac{3}{4}$ mile from touchdown, the Viscount was told that it was 'to the right of the centre line', and at about half a mile from touchdown it was 'well right of centre line'. Four people saw it coming. They noticed nothing unusual about the aircraft. 16.50: the precision approach Controller told the flight that 'if you're overshooting turn left five degrees on overshoot over'. The reply was not quite audible. On the ground they picked up '. . . overshoot. . . .' Several people then heard the aircraft 'rev up' to an engine note 'just like a Viscount taking off'.

16.51: staff in the GCA van heard the aircraft pass overhead sounding like 'a perfectly straightforward overshoot'. Then, a second or two later, there was a 'vivid flash followed by the noise of an explosion'. The aircraft had crashed. The engines had been running up to the moment of impact. All on board were killed.

The subsequent investigation ended with a Public Inquiry. 'The problem for the court was to determine the cause of this change from the apparently normal to the catastrophic.' Despite the tremendous goodwill and very conscientious effort that went into the investigation and the public inquiry, the results were only negative. Men and machine were exonerated. Experts studied the possibility of various manoeuvres which 'would be of a fairly violent nature' and could cause such a catastrophe. 'It is therefore necessary to face the possibility that *something may have deceived the pilot* . . .' (author's italics). Nine lawyers asked

343

the necessary questions in court, twenty-nine witnesses, including the investigators, gave the necessary answers, but the then current state of the art prevented the discovery of what that 'something' that had deceived the pilot could be, and the unhappy conclusion was reached that 'this must remain a wholly unexplained calamity'.

Investigators, specialists and interested parties had known the answers before the inquiry began, so that there was no room for anything unexpected or dramatic. Not until the word 'screwdriver' was mentioned. For at last, here was something readily understandable to everybody, something that could fire the imagination of the public, make good, dramatic headlines, permit speculations and theories, and give an opportunity to lawyers to display brilliant rhetoric.

It was found among 'general debris' on the second or third day after the wreckage had been taken to a hangar for examination. It was of the type commonly used by electricians and it was in a badly distorted condition. Apart from its inexplicable presence in the wreckage, there were many suspicious circumstances. The AIB investigator put it aside in a box with some other small components which were awaiting more detailed scrutiny. Police guarded the hangar, yet the screwdriver disappeared a few days later. The AIB investigator made inquiries as soon as he had found it missing, and discovered that it had been taken by a worker who had straightened it and used it 'in all innocence and good faith'.

A television detective would have spotted, no doubt, the work of evil forces in placing the screwdriver in the cockpit and removing it from the wreckage to destroy evidence. The accident investigator placed more reliance on facts, but followed up the clues with no less imagination or perspicacity. During maintenance, loose objects are sometimes left behind in the aircraft. Although BEA, like other companies, always paid special attention to this problem (at Farnborough, they have now invented an 'aviation flypaper' to catch such objects which are left behind despite all precautions) it was possible that the tool had been left behind the panels of the cockpit. It was also conceivable that the screwdriver would then find its way into the controls mechanism with the effect of jamming it. This, in turn, would cause the same kind of accident as had occurred.

And there were even more ominous clues. As we have seen, the manufacturers, in this case Vickers, never stop studying the performance and safety of their aircraft. It was in this way that engineers foresaw the possibility of 'foreign objects' falling through a certain gap and interfering with the controls. Therefore, a month before the Nutts Corner accident, a modification of covering that aperture was recommended to all users. The modification was rated as 'desirable' — not 'essential' or even 'highly desirable' — for there had never been an incident caused in this way. The airlines study these suggestions (there are always a large number of them) and, if an idea is approved, it is implemented. This particular modification had a low priority rating and so it was not carried out before the accident.

There had been no such incidents *before* the crash, but there were *two within a fortnight after it.* In both cases, tools fell through that particular aperture and jammed the controls. If the same had happened at Nutts Corner in a critical moment, it would have caused at least a slight delay in operating the controls — and that delay would have been fatal.

The investigators did not wait for the court to tell them that much. All aspects of this possibility were looked at meticulously. It was found that none of the controls had been jammed before impact. It was also established that 'there is not in this case a shred of evidence which would justify a finding that any interference with the controls had anything to do with the fatality'. A series of experiments was made on the screwdriver itself and the damage to it was studied. The distortions in the screwdriver could have been caused by a 'multitude of conditions' in this crash — but no corresponding damages were found between the controls and the 'suspect'. Therefore this attractive theory was ruled out.

Yet when the screwdriver was mentioned in court — as it had to be — nothing could stop the publicity, the public interest and so the complete diversion of the proceedings. Crash detectives called it 'the typical red herring that appears during public inquiries' which, nevertheless, led to a great waste of money and effort of the court, lengthened the inquiry by several days, occupied almost a third of the final report without enhancing air safety, and merely allowed *the public to see justice being done.*

How much the public can *see* of what is shown to them is yet another matter. 'That is the rather terrifying thing about aircraft structure: it has got so much into the hands of a small band of experts that, save in the exceptional case such as a string of break-ups in the air, public comment is well nigh impossible.'* And the same can be said about practically any aspect of aviation. Therefore the word 'public' (public inquiry, public hearing) is one of the major anachronisms which make a mockery of the system. The public can no longer exercise pressure except in two ways: by not flying with certain airlines or in certain aircraft if their suspicion has been roused, and by supporting expert pressure groups and the few well-versed politicians whose views and action guide rather than react to public demand. In the highly-specialised field of air accident investigation there is no room left for democracy.

If in these cases the public are meant to be represented by specialists in an unofficial status, the facts ought to be made known to them much sooner after the accident, and the

* 'CCI's column,' New Perspectives, *Flight International*, June 30, 1966.

examination of the findings ought to be conducted in the manner of an informal, freely accessible tribunal rather than in the style of the courts, so that anybody who has something worthwhile to contribute — for instance a witness who has not been called — could make observations and suggestions or volunteer information early in the investigation. There have been numerous reform propositions from legal, ethical and practical points of view aimed at improvements and at least *some* international uniformity of procedures, but it is not our duty to examine them here in detail. Our main concern is whether the present variety of final national inquiry systems — in public or otherwise — can truly support the process of finding the real causes of accidents or not.

Critics of air accident investigations often claim that the public form of the final inquiry is a defence against anybody *rigging the investigation.* But the fact is that today, when an immense number of people are involved representing numerous parties of conflicting interests, the cheating would have to be done in the investigation stage in one of two ways: by a vast general conspiracy to distort facts, withhold findings, and deliberately 'overlook' logical conclusions, or by persuading one party like the pilot to accept responsibility for the mistake of another, say, a traffic controller, which again would inevitably require the connivance of the others. Both of these are, of course, possible only in theory.

In practice, most crash detectives in various countries admit that they often work under pressure from various interested parties. The pressure is usually subtle and psychological in a professional guise. It may take the form of promoting theories and emphasising the importance of certain findings which would channel the investigation in a particular direction. Another form may be that, especially from flying or handling and therefore less factual aspects, one or

347

another member of the team will try to ridicule the ways of reasoning which imply that his firm's product or his government's regulations or a pilot of his union may have been responsible for the accident.

Very infrequently, and mainly in countries where the investigation is done by one man or a miniature team, the pressure may aim at inducing negligent investigation or, in a very extreme case, may take a more active role: during interviews, two such cases have been mentioned to this author. In one of them, the investigator was invited to a bar for drinks while, he later found, somebody with access to the site climbed into the wrecked cockpit and moved some controls into the more appropriate position. Whoever interfered with the settings — the person was never found — must have overlooked the fact that the investigator had photographed all the interior of the cockpit well before he spared the time for a few drinks in the bar. In the other case, the lawyer of a small airline tried to intimidate an investigator whose wife he threatened with blackmail. The crash detective contacted the police, a trap was laid, but when the wife telephoned the lawyer to arrange a second meeting, he probably grew suspicious, claimed he had never met her and threw down the receiver in simulated annoyance.

In an important case, the multitude of interested parties is still the greatest deterrent to rigging the conclusions; and, it must be emphasised, every single participant (even the government investigator) becomes an *interested party* one way or another so that nobody can remain absolutely impartial. The independent scientist who is consulted may for instance, put forward one of his pet theories as an explanation of the accident, and it will be his professional pride which flavours his argument with subjectivity.

Unfortunately for those who are entrusted (or burdened?) with *writing* these accident reports, the analysis of facts is liable, at least in certain aspects, to individual interpretation.

The task is comparable to walking the tightrope a thousand feet above the ground. Any sign of really or apparently wavering impartiality is bound to provoke all-round condemnation, and even the most acutely accurate and objective reports inevitably draw unfavourable comments from interested parties. (The two most frequent types of attacks on reports claim, as we have seen, that 'the conclusion of pilot error' was unjustified or that 'one government agency tried to defend and cover up for another'.)

Air accident reports have grown tremendously in length, complexity and importance during the past decade. From six to eight pages they have expanded to a volume of sixty pages or more and even then they can contain only brief summaries of months or years of research in many highly specialised fields, and must leave out the great deal of detailed evidence which has led to the final conclusions. (In some countries, like Japan, the reports are still as short as the American ones used to be some twenty years ago, but there is a tendency to greater elaboration everywhere, and in one European country, it is alleged, the government is so anxious to get really detailed reports that they pay independent investigators according to linage!)

Writers and signatories of the accident reports are therefore the most likely to be exposed to the charge of having 'rigged the investigation'. Apart from this cross they have to carry and in addition to their tremendous reponsibility to air safety in general, what makes their existence even more precarious is another major anachronism of the entire system: it is a universal claim that accident investigation is concerned solely with finding the *truth* — yet invariably, the discovery of that truth means an attachment of *blame* to something or somebody, and it becomes what amounts to an indictment when the cause of an accident is expounded in the report.

It is true that the reports are not final, they speak about

the 'probable cause', they suffer from the limitations of the 'state of the art', they can be and are frequently argued, they are not meant to be used in court or as a basis for insurance claims, disciplinary action, etc., and they may be contradicted by subsequent legal action which may name a cause and blame a party different from those in the accident report. On the other hand it is indisputable that it is extremely difficult to substantiate charges contrary to these reports, that it is even harder to get reports altered on the basis of new evidence, and that the reports exert very considerable influence in all directions including subsequent litigation and disciplinary measures. Therefore, the blame that naturally arises from the pinpointed causes will stick and give a bad name to individuals, an airline, an aircraft, a manufacturer, an airport or a government agency at least for a number of years, until the evidence is revalued and mistakes are corrected.

This responsibility, too, must be shouldered by those who write and issue the accident reports so that they must take into account the fact that their truth-finding exercise is turned into a lawyers' battlefield where a legal smoke-screen protects individual parties from the lurking threat of blame, and where those who refuse to divulge self-incriminating information are not fired at — even if this means a delay in the investigation and *an extended period of threat to air safety*. Because there is no evidence to the contrary, it is generally believed that all such information that had been withheld from the investigators came to light eventually, but in some cases the delays were accessories to further accidents and the loss of many lives.

Joseph O. Fluet, chief of the Investigation Division of NTSB, says 'it is infuriating to know that we would have to work for months to learn what somebody could have told us in ten minutes, but in return for that information we would have had to offer complete immunity and also secrecy from all but investigating authorities — the very guarantees we cannot give.'

In the United States, public hearings are of a technical, factual nature — but they are closely followed by lawyers to whom, later, all the files are open for examination. Because of this, every word of evidence is very cautiously considered and nobody is required to say anything which may incriminate him or the organisation he represents.

In some European countries, accident investigation is in the hands of the judiciary to the extent that in France, for instance, a local court must decide if there was any crime or a misdemeanour *before* the technical investigation is completed. Quite frequently this means that the investigator can look at the wreckage but not at a particular piece which has been taken away by the court.

In Italy, even the effectiveness of ICAO conventions (like Annex 13 which ought to ensure automatically the right of relevant foreign participation in the investigation) depends on judicial permission.

In Sweden, Switzerland and Germany, there is no public inquiry. The work is done by a board of experts from government aviation authorities. *After* their conclusions have been reached, the files can be inspected by those who have a legitimate interest in the case. This arrangement may have the advantage that at least specialists and not lawyers are dealing with aviation problems, but one is soon driven to realise that it openly combines safety-conscious crash detective work with law-enforcement and blame-apportioning. In Sweden, the investigator reports to the board which then determines the probable cause of the accident and decides if anybody should be charged in court with, say, negligence.

In Switzerland a similar board finalises the report and against this no appeal can be made. As in Germany (for instance, the Munich crash case), individuals who are blamed for something in the report can make statements to the board but cannot defend themselves against accusations, cannot object to the way a verdict is reached, and cannot insist on having their objections stated side by side with the views of the board. The answer to them invariably is that this is not a blame-finding inquiry and that anybody who has been criticised will have the opportunity to defend himself in court or when disciplinary measures, like licence endorsement or withdrawal, are instituted. This argument ignores the fact that by that time the accused will already have the disadvantage of being blamed by a final accident report.

In the Soviet Union, even the accidents are never reported — unless foreigners are involved — and so the inquiry, too, is shrouded in secrecy. According to an executive of Aeroflot who insisted on remaining anonymous, the Inspection Department of the Ministry of Civil Aviation which checks and licenses airlines, aircraft and pilots, is also charged with the investigation of accidents. In a very serious case, like the crash of the TU–114 in Moscow on February 17, 1966, a special commission is formed. (The accident occurred during take-off. At the time, the TU–114 was the world's biggest airliner with a seating capacity of 170. A long-delayed official announcement admitted the death of the crew and six passengers, but various reports estimated the toll to be much greater.) The commission has from six to twelve members who represent interested parties. It suggests punitive measures which are automatically accepted by the various authorities which participate in the investigation anyway. Its report is only for internal use. If anything, a brief and rather vague communiqué may be published.

While the inquiry in public does not really help the quest for aviation safety, at least it gives a fair deal to those who may be in danger of being blamed; on the other hand, the summary method of jurisdiction deprives the 'accused' of proper legal and specialist defence as well as the opportunity to appeal for support to the public in general and independent experts in particular *before* a verdict has been reached. Therefore, it is impossible to recommend an 'inquiry in camera' as a replacement for the inquiry in public, because neither will really advance the main purpose of the investigation which is finding out the truth.

It was typical of this self-contradictory situation that in Britain, where at least once a solution was sought to it, the suggested course of action came under heavy criticism because 'impossible' seemed as appropriate a comment on it as 'ridiculous'. There are two forms of investigation in Britain: an Inspector's Investigation at the discretion of the Chief Inspector of Accidents, and a Public Inquiry ordered by the minister responsible for aviation. Officially, it has always been maintained that neither form is a trial or a prosecution. If, however, 'a charge is made against any person, that person shall be provided an opportunity of making a defence.'*

The Public Inquiry is completely in the hands of laymen, who happen to be lawyers. They are assisted by specialists whose devotion and knowledge are sometimes lost in the ghosting process through solicitors to counsel, the man who may speak in court. These courts are usually bent on convicting or exonerating various parties despite fervent claims to the contrary. The minister orders the Public Inquiry to search for truth and allay public anxiety. Then, in turn, the various parties wash their hands — they most willingly assist the inquiry as far as the other parties are concerned — because subsequent legal claims or disciplinary action against them will be based largely on these findings.

In 1961 the Cairns Committee Report† spotted various anachronisms in the system. It proposed, for instance, 'to

* J. D. Rose, former Deputy Chief Inspector of Accidents, AIB.
† Op. cit.

omit from the questions asked of the Commissioner "was the accident due to, or contributed to by, the wrongful act or default of any party?", because this, together with the Commissioner's former right to recommend disciplinary action, clearly turned the inquiry into trial.' The question can still be asked, but recently it has been omitted quietly. Another recommendation was carried out after a mere six years' delay: for the first time, in 1967, the AIB regulations stated that the aim of the investigations was to prevent repetitions and not to blame anybody for the accident. Further suggestions, like the use of appeal tribunals, went through a great deal of consultations and reached the *proposal* stage in 1968.

The one recommendation which was dubbed 'ridiculous' and 'impossible' had to remain conveniently forgotten. It called for the use of the power of the Public Inquiry to hold its proceedings in private when it is hearing the evidence of a witness whose answer may incriminate him. Impossible? Perhaps. Because the change in proceedings may in itself incriminate a witness. But surely it is not ridiculous because it only reflects the urgent need for both kinds of inquiries! And if the method of the U.S. Air Force were adopted, the public and private inquiries together could achieve what the public inquiry followed by legal action never will.

The USAF have an *accident investigation* and a *collateral investigation*. To the accident investigation board, any witness can give testimony 'freely without fear of disciplinary action, civil action or other penalty' because without this immunity 'the accident prevention program would be severely compromised. Witnesses would be inclined to withhold evidence or invoke their constitutional rights against self-incrimination'.* Their statements may not be

* USAF Aircraft Accident Prevention and Investigation, AFM 127–1, September 20, 1963.

354

compared with those given to the collateral board, and may not be used 'for any other purpose than the prevention of aircraft accidents'. Witnesses 'may not appear before a collateral board until they have been released by the accident investigation board. No member of the collateral board may attend the aircraft accident board proceedings' concerning the same acident. Members of one board must not be assigned to assist the other. These precautions are vital because the collateral board compiles information which can be used for *any* purpose including evidence in civil or military court, basis of compensation claims and disciplinary measures.

A system like this, applied to the different nature of civilian aviation, would be particularly useful in cases which involve two or more countries and frequently create a conflict of real or imaginary national interests. There is a clearly growing urgency for creating a pool of international crash detectives who could help countries which have inadequately trained personnel and insufficient experience. Today there is still a great deal of suspicion against foreign assistance, resentment of 'interference', and so even the implementation of international agreements depends on the tact and diplomacy of individuals. But if these international teams never published their reports which would be used purely for 'accident prevention', no country would suffer loss of face and a national collateral board could then get to work on the legal implications, and could even carry out the diplomatic mud-slinging which often seems essential in the preservation of national pride.

There are probably thousands of practical objections to a plan like this. But with a sufficient amount of goodwill — perhaps this is asking for too much — these could probably be sorted out. The majority of the most experienced crash detectives are convinced that such a 'dual standard of investigation' would be ideal from the safety point of view, but its viability would certainly be endangered by a public outcry against it.

It is true, the public would suspect the secrecy, governments, airlines, manufacturers and other interested parties would hate the delayed and inadequate clearance of blame, and the cost of the inquiry would increase even though crash detectives could give the same evidence to both boards of investigation. But the question is: what kind of a public outcry will there be when the *second* supersonic or the *second* plane with five hundred passengers crashes?

CHAPTER EIGHTEEN

1984 — SAFETY OR NON-SAFETY?

THE original version and the subsequent editions of this book contained the following paragraph:

'Bo Lundberg, the Swedish air safety expert, estimated that if we can do no better than just preserve the present safety level proportionately to the growing traffic, we will have 60,000 fatalities in the year 2000 alone. Our chances are, in fact, better. New aircraft going into production are now tested more thoroughly and in many more ingenious ways than any others in the past. The chances of failures slipping through undetected are growing slimmer. But if the few that may get through and may cause accidents remain, even then, mysteries, if the investigators cannot learn the vital lessons from those tragedies — a thought that haunts them most persistently in every case they handle — then Lundberg's pessimistic estimate may be proved even optimistic.'

Fortunately, Lundberg's forecast still appears to be pessimistic in 1975; but not that pessimistic any more. Some disturbing events and dark clouds of uncertainty loom now large on the horizon of aviation and, unlike in 1968, this author would hesitate to offer a totally unequivocal reassurance to all air travellers.

The present picture is not all black. Far from it. There is still an abundance of cheering news. Some countries continue to improve their safety record, new aircraft prove to be more reliable even in the learning period than others used to be for years in the early part of their flying career, and

Qantas, the Australian international airline, has still not lost a single passenger or crew member since 1946 – a virtually unique achievement through a combination of skill and care, which could be the subject of a special case study in safety – reassuring everybody that yes, it can be done, and we should not settle for anything less.

Yet there is a steady accumulation of indicators which may seem insignificant individually but add up to the warning that all may not be well in the state of aviation. And it is not only the horror and magnitude of the modern air disaster (a Turkish DC–10 set a new record of air slaughter by killing 346 people in a single crash near Paris in 1974) that worry all who care about air safety: the truly disturbing evidence comes from the details of those accidents. The causes, the explanations, the excuses, the lacking sense of absolute inevitability, the discovery of tiny yet fatal loopholes, blunders of bureaucracy, and all-round greed, including strikes, fuel prices, cut-throat competition and measures of false economy are among the symptoms that become, in combination, a massive confidence-shaker.

In 1968, this book argued that with due respect to scientists, designers, law-makers, manufacturers, operators and many others, the accident investigators deserve a special place of honour in the achievement of the 'present amazingly high level of aviation safety that has given flying a place among the safest forms of travel'.

Amazingly high level is, of course, a vague and unqualified description of safety. It has been used on purpose. There are many ways to describe safety level. Robert J. Serling, in his excellent book *The Probable Cause*, used the illustration that the baby who was born and grew up without ever leaving an airliner in non-stop service would not be involved in a fatal accident before his seventy-sixth birthday.

There are many well-known and somewhat cheap

358

methods of giving such reassurances. It is true and it sounds convincing that flying is twice as safe as road transport, but when you look at the figures more closely you find serious discrepancies. Cars are from six to eight times more dangerous than aeroplanes and in America alone, during an Independence weekend, a Christmas or a Thanksgiving holiday, as many road accidents occur as the number of victims of the entire international aviation in an average year — but cars are not public transport, and if you are driven by somebody else, you have a chance to assess the driver and the car, avoid accident blackspots, and get out of the car at any point if the road is icy or the brake does not work properly. Buses and trains are, on the other hand, almost three times as safe as scheduled air carriers on a passenger–mile basis, and many times safer on a travelling time — length of exposure — basis. (There are, of course, some exceptionally good years for aviation: in 1966 U.S. airlines had twice as good a safety record as the railroads on a passenger–miles basis; in 1961 and 1962 the American airlines had no accident, therefore their record was naturally better than that of any form of ground transport.)

The main problem with these and even the more detailed statistics is that their validity can be disputed and they do not serve as a guide to what aircraft detectives need most: information about hazards (in design, manufacture, maintenance, and operation) by revealing, for instance, that the techniques of take-off and landing contain many more dubious safety factors than those in cruising for a million miles. Therefore investigators, airlines, manufacturers and various aviation authorities have already begun to use statistics for keeping an eye on trends so that they could spot a potential killer almost at birth.

Flying has an 'amazingly high level' of safety, but nevertheless we have a right to demand most strenuously still greater improvements by allocating more funds for research and by more stringent regulations. Investigators have proved that a lot more and more quickly could be done. But to demand *perfect* safety, as some critics do, is sheer nonsense.

Aviation will never be *perfectly* safe. Just as nothing will ever be as long as the major hazard in life — death — remains. If this sounds fatalistic, then this is grossly unfair to aviation which is anything but fatalistic. Today, when such enormous efforts and investments are used to make aviation safer, the cost of any further, even slight, potential safety improvement is astronomical. Design for 'perfect safety' would have to contend with further possibilities of man-made mistakes, and add so much extra weight to aircraft that they could carry only ten passengers, each of whom would have to pay £1,000 for a single transatlantic flight. But safety at such an extreme is not what the travelling public — or even headline-conscious politicians on the eve of elections — want. Beyond a certain level of safety, the public want speed and comfort at a low cost, otherwise we would go to Hong Kong by ox-cart. And we would ban cars from the road, ships from the sea, electrical appliances and staircases from the house, and people from a five-mile stretch round the coast.

This attitude is not new. In the 1930's Imperial Airways used the Heracles, a vast biplane with a wing-span of 130 feet, which had a most luxurious interior, needed only a small airfield with a short runway, and which in some ten years of service never killed a single passenger. But it had a drawback: it could reach only 100 mph and, in the European skies, German and American aircraft beat it to the post. Passengers showed preference for speed and cheaper fares — the Heracles had to be forgotten if competition was to be maintained.

Or take the latest blind landing system. With its duplicated and triplicated fail-safe mechanisms, it has been designed to a ten million to one safety level. It is a fantastic figure. No airliner can expect to live for ten million landings. But the odd one chance may come much earlier. So it is not *perfectly* safe. Could it be safer? Yes. With further triplications of extra safety devices, with new systems that safeguard against the additional hazards created by the complexity of extra safety equipment, it would be possible to raise the odds to, say, a hundred million to one. But the extra weight and expense would be so tremendous, and the extra margin so thin, that it is not yet a feasible proposition.

Just as aerodynamicists have always come up against structural experts in the lift versus strength battle, so investigators have always found their less than vitally important findings measured against commercial considerations. (See, for instance, the use of ill-equipped 'marginal' airports.) The American Federal Aviation Agency (FAA) said in a policy statement in 1965: 'It is simply not possible to pursue safety for safety's sake in an effort to achieve the highest level of safety without being seriously limited by the compromises necessary in the interest of a reasonably costed, efficient and viable system.' It sounds cruel but it is quite understandable in the light of what individual investigators admitted frankly:

'If we find something really big, licensing authorities will see it through. There can be no doubt about that. The problem arises with the more marginal questions which are open to considerations. One airline has a magnificent variable formula to define its task: the operator's duty is "To carry passengers and freight from one place to another with the maximum of safety, comfort and economy". For the government, they use the formula as it is. For sales and public relations "comfort" comes first. For board meetings, "economy" precedes the other two.'

In the interest of public relations severe changes will have to come — or, to some extent, are already on their way — which will, no doubt, affect the variations of this formula by making safety an economically more essential factor.

Thus in 1968, three crucial elements supported an optimistic view of aviation safety: (1) statistics, (2) the level where safety considerations were permitted to become marginal, and (3) the healthy state of the economy of flying. The changes since then are quite dramatic in all three respects.

(1) Until 1965, there was a regular and steady improvement in safety statistics. After that disastrous 1966, the ups and downs of the death-per-mile graphs did not look too alarming at a glance, but the tremendous increase of distances flown concealed some appalling facts: the five-year average to 1972 showed that the trend in safety improvements had been reversed for the first time; the actual number of crashes was increasing and the number of deaths rose above the 1,000 mark in 1971; and then came another year of disaster with 2,124 fatalities in twenty-five crashes; on that basis, we were lucky in 1973, when there were thirty major jet accidents with 'only' 933 people killed.

When *Flight International* examined the more meaningful figures — the number of deaths for each million flights surveyed for the decade to 1972 — some countries could look back with pride, while others had to swallow rather unpalatable facts. Holland had no accident and topped the safety chart. Britain sank to ninth place — killing five times more passengers per million flights than Scandinavia or the United States. British airlines could find no consolation in the fact that Japan and France had an even poorer record, that Indian aircraft had lost more than twice as many passengers, and that the Russians, for the first time, began to admit air disasters (already reported by hundreds of international eye witnesses).

Most of the blame had to be taken by the independent

airlines. While some could proudly continue to claim that they never had a fatal accident, others had plenty and pulled down the level of British air safety: in the decade to January 1973, British independent airlines, carried a quarter of the traffic but had 60 per cent of the accidents and fatalities.

The figures also showed that most of the victims were travelling on scheduled, not charter, flights — with renewed emphasis on the fact that the inherent danger was not to be found in the name or nature of the operation, but in the individual operator's ways of running an airline.

Aviation insurers work on the basis of statistics. Flight insurance for passengers is cheap because the odds against them improved from 25,000 to 200,000 to one in the 1950s and 1960s. For life cover, some companies charge only as much to pilots as to bank clerks: whereas in the 1920s, one in every four commerical pilots was killed annually, in the 1930s, the ratio was one in fifty, and in the 1960s, it was only one in 1,600. Despite fast-rising aircraft values and passenger liabilities, insurers could hold down premiums in the light of past safety record, and so the comparative cost of insurance actually dropped. But now an increase is inevitable. In April, 1974, alone, there were ten major losses, followed by two more in September, and then five more in quick succession. Total write-offs included costly hulls such as a DC–10 and a 747. The time is near when all the foreseeable liabilities will amount to about a hundred million pounds per accident.

The statistical cause for optimism has thus become questionable.

(2) Further doubts must be admitted as a result of the examination of accidents. The level at which airlines, manufacturers, and various authorities now permit safety considerations to become 'marginal' seems to approach the point where some blatantly obvious hazards could be just a matter of argument. The following is a random sample.

*An independent re-investigation of accidents showed up

pilot fatigue as a greater menace than hitherto thought in causing the often inexplicable *human error* that leads to mysterious accidents. (While much of the evidence was inconclusive and out of international context, the authorities must review regularly the questions of duty and rest periods, demands of modern aviation, and the pilots' spare time activities — moonlighting as pilots or simply second-jobbing in some other capacity.)

*Since 1968, more evidence has been gathered about inadequate airports and ground control services. Accident investigations revealed that the hazards were known but were regarded much too easily as 'marginal'. Only magnificent airmanship prevented a collision between a British and an American aircraft at Miami airport in 1973. The investigation found some gaps in the safety regulations yet not all were immediately plugged. International knowledge of insufficient radar installations at busy airports such as Rome's Fiumicino (totally overcrowded), of malfunctioning equipment and a shortened, partly unserviceable runway at New Delhi's Palam (protests by Japan, Qantas, IFALPA and others), and of the horror stories about Kano, Nigeria (until an accident killed 176 people in 1973), failed to lead to immediate and satisfactory measures by the relevant authorities or to determined action by the pilots and the airlines. At New York's Kennedy, the ILS is often lost in bad weather. To avoid Manhattan, planes must then take the Conarsie VOR approach: a constant turn, over the high International Hotel and a 'dive' to the runway — causing frequent overshoots.

*In 1973, the *Guardian* quoted from an official report that 'nearly 90 per cent of Britain's state-employed air traffic controllers rate their equipment unsatisfactory'. The report remained unpublished and far too little was done about its findings.

*In March 1973, two Spanish airliners collided in the air

over France. One of them, an Iberia DC–9, crashed near Nantes, killing 68 people. The other, a Convair Coronado of Spantax, the large Spanish charter line, managed to land with its 99 people on board although one of its engines was on fire and its starboard wing was badly damaged.

French authorities were quick to accuse one of the pilots and blame 'a series of errors in the air' for the disaster. Yet much too obvious facts weakened the French case. At the time of the accident, French air traffic controllers were on strike. Industrial action and the confusion it caused embarrassed the government on the eve of the General Elections, and therefore, military air traffic controllers were brought in to take over. The plan for this action had existed from 1968, and was known to be riddled with safety hazards. In the first 12 days of the strike, in late February and early March, several near-misses were reported, and the pilots' union warned the government — although never banned its members from flying under these questionable control conditions. When the collision occurred, a powerful civilian radar not only noted but also recorded with its automatic camera on film the converging courses of the two airliners. But the military operators had paid no attention to the civilian equipment.

The British Airline Pilots' Association imposed a ban on flights over France for the duration of the strike and the military air traffic control. Within 24 hours, most of the world airlines began to by-pass France. The French government — 'We would never negotiate with law-breakers' — was forced to eat its words and get in touch with the 'illegal strikers'. (The strike was for better pensions and for the right to strike.) But in the meantime, the detour proved to be a costly business for the airlines: each BEA Trident, for instance, making a 30-minute diversion, used up some 600 gallons of extra fuel. Boycotting French air space was to cost Britain alone a couple of millions within a few days.

Other airlines were equally concerned and everybody tried to find a way out.

KLM was among the first to re-start flights over France, but when a Dutch pilot filed another near-miss report, Holland (the country with the best safety record in the previous decade) re-imposed its ban and kept it in force for the duration of the strike even though Britain and other countries sought, received and accepted renewed assurances from the French military in order to resume normal services ... and save on the fuel bill. (Beyond the wild accusations, even the immediate, and obviously inadequate, investigation revealed appalling misunderstandings, big holes in the radar coverage, insufficient knowledge of English — the language of the air — and other dangerous shortcomings.)

*In March 1974, when the new Paris airport at Roissy was opened, French airline pilots and traffic controllers protested against its 'outdated and shoddy' equipment including a radar with limited range and a coverage 'as full of holes as a gruyere cheese', against 'virtually unworkable' regulations and the arrangement for civilians to handle part of the military traffic. The government satisfied itself with cutting back traffic for a 'familiarisation period'.

*108 people from four Somerset villages died in the Vanguard crash into a mountain near Basle. There were thirty-seven survivors. The 'shoppers' special' day trip arrived at the airport in a blinding snowstorm, in April 1973. Instead of diverting to Zurich, the pilot tried three times to get in. Irrespective of the lengthy investigation, the main immediately worrying aspect of the case was that, to the best of this author's knowledge, no immediate preventive action was taken to eliminate all the suspects that could cause a replica of this disaster before the probable cause would be found. Just before the crash, the pilot reported 'trouble with my Automatic Direction Finder'. The crash occurred when the plane flew in the wrong direction. The ADF was known to give trouble particularly in snowstorms. Yet no new procedure or checking of all these instruments was made compulsory without delay. (Defective electrical circuits in navigation aids were due to shoddy repairs.)

The plane belonged to Invicta International Airlines which temporarily ceased operations three months before the crash, because its leased fleet — five Vanguards — had been repossessed by Air Holdings, the vendors. In February, a shipping group acquired control of the company, and operations were due to be re-started as soon as the fleet could be purchased from the owners. After several postponements, the 'shoppers' special' took off to disaster. In the storm, with malfunctioning equipment, there was a tremendous overload on the pilots. Only Andrew Wilson raised the question in *The Observer*: 'should the Vanguard have been required to carry a third pilot, as do BEA Vanguards?' (Later the investigation found 'failures and discrepancies' in the flying career of the pilot in command.) Another hazard dismissed as 'marginal' was the laxity of the French air traffic control near the Swiss border. (France barred the appearance of key witnesses.)

*Defect and Incident Reporting — an admittedly complicated subject — was discussed and discussed by expert committees and air authorities without sufficient practical progress in creating a workable mandatory or voluntary system which could have prevented numerous serious accidents. (Reports of previous incidents, with sufficient follow-up warnings, might have helped a Trident crew, for example, to be better prepared to meet an emergency caused by 'premature droop retraction' and thus, perhaps, to avoid the accident that killed them as well as all their crew and passengers, 118 in all, at Staines in June 1972.)

*When one thinks about avoidable accidents, nothing seems a less inevitable disaster and a more senseless slaughter than the biggest of them all — that Turkish DC–10 over France in 1974.

In June 1972 only six days before the Staines crash, a near-disastrous incident and a magnificent feat of airmanship were noted at Windsor, Ontario. The crew managed to land a crippled DC–10 of American Airlines. NTSB investigators quickly discovered what happened: a huge outward-opening cargo door flew open and was torn off in flight; it caused explosive decompression in the hold and this, in turn, made the floor of the passenger cabin collapse; had there been any passengers seated there, they would have been sucked out of the plane; the flying controls to the tail section and the rear-mounted engine ran under the floor and the collapse ruptured and partially jammed them.

With superb presence of mind, the pilot shut down that engine and nursed the rudder, veering dangerously to the right, to a successful emergency landing.

Most aircraft have 'teething troubles'. Some hidden design problems may manifest themselves only in regular service, perhaps only once in ten thousand flights. Many new aircraft have achieved a truly high level of safety only after one or two initial disasters. The DC–10 was lucky: it got away with this nasty shock. Luckier still: the manufacturers admitted to investigators that this was not the first incident — there had been another hundred complaints from the users of some 130 planes before that.

Once the problem was discovered, the NTSB only needed to put through its recommendations: make the closing mechanism of the door fail-safe — and strengthen that floor.

What exactly happened is, in fact, the subject of lengthy investigations, Congressional hearings, and endless legal wrangling about responsibility and compensation. But a fair number of facts have emerged clearly even in the preliminary stages. A report by the House of Representatives criticises the FAA for trying to balance the 'competing interests' of promoting industry against safety, and 'dollars against lives'. This problem, affecting FAA policy, was clearly stated for all to see in 1965. (Quoted on page 362.) Unfortunately the investigators' qualifying statements, the saving grace of 'if we find something really big, licensing authorities will see it through . . .', were lost over the years towards the end of the 1960s and the beginning of the Nixon administration, when the FAA would start playing politics and make 'gentlemen's agreements' with instead of issuing firm directives to the air industry.

Until 1969, about 90 per cent of the NTSB recommendations were accepted and enforced by FAA. After 1969, the average was just over half, Many kinds of recommendations which used to become the subject of mandatory Airworthiness Directives (something that is always widely publicised and urgently carried out by manufacturers as well as users all over the world), were now 'quietly' handled as gentlemen's agreements, with notifications via seemingly dull and insignificant 'service bulletins' (usually non-mandatory) sent by ordinary mail instead of Telex or priority telegrams. Apparently, this 'voluntary' system worked well in many cases with several manufacturers (e.g. Boeing), including McDonnell Douglas — most of the time.

The cargo door was to be made fail-safe in two new ways. Users were notified about these (but only one of them carried the urgency and emphasis of an 'alert' — the other, perhaps more important measure, became only a routine service bulletin). Not all users carried out the modifications without delay because they did not appear to be all that important.

The manufacturers also agreed as gentlemen to do both modifications on the cargo doors of new aircraft coming off the assembly line, before delivery to customers. Yet it appears that inside the factory, the checking of work — including these modifications — was also carried out, at least occasionally, by gentlemen's agreement. Thus Douglas continued to deliver some aircraft without the necessary modifications ... although the documentation showed that the newly required fail-safe devices had been fitted and checked.

One of these aircraft was delivered to Turkish Airlines in 1973.

Both modifications were simple. One required the fitting of a plate to prevent the locking handle being forced (as in the case of the plane that had the Windsor incident). The Turkish DC–10 was not fitted with that plate, but it was equipped with a peephole to check the locking mechanism of the door. This modification No. 2 also required a printed notice about the usage of the peephole and the warning that the handle must not be forced.

Disaster was now on the cards, but it was still not inevitable. In February 1974, the American government asked the manufacturers to study the problem of explosive decompression. The company thought that the FAA ought to pay for this because of the magnitude of the problem affecting the entire industry.

Only six days later, an allegedly illiterate airport worker closed the cargo door of the above Turkish DC–10. He later claimed that he had fastened that door correctly. Safety experts argued that he made a mistake because he could not read the warning. (A point that would only increase the makers' and operators' responsibility for failing to foresee such a situation.)

Nine minutes after take-off, at about 13,000 feet, the cargo door flew open, explosive decompression made the cabin floor collapse, the door was torn off and six passengers were sucked out (later to be found seven miles away from the main wreckage area), the controls were ruptured and jammed, and the plane crashed into Ermenonville forest, killing everybody on board.

Those immediately suspect cargo doors were now checked, double checked and fastened all over the world.

As a prelude to the legal battles, numerous deadly shots of accusations and counter-accusations were urgently fired. McDonnell Douglas alleged gross technical incompetence by Turkish Airlines (THY), the operators who, in turn, returned the compliment with a mention of the defective cargo door and the false documents about the completion of the recommended patch-up measures for safety. The Turks also blamed Convair who produced the hull and the door as sub-contractors. But Convair had a great deal of ammunition in reserve: they had to follow design specifications precisely, and what is more, they had noticed the hazard — and had said so in writing!

A Congressional investigation published the Convair study which predicted the disaster with uncanny accuracy. It claimed soon after the Windsor incident that due to Murphy's Law, first-aid patch-up modifications, cabin floor weakness and basic design, a blow-out and explosive decompression were inevitable. Convair was prevented by contract from direct approach to Federal safety authorities — and apparently, the manufacturers failed to pass on the warning of doom.

The manufacturers' latest idea for improved safety – some floor strengthening and vents to reduce the risk of explosive decompression – is not new at all. They rejected this as 'impractical' when the NTSB suggested it almost two years before the crash. Meanwhile, they argue that the other American wide-bodied jets (747 and TriStar) are also affected by relatively weak floor structure. (On the 747, only one of the cargo doors is plug-type — the others open outwards.)

This dramatic story will be discussed, no doubt, in many books to come. What one must hope is that those books will not be only the first volume of a continuing tragedy. *Hope* is the key word – and hope can never compete with a surplus margin of structural strength for safety. In June, 1975, a BAC One-eleven of Philippines Airline was descending to Manila when plastic explosives blew up in the lavatory at the rear of the plane. Passengers suffered only minor injuries but the hole in the hull caused a major decompression explosion: the cabin was wrecked, large sections of the wing were torn off – but the main airframe withstood the strain, the engines kept running, the controls continued functioning, and the pilot managed to land the crippled aircraft.

Could a DC-10 (or another wide-bodied jet) survive a proportionately greater explosion initiated by sabotage? The chances are that if anything violent happened to those now carefully modified doors the floor would collapse just the same, the controls would be severed just the same, and death would come just as swiftly and mercilessly as at Ermenonville. *For the strengthening of the floor, one of the NTSB recommendations, is still a matter of argument between government and manufacturers.*

The makers' resistance is understandable — at least from the financial point of view. 'Strengthening' may involve a complete re-thinking and re-designing of this revolutionary wide-bodied jet, at tremendous cost, to the extent of the DC-10 becoming a DC-11 — a different aircraft. Yet is this not what the manufacturers should be forced to do? And if the aviation lobby is too powerful in the United States, shouldn't all other governments and their aviation authorities re-think completely the licensing of the DC-10?

The question all licensing authorities must now ask from themselves is simple: if the DC-10 was submitted to them, in its present form, as a new design by a manufacturer in that country, would they accept it without modification and certify it for airworthiness? They must also face the fact that this would be a very different proposition from simply checking and accepting the American authorities' opinion.

372

It is so different that in Britain, for instance, several specialists hold the view in private, that most countries do no more than rubber-stamp the American airworthiness certificate because the American system and the resulting air safety are known to be so much better than those anywhere else.

On this occasion, however, the American system broke down, and the safety record is threatened from several sides . . . most of all, perhaps, by the third major confidence-shaker: *the financial status of the aviation industry.*

(3) When making inquiries about the DC–10 design, this author was told off several times by specialists: 'What are you after? £1,000-seats for a trans-Atlantic flight? The extra weight used for safety must come out of the weight that can be utilised . . .' the old argument again and again, but certainly, there is a point where they stop convincing and begin simply conning us! It is true that the Jumbo-type planes are revolutionary, that they may be cheaper to run and, carrying far more people, may be a better proposition for the last third of the century — but surely, at the moment, the cost-reduction is not offered to the public who pay by the distance not the type of aircraft. So if the increase of safety in the new wide-bodied jets is a financially crippling proposition, this must clearly be a problem and burden to the manufacturers and the airlines.

For it was a financially crucial question for the makers of the DC–10 that the Windsor, Ontario, incident should not get much embarrassing publicity just when the Rolls-Royce–Lockheed financial struggle gave a tremendous battle-winning opportunity to the DC–10, when a huge sales campaign was to go into operation, and when a DC–10 was to make a round-the-world sales tour. (Two weeks after the Windsor episode, the tour began, the plane helped to win three Turkish orders — the first of which was to cut a mile long swath of trees through France.)

Long gone are the days when a major aircraft — like the

Comet — could be simply grounded and re-designed, no matter what losses of pride and business were involved. As the American and European aircraft manufacturing giants fight for survival, bringing news of bleak economic prospects for their respective countries, governments and their air authorities must try to be at least sympathetic towards the problems. And that is not particularly re-assuring to the flying public.

The situation is no better with the airlines — no matter how big or small they are. With vast investments tied up in hardware, and with constant pressure to keep up with the latest wide-bodied, supersonicised Jumbolic Joneses of avi-ation, too many airlines with too many seats chase too few passengers and dwindling profits. And this is exactly the situation where airlines — the smallest, hardest pressed, most desperate ones in the first place — may be tempted by 'temporary' corner-cutting, 'ingenious' ways of reducing maintenance costs, and the attractions of giving just a bit too much encouragement to pilots who are determined to save money and please the management. (For example, acci-dent investigators have always been suspicious — and not without justification — of the pilot 'who had every oppor-tunity to divert from that fog-bound/storm-torn/ill-equipped etc., airport and yet tried and tried to get in twice, three times, until succeeding ... or crashing into high ground or the sea ...' And a British investigator admitted: 'it's virtually impossible to get proof in most cases, but pilots admit that several companies operate on a shoestring: if a plane-load of holidaymakers must be diverted to an alternative, sometimes more expensive airport, the extra fuel cost and hotel bills for the night might wipe out all the ex-pected profit and may actually turn the flight into an out-right loss. If the plane is the loss, at least the insurers and re-insurers pay for it.')

False hopes for a boom period can cause more financial

disasters than most other miscalculations. And in a way, this is what happened to the aviation industry. Manufacturers, airlines and even travel agents were geared to a constant tremendous expansion of air traffic. Some increase did occur (450 million people travelling 350,000 million passenger miles), but the expected growth never quite materialised.

The relatively smaller lines are, of course, the first to go. In 1973, Donaldson International were told by CAA (Civil Aviation Authority) that they could not operate cheap advance-booking trans-Atlantic charter services and expand until they found more capital. It was not the first warning. The company then decided to sell two of its four Boeing 707s and run a reduced charter service. In 1974, Donaldson had to cease operations. But by that time, much bigger outfits were also in trouble.

The 1973 Middle East war and the subsequent Arab oil embargo forced fuel prices up 140 per cent. Wages were rising incessantly, and borrowing capital became record-expensive. Bankers began to lose confidence in airlines. Passengers began to find that they could not afford all the surcharges. Bookings began to dwindle. Airliners, ordered in brighter days of optimism, were delivered and had to be paid for. (A Lockheed TriStar with essential spares costs near enough ten million pounds these days.) And the profits, already cut to bare minimum to win huge numbers of passengers in cut-throat competition, reached the point where they would turn into losses if those rows and rows of yawning seats could not be filled. (Laker's, an exceptionally successful, tightly controlled ten-jet airline carried a million people — with only 15p. profit on each.) By 1975, leading American lines have been forced to become aircraft sellers: while taking new deliveries of Jumbos — and mothballing them right away — they compete to sell off unused, though secondhand, giant machines to cargo carriers or any bargain-hunters for little more than half the manufacturers price.

The biggest British charter operator, Court Line Aviation, was valued at about £80 million and made a profit of £4,700,000 in 1973. It owned hotels in several countries, had shipping interests, owned the millionaire holiday and travel chains which used to be its best customers, employed ten thousand people, ran a good fleet of modern jets, ordered the latest designs, carried two million passengers in 1973 — and crashed in 1974.

Many of Britain's twenty charter airlines suffered a thirty per cent drop in bookings, while fuel costs grew one-third to two-thirds of their operating expenditure. Britannia Airways needed the support of the Thomson organisation, its parent company. British Caledonian reduced its dependence on low-profit charter work and added more of its three dozen jets to the crowded skies of scheduled services.

Yet the hunt for the individual passenger is just as desperate as the need of the charter aircraft-fodder, with the situation being worse over the North Atlantic. David Nicholson, chairman of British Airways, the huge state airline formed by the merger of BEA and BOAC, told an aviation conference in May 1974, that his company's Atlantic-crossing capacity was the equivalent of eleven Jumbos a day — of which five were always empty. In fact, stepping inside almost any of those scheduled planes to New York, one easily gets the impression that they could advertise and offer not only 'more leg-room' but also your own patch of vegetable garden. (For the year ending in April 1974, British Airways trebled its net profits, making £16 million. But by the summer of 1974, the picture was not so rosy: the company had to raise twenty million pounds to pay wages and running expenses, and the prospect was that the airline would end the year about £20 million in the red. Soon after that, some five dozen pilots have been grounded on full pay — 300 others are already without jobs — due to the fall in air traffic and the financial situation that may bankrupt even a State airline.

With all those empty seats in mind, for the first time, everybody began to think seriously about pooling aircraft and sharing resources over the North Atlantic. Although, at the same time, American authorities want to license additional airlines for that packed bit of sky, the two biggest aviation household names, TWA and PanAm agreed to split up most of their routes and compete only on the London and Lisbon runs. This was to give them higher load-factors, cut costs and boost profits — everything that even these giants need badly. Both these organisations have the reputation of being smooth money-printing machines. Yet they are losing heavily. PanAm's deficits have mounted incessantly for six years. In 1974, the airline lost some 70 million dollars, an all-time record, four times more than the deficit in 1973. Yet this record was almost equalled in half the time, the first six months of 1975. In order to secure further credits from its 36 bankers, the airline had to mortgage its assets to the hilt and hope for the best in the negotiations of a $300-million Persian rescue deal.*

*Joining forces and pooling aircraft may soon be the only viable proposition for smaller airlines, too. The problem would deserve urgent attention for the complexity of modern aviation affects safety. Air Ceylon is a good example. It is profitable and — due to care, national pride and enthusiasm, government backing and operations contracted out to major international carriers — it has an accident-free record. But accident statistics are meaningless: one DC-8 constitutes the airline's long-range international fleet, and it is statistically unlikely that an entire airline should be wiped out by a single accident. On the other hand, even the combined finances of Sri Lanka aviation authorities and Air Ceylon would be overstretched if they had to employ enough people to deal meaningfully with *all* the information pouring in about accidents, incidents, new regulations, technical and commercial developments etc. "We have learned to avoid transport dependence on other countries," said Engineering Manager Fonseka, "but capacity-sharing may be the only way to ensure that we remain safe and profitable".

All this seems to be merely a matter of finances, not safety. But are the two truly separable? Is it just a coincidence that in 1974, the American government ordered an investigation into the operations of PanAm whose Boeing 707s had been involved in four crashes within a single year, killing almost three hundred people? And it is the number of accidents, not the number of deaths that must ring alarm bells because the 707 is one of the best-tried, most widely used work-horses of this age. The investigators will now examine several aspects of PanAm practices, including crew training, operation procedures, pilot supervision and crew scheduling.

If, at the same time, one thinks about the huge sums that may be involved in covering the losses of and compensations for the DC–10 accident, one can, perhaps, begin to envisage the advent of the 'safety as a commercial proposition' era.

In August 1974, National Airlines of the United States announced a record profit of thirty million dollars for the year that had ended on June 30, and distributed another million dollars of tax-free bonus among its employees. David Green remarked in the *Daily Telegraph* on August 28, 1974: 'National, famous for its off-beat "Fly Me" advertisements,' will perhaps 'amend the slogan to "Fly me, I make a profit".'

Which may not be a bad proposition at all. It may lead to a new routine of airlines offering their healthy balance sheets instead of costly and glossy adverts as an inducement to the seat-filling load factor — our beloved passenger.

The only unanswered question would be: what does a healthy balance sheet imply — efficient cost-cutting or reckless corner-cutting? This is why it is such a great pity that National, a big airline, one of the few with healthy finances and good records of safety and efficiency, should be unlucky enough to own *Barbara*, a DC–10, probably the unluckiest jet in the world. *Barbara* suffered numerous serious incidents, punctured fuselage, damaged engines and wings, broken window through which a passenger was sucked out, flight cancellations and potentially catastrophic mishaps as well as minor, irritating deficiencies. *Barbara*'s defective cargo door, subject of the McDonnell Douglas warning (service bulletin) of 1972, was not yet repaired in 1974, at the time of the Turkish accident. At a recent Congressional hearing, an investigator remarked: 'Her slogan should be — "I'm Barbara . . . take a chance on me to Miami".'

* * * * * * *

The original version of this book ended on a note of clear optimism and reassurance. It described a routine flight from London to Frankfurt:

'. . . 11 minutes before scheduled arrival time, the Trident landed on Frankfurt runway 25R at 10.24. As usual, the passengers were asked to remain seated until the aircraft came to a complete stop.

'As the disembarkation began, some passengers sighed with relief. Many of them must have thought about the unforgettable pictures of burning wreckages they had seen in newspapers from time to time. It never occurred to most of them that they were only eighty-four out of more than a million people who completed their journeys by air in perfect safety on that single day in June.'

Today, a note of doubt must prevail. Are we in the process of wasting all the effort, ingenuity and great achievements of aircrash detectives and the entire aviation community? Is it possible that despite all the talks, plans and promises we are witnessing the emergence of new blueprints for disasters to come? Will it remain only a quite unique case that due to the lack of proper information ex-

379

change even about serious incidents and to the lack of speedy and compulsory modifications, aviation failed to help preventing a 747-accident that murdered 59 people? And will the NTSB's warning about the vulnerability of the centre engines on wide-bodied aircraft (DC–10 and TriStar) remain just another space-waster on the shelves of the licensing authorities, and will only an icing disaster blow away the gathering dust from the file?

It is for the entire air transport industry to prevent the development of new dangerous trends — and reassure us all with facts once again.

SELECTED BIBLIOGRAPHY

EXTENSIVE use has been made of accident reports, national and international statistics, ICAO and IATA publications, accident reports published by HMSO, NTSB, etc., FSF papers and seminars, university lectures, papers read at the University of Southern California accident investigation course and also at the American investigators' school, national and airline accident investigation regulations, American and European aviation journals and newspapers.

AIRCRAFT ACCIDENT INQUIRY, Annex 13 (and Amendments) to the Convention of International Civil Aviation, ICAO, Montreal, Canada.

AIRCRAFT ACCIDENT PREVENTION AND INVESTIGATION, *U.S. Air Force Manual,* Department of the Air Force, Washington, 1963.

AIR SAFETY GROUP, A Review of the Aviation Fuel Controversy, London, 1966.
Cabin Staff and Air Safety, London, 1967.

BEATY, D., The human factor in aircraft accidents, Secker & Warburg, London, 1969.

CAB BUREAU OF SAFETY, A study of U.S. air carrier accidents involving fire 1955–1964, Washington, 1965.

FELTHAM, R. G., Aircraft Accident Data Recording Systems, HMSO, London, 1973.

HANDBOOK FOR AIRCRAFT ACCIDENT INVESTI-
GATORS, PAM 95-5, U.S.A. Government Printing Office,
Washington.

JONES, F. H., Aircraft accident investigation – the analysis
of the wreckage, *Canadian Aeronautics and Space Journal*,
December 1962.

MANUAL OF AIRCRAFT ACCIDENT INVESTIGATION,
ICAO.

MASON, J. K., *Aviation accident pathology*, Butterworth,
London, 1962.

NATIONAL TRANSPORTATION SAFETY BOARD, Working paper on history and duties of NTSB, 1968.

NEWTON, E., The investigation of aircraft accidents,
Journal of the Royal Aeronautical Society, March 1964.

SERLING, R. J., *The probable cause*, Doubleday & Co. Inc.,
New York, 1962.

WHITNAH, D. R., *Safer Skyways*, *Federal control of
aviation 1926–1966*, Iowa State University Press, Ames,
Iowa, 1966.

INDEX

INDEX

Names of airlines and crews involved in accidents have been omitted from the list of index headings. Accidents and incidents are listed under aircraft types (e.g. TUDOR) and, for cross reference, under the names of geographical locations where the selected accidents and incidents happened.

DC–3 DAKOTA – *cont.*
260–62 – new Lake Gwynant, Caernarvonshire; Jan. 1952; Aer Lingus; navigational error and turbulence

DC–4 (see also Argonaut): 247, 327
160, 161 – Pacific; Sept. 1955; USAF; wrong fuel management
214–17 – Mount Marra, Sudan, May 1960; Balair; navigational error
309 – Perpignan, France; June 1967; Air Ferry; carbon monoxide poisoning

DC–6: 139, 140, 202, 339
95, 100 – near Bolivia, N. Carolina; Jan. 1960; National Airlines; sabotage
114 – Bryce Canyon; 1947; fire in the air
139 – Rikers Island; Jan. 1957; Northeast Airlines; fire
308 – Ndola, Rhodesia; 1961
334 – New York; Dec. 1954; Alitalia; pilot error

DC–7:
148, 298 – Grand Canyon, Arizona; June 1956; UAL; collision with Constellation
280 – New York; Nov. 1962; EAL; pilot error

DC–8: 122, 202, 247, 268, 274, 377
110 – 1967; Swissair; incident
129 – New York; 1961; Aeronaves de Mexico; aborted take-off and fire.
130, 140 – Denver; July 1961; UAL; collision with a truck on landing and fire
131 – Holland; June 1968; KLM; fuel explosion
238–40 – London; Nov. 1963; Trans-Canada Airlines; aborted take-off
256, 269 – near Dulles International Airport, Virginia; Aug. 1963 CAT incident
258, 269 – over Texas; Nov. 1963; EAL; CAT incident
259 – Trans-Canada Airlines; CAT
259 – Lake Pontchartrain, Louisiana; Feb. 1964; EAL; turbulence
269 – near Prestwick; Jan. 1966; Air Canada; turbulence
24, 293–5 – over Staten Island, New York; Dec. 1960; UAL; collision with Constellation
317, 318 – Tokyo; Aug. 1966; KLM; co-pilot save a/c after Captain's heart attack

DC–9: 122, 189, 199
110 – Brussels; March 1967; Swissair; incident
365 – Nantes; March 1973; Iberia; collision

DC–10: 89, 358, 363, 371–2, 377
358, 368 – Paris: Feb. 1974; Turkish Airlines; decompression due to faulty closure of cargo door
368, 372 – Windsor, Ontario; June 1972; AA: incident

Derry, J.: 150, 151
Doyle, B.: 50, 142, 242
Doyle, C.: 34

ELECTRA: 327
110, 184 – Chicago, Ill; Sept. 1961; Northwest Airlines maintenance
117, – near Buffalo, Texas; Sept. 1959; break-up in the air (another case in 1960)
158, 310–14 – Ardmore, Oklahoma; April 1966; American Flyers Airline Corporation; pilot's heart failure

SEX SLAVERY

Stephen Barlay

Many would deny that sex slavery even exists today. They maintain that the white slave trade is no more than a dark shadow on the face of history. But Stephen Barlay's far-reaching investigations show that not only does white slavery still exist, but it has now become a profitable and wide-ranging international trade.

The modern slave need be neither white nor a prostitute. There are ways of forcing any girl into sex slavery. The slavers have diversified their operations and employ new methods to lure the unwary. The trade now operates through the devices of professional pick-up men, bogus marriage bureaux, misuse of theatrical agencies and blackmail. The slavers' greatest advantage is public ignorance about their activities. But no-one who has read this horrifying report can fail to realize that sex slavery — with all its horrors — still threatens the unwary.

An international bestseller in hardback, SEX SLAVERY has been fully revised and brought up to date for paperback publication.

CORONET BOOKS

SUPERNATURE

Lyall Watson

Did *you* know that

A blunt razor blade left overnight inside a cardboard model of the Great Pyramid of Cheops will be sharp again in the morning.

A Chicago hotel porter can produce photographs by *staring* into cameras.

A potted plant registered emotion on a lie detector when an experimenter just *decided* to burn one of its leaves.

Dr. Lyall Watson has challenged scientific orthodoxy by applying new criteria to the investigation of supernatural phenomena. His fascinating and open-minded scientific study proves beyond doubt that science is stranger than the supernatural.

CORONET BOOKS

THE RAVENOUS EYE

Milton Shulman

Violence appears to be increasing at an alarming rate. Contempt for politicians appears to be endemic. The problems concerning the usage of dangerous drugs in our society appear to become more manifold. The generation gap between children and their parents appears to widen too quickly. Sexual permissiveness appears to permeate many western societies.

HOW MUCH OF THIS ACCELERATION IN BOTH FACT AND SENSIBILITY IS DUE TO THE IMPACT OF TELEVISION?

'A civilised, reasonable and reasoned book. No one concerned with broadcasting should ignore it, but it will be particularly useful to the intelligent layman in his role as critical viewer' — *The Sunday Times*

'A formidable attack' — *The Observer*

'A serious and powerful case' — *The Guardian*

'He argues with passion and intelligent vigour ... a thoughtful and stimulating book ... a worthy one on an important subject' — *Variety*

CORONET BOOKS

THE COSMIC CONNECTION

Carl Sagan

'A daring view of the Universe by the wittiest, most rational and most clear-thinking astronomer alive today' — *Isaac Asimov*

'I recommend THE COSMIC CONNECTION to everybody — it's short, exciting, enjoyable, and everybody can understand it ... Fascinating ... Delightful ... A wonderbook' — *The Sunday Times*

'A delightful series of essays ... Carl Sagan, widely regarded as the leader in his field is not afraid to speculate' — *Patrick Moore, Journal of the British Astronomical Association*

CORONET BOOKS

CORONET BESTSELLERS

☐ 19679 3	**Stephen Barlay** Sex Slavery	45p
☐ 18637 2	**Kenneth Allsop** In The Country	40p
☐ 14986 8	**Robert Townsend** Up The Organization	30p
☐ 20445 1	**James Clavell** King Rat	60p
☐ 18833 2	**Lyall Watson** Supernature	50p
☐ 19855 9	**Milton Shulman** The Ravenous Eye	75p
☐ 19846 X	**Ruth Aliav & Peggy Mann** The Last Escape	90p
☐ 15817 4	**David Niven** The Moon's A Balloon	60p
☐ 19881 8	**Pierre Rey** The Greek	75p
☐ 18764 6	**James Grady** Six Days Of The Condor	40p
☐ 19682 3	**Carl Sagan** The Cosmic Connection	85p
☐ 18802 2	**Eilis Dillon** Across The Bitter Sea	80p

All these books are available at your local bookshop or newsagent, or can be ordered direct from the publisher. Just tick the titles you want and fill in the form below.
Prices are subject to change without notice.

CORONET BOOKS, P.O. Box 11, Falmouth, Cornwall.

Please send cheque or postal order, and allowing the following for postage and packing:

U.K. and Eire — 15p for the first book plus 5p per copy for each additional book ordered to a maximum charge of 50p.

Overseas Customers and B.F.P.O. — please allow 20p for the first book and 10p per copy for each additional book.

Name ....

Address ....

....